Percy Blandford's Complete Outdoor Buildings Book

Percy Blandford's Complete Outdoor Buildings Book

Percy W. Blandford

TAB BOOKS
Blue Ridge Summit, PA

FIRST EDITION
SECOND PRINTING

© 1992 by **TAB Books**.
TAB Books is a division of McGraw-Hill, Inc.

Library of Congress Cataloging-in-Publication Data

Blandford, Percy W.
   [Complete outdoor buildings book]
   Percy Blandford's complete outdoor buildings book / by Percy W.
Blandford.
     p.   cm.
   Includes index.
   ISBN 0-8306-3608-0 (h)
   1. Outbuildings—Design and construction—Amateurs' manuals.
I. Title. II. Title: Complete outdoor buildings book.
TH4955.B56 1992
690'.89—dc20   91-34359
                                                 CIP

TAB Books offers software for sale. For information and a catalog, please contact
TAB Software Department, Blue Ridge Summit, PA 17294-0850.

Acquisitions Editor: Kimberly Tabor
Book Editor: April D. Nolan
Director of Production: Katherine G. Brown
Book Design: Jaclyn J. Boone   HT3

Contents

Introduction

This book covers the making of a great variety of small buildings, mainly from wood. They are not homes to live in, but they are the places you might like to have in your yard or garden, at a weekend retreat, on a sport or recreation field, or anywhere that storage facilities or shelter would be needed.

The following pages contain nearly all the instructions and projects in *Small Buildings* (TAB. 3144), together with nearly as many more new projects, resulting in a collection of detailed instructions for small wooden building construction that must be the largest ever published. You should be able to find a design that will suit your needs as it is or can be adapted, accompanied by the full instructions you require.

The buildings range in size from little more than lockers to places to house vehicles, equipment, or stock. Perhaps your first reaction is that anything so big would make a daunting project. It need not be so. You will be handling large pieces of wood and will need space to work, but the actual construction processes are generally simpler than making furniture or toys. You will make more use of hammer and nails. Nearly all joints are simpler. Extreme precision is less important.

If you have done simple woodwork around the home, made basic furniture items, or amused the children with homemade toys, you have the skill to make any building described in this book. If you have a few basic hand tools, you can make almost any of the buildings included in these pages. If you are already a skilled carpenter or cabinetmaker and have a well-equipped shop, that is an obvious advantage, but the beginner with the necessary hand tools can get the same results; it will just take a little longer. Size might make parts heavier, but cutting a joint on wood 15 feet long is no more difficult than it is on a piece 2 feet long.

You might be worried that a building you make might be out of shape and that your mistake will be obvious to anyone who sees it. To avoid this, your approach to marking and setting out must be different than with other wood-working projects. You can use squares and rules on individual pieces of wood, but they are of little use when you need to set out a square of 20 feet or so. Actually, the techniques for squaring a building in all directions are simple and interesting, as you will discover in later pages. A hexagonal form or a hip roof are a little more complicated, but they are straightforward when you follow the steps given.

Don't let the making and erecting of small buildings put you off simply because it is a less compact form of woodworking. You can prefabricate many parts on a flat piece of ground. While you will have to prepare a site and perhaps even pour concrete, it will be much easier if you do all you can to individual pieces before building them into an assembly. After all, it is usually easier to make a cut or drill a hole on the bench. All of the processes involve the wood-work you know already, but on a larger scale.

Making a small wooden building is a very satisfying form of carpentry. At the end of the work, your product is certainly large enough for others to see. You can look at it and say , "I made that," and others will look at it and ask where you got such a marvelous building!

With individual work you can fit a building to suit needs or a particular space or situation. You can place doors and windows where they suit needs best. Any building you make to your own specifications will be much better than a mass-produced building that has to be accepted as a set design. If you make one or more buildings for your own use and this sort of woodworking appeals to you, neighbors might ask you to make small buildings for them. If you wish, you could find yourself fully occupied in a custom-building small business.

In my many woodworking activities, I have found making small buildings among the most satisfying. I built my own workshop many years ago. It still encourages me to tackle work in it to a high standard, knowing that it is not only well built, but that I planned its size, shape, and arrangement of windows and doors to make the best possible use of the situation. No factory-produced sectional building could compete.

I hope you will find buildings described in the following pages that will show you the work is well within your scope. In a short time you will have the satisfaction of looking at and using your own shed, shop, playhouse, barn, or whatever appeals to you.

Note: Sizes on drawings and in materials lists are nearly all in inches. A few longer measurements are in feet and inches. Widths and thicknesses quoted are nominal, but lengths are mostly a little full. If you don't know any of the building terms, the glossary should help you.

1

Preparations

Even the smallest building is probably bigger than the majority of woodworking projects you make, and its size introduces a few special considerations. Instead of doing layout and squaring assemblies on the bench, you are faced with floor areas and structures larger than your normal equipment can span. It would be unwise, for instance, to use a 12-inch square and extend its line to 6 feet, as the possible error at the limit could be more than would be acceptable. Instead, it is better to use geometric methods, preferably to a size larger than the final result has to be so you can avoid possible errors.

It should be safe to assume that the corners of a sheet of 4-×-4-foot plywood are square, so within the limits of that size, you can use a sheet of plywood for marking and checking corners. It might be worthwhile to make a 45-degree triangle by cutting from the corner of a sheet equal lengths along each side. You could use the edge of a sheet of plywood as a straightedge, but it would be better to find your straightest piece of wood of greater length than that, and use it as a straightedge. You can check its straightness by drawing a line against it on a flat surface, then turning it over to see if the line matches (FIG. 1-1A).

If you want to mark long lines, it is better to use a chalk line. Rub a piece of fine line (crochet cotton is suitable) with chalk, without jerking it so the chalk is shaken off. Stretch the line, and have an assistant hold one end down, or use an awl (FIG. 1-1B). Reach as far along as you can, then lift the line a few inches and let it go, to deposit a fine line of chalk on the floor (FIG. 1-1C). If the length is so great that you cannot reach near the middle of the line, get someone else to "snap" the line at its center.

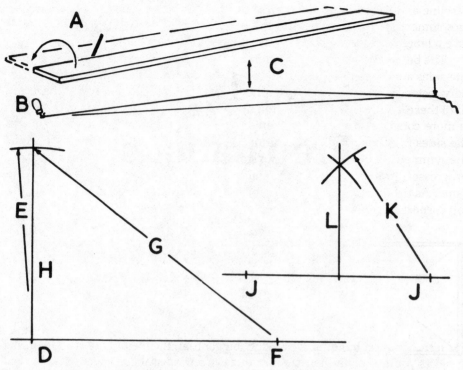

Fig. 1-1. *Check straightness by turning a board over. Striking a cord (B) will produce a long line. Make right angles by measuring (D,E,F,G,H) or drawing arcs (J,K,L).*

If you need to get a large corner square, as you would for a foundation or floor, draw a baseline longer than you will need. Mark on it where the square line is to come (FIG. 1-1D). Now use the geometric property of right-angled triangles (90 degrees) with sides 3:4:5 proportionally. The right angle is between the two shorter sides.

Choose sizes for the sides of the triangle that will result in the square line you draw being at least as long as the final size you need. Suppose you need 12 feet. If that is the "3" side of the triangle, the unit to use is 4 feet, making the triangle sides 12 feet, 16 feet, and 20 feet. Use a steel tape measure or other convenient means of measuring to draw a short arc from the point on the baseline at 12 feet radius (FIG. 1-1E). The arc should swing over what obviously will be the position of the square line. From the point, measure 16 feet along the baseline (FIG. 1-1F). From that point, measure 20 feet to a position on the arc (FIG. 1-1G). From the starting point, draw a line through the mark on the arc with a chalk line or a long straightedge (FIG. 1-1H). This line will be square to the baseline. Measure other lines parallel to it or the baseline.

If you want to erect a line square to the baseline away from a corner, you can measure equal distances on each side of where it is to be (FIG. 1-1J), then swing arcs from these points (FIG. 1-1K). Draw your square line through the point on the baseline and the crossing of the arcs (FIG. 1-1L). Arrange sizes so the radii of the arcs come at about 45 degrees to the baseline to get a crossing high enough to give a length of square line as big as you need.

The best way to check the squareness of anything you assemble, when opposite sides are the same length, is to compare diagonal measurements. In an ordinary rectangular frame, measure corner to corner (FIG. 1-2A) and adjust the frame until these lengths are the same. You do not have to use the extreme corners. If it is more convenient, take other points that should be square, or measure along the sides from the corners (FIG. 1-2B). You can use the same technique to check the symmetry of anything that is not square (FIG. 1-2C). As assembly of a building progresses, you can compare diagonal or other measurements that should be the same. As the building takes a cubic form, you can compare the distance from the top corner of one side with the bottom corner of another.

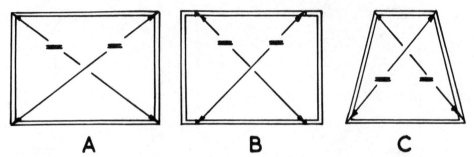

Fig. 1-2. To check squareness and symmetry, compare diagonal measurements.

Rigidity of Small Buildings

It is useless to try to achieve squareness if what you make is so poorly designed or made that it goes out of shape. The ability to hold a shape depends mainly on triangulation. If you join four pieces loosely at the corners and one corner is pushed, the frame will go out of shape (FIG. 1-3A). If you make a three-piece frame (FIG. 1-3B), nothing can push it out of shape. Put a diagonal piece across the four-sided frame, and you have two triangles (FIG. 1-3C). Providing no parts bend, this framework will hold its shape. Smaller triangles might be sufficient (FIG. 1-3D). If you cover a framework with plywood, you have thoroughly triangulated it, and its shape will hold, but if you nail boards across, movement is still possible and it is advisable to add one or more struts to provide triangulation.

In a roof truss, you have the rigidity of a triangle, whether the tie-in is at the eave's level or higher (FIG. 1-3E) to provide head room. Any other framing in a roof truss is there to provide stiffness, but it also contributes to rigidity.

In a large roof, you support the covering on lengthwise purlins attached to the rafters. The assembly is comparable to a squared framework. Some stiffness comes from the building below, but triangulating the roof will relieve that of the excessive load. If the roof covering is made up of large sheets of stiff plywood

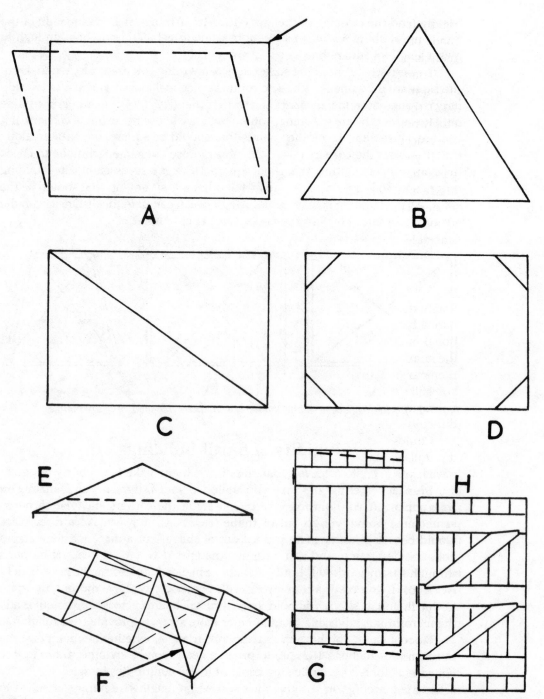

Fig. 1-3. *A four-sided assembly might push out of shape (A). A three-sided figure will not push out of shape (B). Stiffen four-sided frames by triangulating them (C,D,E,F). To prevent a door from sagging, use diagonal braces (G,H).*

rigidly fixed down, that will be sufficient. On the other hand, if the covering is made of many sheets of corrugated metal, plastic, or something similar, movement is possible and diagonal wind bracing (FIG. 1-3F) might be advisable.

Triangulation also might be necessary in smaller assemblies, such as doors. If you make a door with several upright boards and ledgers nailed across (FIG. 1-3G), the door will soon sag. To prevent this sagging, add braces (FIG. 1-3H), preferably notched into the ledgers. If the door tries to sag, the compression loads on the braces stop it.

If you are making the side of a shed or something similar, consider all the parts that are being built in, such as windows and doors or anything that will be inside and attached. If there will not be an absolutely rigid skin and the lines are all parallel in two directions, add some diagonal struts to keep the assembly in shape. Long struts are most effective, but smaller, diagonal braces can give considerable stiffness.

Foundations of Small Buildings

Rarely do you erect a building directly on the ground. Usually you have to prepare a base on which it stands and to support it. You might want to use a sectional building temporarily—such as with a shed used for garden tools during the summer months only, or another building you plan to use only briefly and then move it to another position. A dirt floor might be acceptable in this case, but you still must level it. Even a temporary building that is obviously not level looks wrong to you and all other observers. If you erect walls out of true, you will have difficulty fitting the roof.

Compacted soil might take the weight of a small building, but you must ram it or roll it hard before you put a building on it. If soil settles under the weight of a wall, you might have difficulty lifting and supporting it to make it level.

Even if you are satisfied with a dirt floor, it is usually better to arrange more solid supports under the walls. You could dig out a shallow trench and fill it with sand and small stones rammed tightly together (FIG. 1-4A). Better solutions would be to use concrete for the top few inches (FIG. 1-4B) or to embed anchor bolts as shown in FIG. 1-4C. With stones only, you will have to drive spikes through them into the ground.

Another alternative is to use bricks or concrete blocks. It might be satisfactory to put them in line (FIG. 1-4D), but you can spread the load better if you place them crosswise (FIG. 1-4E).

Wood as a foundation material can rot. Some woods have a good resistance to rot, and woods soaked in preservative will certainly have a reasonable life. However, keep in mind that merely painting preservative on your wood does not achieve much penetration and would have little effect. Old railroad ties are a very good source because they are saturated with preservative and should be immune to rot.

The most common foundations for wooden buildings consist of an all-over

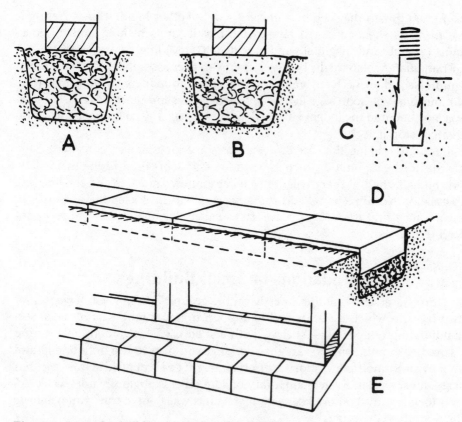

***Fig. 1-4.** A wooden building needs firm foundations.*

concrete pad. You can extend it outside to form a path or patio; you also can use it as the floor of the building if that will suit its use.

A floor made of something other than dirt is also a good seal against moisture and rodents. The thickness and the way you form the foundation will depend on the state of the ground. On a hard soil, you could cover a few inches of rammed, small stones with 3 inches of concrete, but if the soil is loose and sandy, you would need to increase both thicknesses.

Most ground is not as level as you would wish. If you want to put the building on the side of a hill, the slope is obvious. You might have to make a foundation pad partly into the slope at the back and build it up at the front.

On apparently level ground you might find a few inches difference in the length of the building, and you must allow for that. You must consider the circumstances and decide if you want one end above the surrounding ground or if you should go deeper at the other end. A compromise might be more appropriate. This decision applies whether you are putting down foundations under the walls only or laying an over-all pad.

For leveling, use the longest possible level, but supplement it with a long, straight board, preferably to span the whole foundation diagonally. It would be unwise to use the level alone to check a distance much greater than its own length.

Start with one side. If you will be putting down blocks, drive in several pegs as guides so their tops are level (FIG. 1-5A). You can use this procedure for a concrete foundation, or you might put down the shuttering strip, making sure its top is level with what will be the top surface of the concrete (FIG. 1-5B). Use pegs on both sides of the strip and pack it so it cannot move once you have it level and straight.

Next, work square to the first side, setting out the angle as described earlier. Level the pegs or shuttering in the same way. As a final check on that side, put your leveling strip across diagonally (FIG.1-5C). If your leveling strip does not show a true level, test the other ways again—you do not want a twist in the foundation.

Level the remaining two sides in the same way. Mark them parallel to the first sides. Level each in the same way as the first side (FIG. 1-5D). Also, check both diagonals. If you will be putting down a complete pad of concrete, put a few pegs in so that their tops are level with the shuttering in the body of the base (FIG. 1-5E). Use them as guides to leveling or laying the stones over which you will put the concrete. Pull them out as you lay the concrete.

If you are only laying concrete under the walls, put in the inner shuttering (FIG. 1-5F), making sure it is level as you progress. If you are putting down bricks, blocks, railroad ties, or other sectional-foundation material, lay it with the pegs as guides, but check it frequently with your level. You can do little to correct unlevel surfaces once the mixture has set.

This is not a book on concrete work, so you should always follow the supplier's recommendations. If your foundation is in a position where you can have ready-mixed concrete delivered and shot, that might be the best way of preparing a foundation. You probably will settle for more than adequate thickness. If you mix the concrete yourself, do not be tempted to lay only a thin layer to save money or time. Have a good, consolidated base of sand and stones, with about 3 inches of concrete, even if the only weight on it will be light storage and standing people. For storage of yard machinery or a car, use an increased thickness of concrete. Thin concrete might crack, even if you do not load it heavily.

An alternative to laying concrete as a one-piece foundation, especially where it also will be the floor, is to put down precast concrete slabs. You can buy them plain or with decorated or stone-like surfaces. You can spread slabs about 24 inches square over a large area quickly. Bed them in sand and small stones, making sure they are level as you progress. They need not have anything between them, although you can seal spaces with concrete. If you seal the spaces with concrete, make sure it is more than 1/2 inch thick; very thin concrete mortar tends to crack and break away. Open spaces filled with soil are appropriate to the floors of summerhouses or sun lounges, where you might consider grass or small plants taking root there attractive.

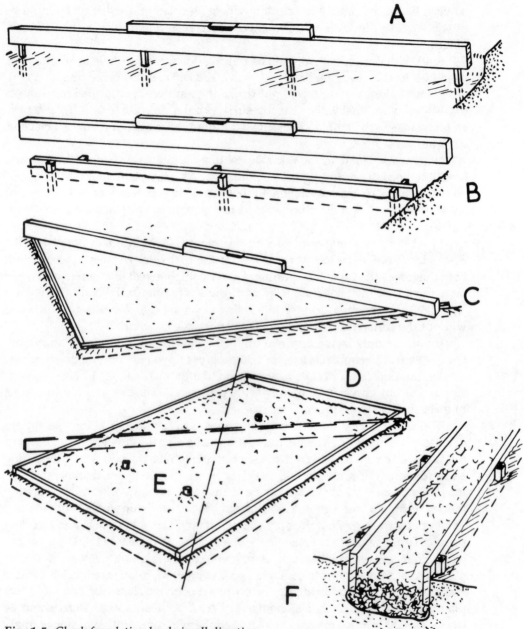

Fig. 1-5. Check foundation levels in all directions.

Floors of Small Buildings

In many buildings, the floor and the foundation will be the same thing. A concrete floor is acceptable for many purposes. If you will be driving a car or a tractor over it or if there is a risk of spilling oil or water on it, concrete should be the choice. If it is a workshop or other building where you will spend some time and might drop tools or equipment, a wooden floor is more comfortable and less liable to damage dropped tools. If it is a building for year-round use, a wooden floor gives a more equitable temperature underfoot. You can coat concrete with rubberized or plastic sealants that might give you 1/4 inch of insulation and a more comfortable surface, but these are not as satisfactory as wood for long-term standing.

The usual wooden floor in a small building might be very similar to the floors in many houses, with boards laid over joists (FIG. 1-6A). Sections of wood and spacing of the wood will depend on the size of the floor and the amount of support needed. As a guide, you can support boards which are 7/8 inch thick on 2-×-4-inch joists at 15-inch centers in an average small building (FIG. 1-6B). In a very small building, the joists need only be 3 inches deep. Particleboard, at least 3/4

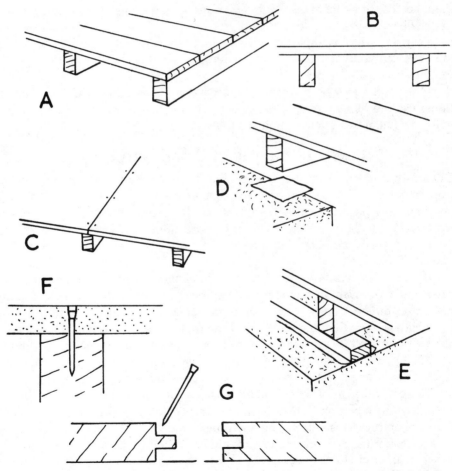

Fig. 1-6. *A floor may be boards or particleboard on joists (A,B,C). Insulate wood from concrete (D,E). Conceal nails (F,G).*

inch thick, makes a good alternative to parallel boards. With joints on joists, you have the minimum of gaps (FIG. 1-6C).

Avoid joists or other wood resting directly on concrete, brick, or stone. If you are supporting the ends of joists at wall foundations, insulate them from moisture (FIG. 1-6D). This insulation might be material sold for damp-proofing or for roof covering, or just pieces of plastic sheeting. If you intend to support the length of the joists by the concrete foundation, put strips of plastic under them or cover the whole concrete surface with plastic sheeting. It might be better to raise the wooden floor above the foundations, especially if the concrete is not level in the main area. Even if the wooden floor starts apparently level, eventually it might take the uneven shape of the concrete below. A strip over damp-proofing might support the joists (FIG. 1-6E) above the concrete. In some buildings, the bottom member of the wall might support the joists.

Punch nails through particleboard below the surface (FIG. 1-6F). If you use plain boards, bring them tightly together and sink their nails below the surface. Better floor boards have tongue-and-groove joints. They will maintain a more even surface, which is important if you want to lay carpeting or other floor covering. You can conceal most of their nailing by driving diagonally through the tongues (FIG. 1-6G).

One surprisingly hard-wearing floor covering is hardboard. In damp conditions, use the oil-tempered variety. Fasten it down with plenty of fine pins or nails. An initial wax spray or polish should seal it for life.

Sizes and Shapes of Small Buildings

Obviously, it is important that the building you make can accommodate all you want to put in it. Too many people find that after a period of use, they wish their building were bigger. For this reason, if you have sufficient space, it might be worthwhile to plan sizes that will suit more than your initial needs. If, for instance, you are planning a building 10 feet long, it costs relatively little more to make it 12 feet long.

If your building is purely utilitarian, a functional appearance might be all you need, but if you want to consider visual appeal, remember that having all three main sizes different has a better look than if they are almost the same. Usually, the length is more than the width, and the roof shape breaks up the height.

Plywood and many manufactured building boards come in 4-×-8-foot sheets. If you will be using any of these materials, plan sizes to suit them whole, or cut in only one direction, for economy in cost and effort.

The ground plan of most buildings is rectangular, and there is usually no advantage in departing from this shape. The building is simple to make, and there are no problems with fitting any type of roof. Tapering the plan is unwise because you must then adapt the roof, either by sloping its ridge or sloping the eaves—neither of which looks right.

An L shape is possible, maybe to provide a porch for the door, to keep the main floor clear, or to reduce drafts (FIG. 1-7A). For a pergola or summerhouse,

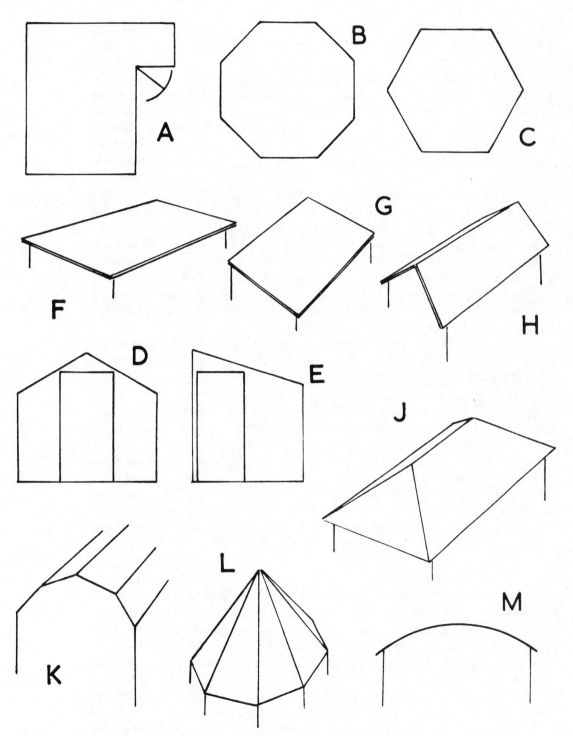

Fig. 1-7. You can plan buildings in many shapes and with different roofs.

you could have an *octagon* shape (FIG. 1-7B) or a *hexagon* shape (FIG. 1-7C). The former is slightly simpler at roof level because you are basically working with a square with its corners cut off.

You need at least 75 inches of clearance for comfortable head room. A storage shed where you do not expect to spend much time inside might have less, or you might provide standing head room over only part of the area. With a *ridge roof*, you can provide this area by using a central end door (FIG. 1-7D). With a *sloping roof*, you might have the door at the higher side of the building (FIG. 1-7E). If you plan to fill the lower parts with shelves or other storage, the limited height might not matter.

A variety of roofs are possible. The simplest roof is a *flat roof* (FIG. 1-7F). This roof might be adequate for some purposes, but in the long term, it can be more troublesome than any other roof. If it is made absolutely flat, it might sag at the center. A slight slope from one side to the other or from the center outwards is advisable.

Next is the sloping, or *lean-to*, roof (FIG. 1-7G). On a fairly narrow building, this roof might be all you need. A moderate slope will shed rainwater, but if you want it to clear heavy snow, the slope must be greater, and that might affect accommodation and appearance.

A *ridge roof with vertical gables* is most popular (FIG. 1-7H), and for many structures, this is all you need. To most people, it looks right and it does all a roof should do. Inside there is good head room and, if the walls are over 72 inches high, you might arrange storage capacity in the roof area. A change to a *hip roof* reduces wind resistance (FIG. 1-7J). On a building of moderate size, you can make this change at one or both ends to improve appearance.

A *double-slope* roof (FIG. 1-7K) has a typical American barn appearance. More work is involved in making it, but the head room is increased over the central area. If you make a hexagonal building, you must cut some complicated rafter angles. In effect, you are making a hip roof all around (FIG. 1-7L).

Curved roofs are possible (FIG. 1-7M), but they are generally better for larger buildings. They are considerably more work unless you use curved, corrugated metal or plastic sheeting, which is almost self-supporting.

Windows in Small Buildings

With the smallest storage building, you might get sufficient light inside when you open the door, but nearly all other buildings should have windows. Even with a windowless, small, box-like structure, it might be worthwhile to arrange a flap or shutter in a wall or opposite the door, for more light or possibly for passing things through.

Consider the use of the building. A few isolated windows might be all you need if no one expects to spend much time in the building. If it is to be a shop or studio, arrange windows to provide natural light where you need it. A window beside the door and one or more at the sides (FIG. 1-8A) might be adequate for

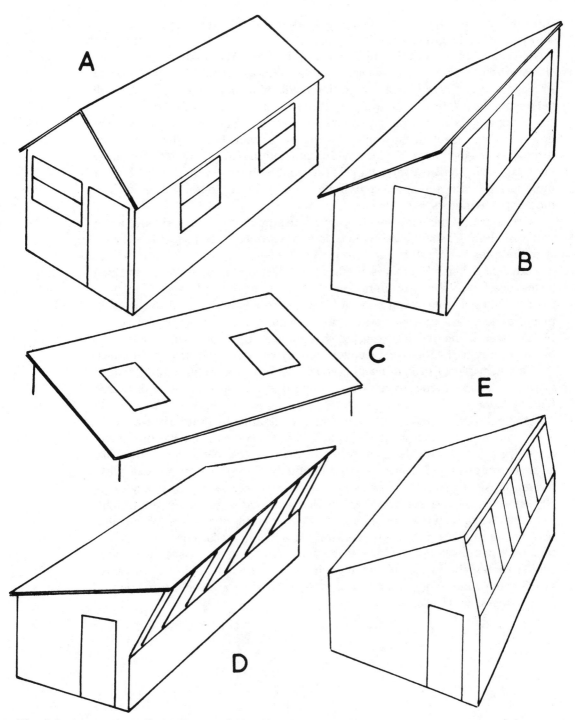

Fig. 1-8. Arrange in walls (A,B) or roof (C). Sloping windows give different types of illumination.

occasional inside activity, but for lengthy work sessions, you will appreciate windows along the length of a side (FIG. 1-8B).

Do you want the sun shining in most of the time? You might if the window side also will serve as a greenhouse. If so, the windows should face south, so far as the location of the building allows. If you will be working at a bench, you will get a more even spread of natural light if the windows face north.

In some parts of the country, you must consider insulation in relation to windows. You can insulate the walls and roof to prevent heat and cold passing through, but large areas of glass might eliminate much of this effect because glass has really no insulating properties. Double glazing would help, but for most small buildings, that is a complication you will want to avoid. It is better to have as few windows as possible.

If you arrange the windows to open, make sure they have a good seal when you close them. A small window in a door is worth considering, as it will help with the spread of natural light.

Daylight through the roof is another possibility for sunlight. When working inside, overhead lighting is often more welcome than side lighting(FIG. 1-8C).

Preventing leakage might be a problem, but roof lights are available to build in as a package. Making your own is not difficult. You easily can fit transparent plastic sheeting into metal-corrugated sheeting. A surprisingly small amount of daylight through the roof will be better than a greater window area in the walls.

To obtain plenty of lighting in a work area with the minimum amount of glare, you might arrange windows all along one wall so they slope outwards (FIG. 1-8D).

Another way to provide maximum and even lighting in a studio or workshop is to make a *north-light roof* (FIG. 1-8E). The name comes from the practice of arranging the roof with the glass facing as near as possible to the north. This arrangement gives you an even spread of natural light throughout the day, without much risk of glare. If the ridge surfaces are at 90 degrees, the eaves angles are 30 degrees and 60 degrees, bringing the glass at a good angle for spreading light.

Windows only in the roof are a good idea for a building where there would be a risk of animals or vandals breaking glass in the walls. However, keep in mind that windows do not have to be glass. Transparent plastic alternatives could be acceptable in a small building where you want light let in, but the finest visibility in or out is not important. If you are building a greenhouse, you will find plastic easier to use.

2
Building Materials

You can use several types of materials to make small buildings. Brick or stone provide the most substantial structures, but you also can make buildings completely of metal, or ones with wooden frames and metal covering. Some plastic materials are suitable for cladding and roofing over wood or metal supports. Using manufactured boards with a wooden base in parts of a building is also acceptable. Nonetheless, most small buildings are made of wood throughout, or with only small amounts of other materials.

This book is for the woodworker who wants to make one or more small buildings and prefers to use the material he knows. Most of the work is quite straightforward and does not have the complications associated with making good furniture or with similar, better-quality woodworking. Obviously, skill is worth having, but you can do much of the work successfully with minimal skill simply by working carefully.

The tools you need are not many. If you have a comprehensive tool kit, you will certainly find uses for it, but it is possible to make many buildings with very few tools, particularly if you get all the wood sawed and planed to size from a lumberyard.

You can use hand or power tools. The main advantages of using power tools are that they can speed up some operations, and they might allow you to gain accuracy, particularly when you prepare parts in the workshop. Once on the site, though, you are more likely to reach for a handsaw or a plane, and you will make much use of a hammer, for which there is no satisfactory power alternative.

The most useful power tool is an electric drill. A router with a few plain cutters will speed up the making of joints. If you have a portable power saw, you will use it, but you can cut most wood for your building easily with a handsaw.

Materials

You can use almost any wood for a small building. Much will depend on what is available in your area. Some woods are more durable than others, but preservatives on the less-durable woods will give them a long life. In general, there is no need to use hardwood. Most hardwoods are harder to work with than softwoods, and they are unnecessarily heavy. Most are also considerably more expensive than softwoods. Some very resinous woods have a good resistance to rot, and you can even use a few of these without treatment on the outside. Consequently, such woods weather to a pleasant color that might blend in well with the surroundings. Normally, though, you should paint or treat most small wooden buildings so they are protected from the effects of sun and rain.

Any of the common softwoods are acceptable choices for your wooden buildings. Wood with a few small knots should work satisfactorily, but for the structural parts, try to get wood with reasonably straight grain and few knots. If a knot is black around its outside, it is loose and will not contribute to strength, even if it does not fall out. Of course, a knot that falls out of cladding or siding would be a nuisance. Knots without black rims are less trouble.

For many parts of most small buildings you can use sawed wood, but where it will show, it is better to use planed wood. Planing at a mill will reduce sizes by about $1/4$ inch, and you must allow for that. For instance, 2-×-4-inch wood planed all around actually will be about $1^3/4 \times 3^3/4$ inches. If the structure will be hidden between the outside covering and an inner lining, you could use sawed wood and get the benefit of extra strength from the thicker wood. It also should be cheaper. Let your supplier see the materials list. If they can provide short pieces, you might get a better price and service than if you tried to buy long lengths to cut yourself.

Plywood

You can use plywood in many thicknesses for several parts of a small building. Sheets are mostly 4×8 feet, so it is wise to scheme building parts to use sheets whole or to cut them economically.

Any wood that can have the log rotated and peeled into thin veneers can be made into plywood. Much of the available plywood is made of Douglas fir, which is satisfactory for buildings, but many other woods are available, some of which have a better appearance and take paint or finish better.

Plywood is available in grades determined mostly by appearance. Prices can vary considerably, and there is no point in paying for plywood free from knots in both surface veneers if one side will be hidden.

More important is the purpose for which you intend to use the plywood.

Today, most glues used in plywood have a good resistance to moisture, but this is not always true. *General-purpose plywood* might be suitable only for indoor use. However, if the inside of a small building will get wet, it is better to avoid general-purpose plywood. *External plywood* has a waterproof glue, which makes it a good choice for the construction of small buildings. *Marine-grade plywood* is even better quality than external plywood, as the plies and their arrangement, as well as the glue, suit boat-building. Marine-grade plywood costs more, though, and external plywood will do the job for your small building projects.

Particleboard

As its name implies, particleboard is made of particles or chips of wood embedded in a resin. Boards are the same size as plywood. For our purpose, it should not be less than 3/4 inch thick for strength and stiffness. You can saw it and plane it, but it is unsuitable for cutting joints.

Most particleboard will suffer if exposed to moisture, so it is unsuitable for outside use, even when you paint it.

Particleboard will make good floors. With its large, overall coverage, it might be better in your building than a floor made of many comparatively narrow boards. Similarly, it makes good one-piece shelves, but would not be suitable in a greenhouse or another place where it would be wet for long periods.

You can nail or screw particleboard. For nails near an edge, it is advisable to drill undersized holes, to avoid breaking out. For screwing into particleboard, a tapping-size hole should be taken as far as the thread will go. A screw will not cut its own way to the full depth, as it will in wood.

Hardboard

Hardboard is made from compressed wood fibers, and the sheets commonly available have one very smooth side and a patterned, opposite side. Sheets are the same size as plywood, but the thickness is only 1/2 inch.

The quality of hardboard available varies tremendously, and is largely dependent on its density. Some of it is little better than cardboard and will disintegrate in a similar way if you allow it to become wet. This hardboard, and even the better- quality, general-purpose hardboard, is unsuitable for use in a small building, except possibly for backs of cupboards or bottoms of drawers in the furnishings of the building. You could use it as a lining, when there is insulation material between it and the outer covering, but the oil-tempered type would be better.

Hardboard might be treated so it has an oil impregnation that gives it a resistance to water. It is not waterproof if subjected to moisture for a long period. Trade names vary, but there is usually something in the name to indicate "oil-tempered." You can use oil-tempered hardboard for the outside surface of a building, but you must paint it constantly. Better coverings are available.

You can obtain hardboard sheets already perforated with a pattern of small holes, probably called *peg board* or something similar. This material is not usually oil-tempered. You can buy a variety of metal clips to hook into these holes, turning the board into a great tool rack. Peg board also will make a ventilated lining, but hardboard has only limited use in a better small building.

Insulation

For many purposes, it might not be necessary to consider insulation for a small building. If it is just a storage place for garden tools, the inside temperature might not be important. If it is a workshop for year-round use, you will want to keep a comfortable temperature whatever the condition is outside.

Wood in itself provides some insulation—better than metal or solid plastic. If you have wood outside and wood or hardboard lining, the air between the two also will provide a temperature barrier. You can improve this barrier by adding one of the insulation materials used in home buildings, such as fiberglass.

Wall insulation will be helpful, but roof insulation is important and not so easy to provide. Because heat rises, much of it could escape through an uninsulated roof. A lining could hold insulation material directly under the roof, or you might fit a ceiling with insulation material above it. A wooden floor, providing the wind cannot blow under it, might be its own sufficient insulation.

Precautions to keep heat in will work in reverse, too, if keeping cool is your problem. You can then have plenty of open windows and doors to increase ventilation. Whether heat or cold is your problem, ventilation is important, otherwise your building could suffer from condensation. Arrange ventilators low and high so air can circulate. You can create a pattern of holes with flaps to cover, if the breeze is in the wrong direction, or you want to keep out rodents.

Wooden Sections

Most of the wood you use in a small building will be plain, rectangular sections and in stock sizes. For covering, you can buy boards that provide weatherproofing, even if they expand and contract. If the boards are to shed water, arrange them horizontally so they overlap. Simple weatherboarding has a tapered section (FIG. 2-1A). Clapboard has the tapered section, and shiplap board is parallel (FIG. 2-1B). Both have rabbets so boards can be fitted to lay flat on their supports. The name *shiplap* comes from the similarity to the way planks are laid in lapstrake boat building.

If you are to lay the boards vertically, you can use tongue-and-groove joints. A plain joint is not as attractive as some others. If the wood shrinks, the gaps are very obvious (FIG. 2-1C). You can make this gap less obvious with chamfers (FIG. 2-1D). Another form that disguises the gap has a bead (FIG. 2-1E). Doors are usually made with vertical boards, even if the wall cladding is horizontal.

The window surround must protect wall-covering boards. In particular, rain must not run behind the boards. At the bottom, there should be a sill with its top sloping to shed water, and, underneath, there should be a groove to prevent water from running back (FIG. 2-1F). Stock sections are available.

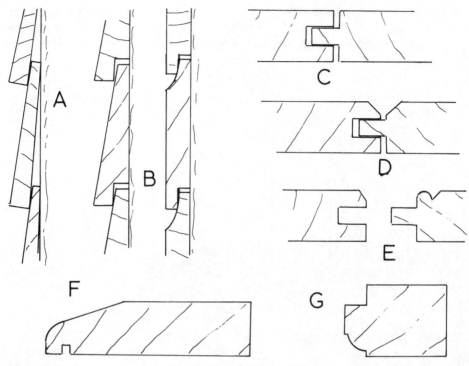

Fig. 2-1. Arrange or join boards in several ways to provide weatherproofness (A,B,C,D,E). A groove under a sill stops water from running underneath (F). You can mold a section with a rabbet (G).

Window glass is fitted best between wood fillets or into a rabbet. If you do not prepare your own, you can buy a stock section. This section might be molded also (FIG. 2-1G). You might be able to find a similar section for a door surround and another for a door step. Unfortunately, some stock sections are meant for home building and might be too big for a small, wooden building. Check what is available locally, and you might be able to plan details of your building to use these standard pieces.

Nailing

In many parts of your small building projects, you might not need to do anything more elaborate than put one piece of wood on top of another and nail it there. Occasionally, screws might be more suitable than nails. Usually there is no need for glue as well as nails, but a waterproof glue will strengthen the joint. Anything less than a fully waterproof glue would have only a brief life.

For most assemblies, you can use common or box nails. If you want the heads to be less prominent or if you want to punch them below the surface, casing or flooring nails with small heads are available. Their grip is not as strong, so you need more of them. For increased hold in the lower piece of wood, *ringshank* or *barbed-ring* nails are available. Another increased-hold nail has a twisted shank. For corrugated roofing, you can use nails with special heads or other roofing nails made with large heads (FIG. 2-2).

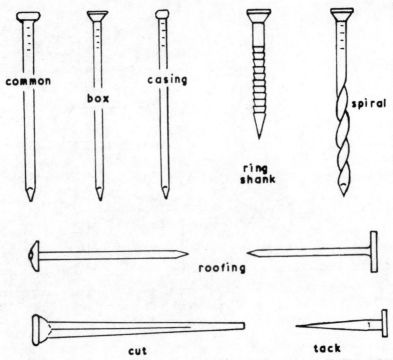

Fig. 2-2. You will use a variety of nails in constructing small wooden buildings.

Driving a nail has a splitting action on the wood fibers. In most positions, this splitting is not enough to matter, but near an end or when using very large nails, it is best to drill before driving. You should drill deep enough to clear, or almost clear, the top piece, and you need to drill an undersized hole in the lower piece (FIG. 2-3A). An increased grip comes from driving nails at alternate slight angles (FIG. 2-3B) to give a dovetail effect. This technique of driving nails with increased grip should be used only when you are certain the joint will never have to be pulled apart. Levering the joint open then might break out fibers or split the wood.

Most often, nails are made of steel, and these will probably be your choice for general construction of a building. Keep in mind, though, that steel will rust. It might not rust enough to matter, but nails in very wet conditions can rust away completely. Rust also might come through the paint and leave brown spots or streaks. You can purchase steel nails that are protected by *galvanizing* (coating with zinc) or other corrosion-resistant metals.

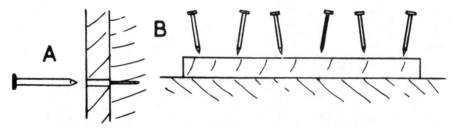

Fig. 2-3. Drill for nails to avoid splitting (A). Dovetail nailing (B) is stronger than straight nailing.

Aluminum nails will not corrode enough to matter. Stainless-steel nails are good to use, but they are very expensive. If you are nailing through metal, it is better to use nails of the same metal to prevent any electrolytic action between different metals, which causes corrosion. This corrosion might happen with aluminum guttering.

Screws and Bolts

Common, flat-head, wood screws are the alternatives to nails in some circumstances. Other types might be more appropriate to hinges or other metal attachments. In some buildings, there is a need for very large screws. You then need a *lag* or *coach screw*, which has a head to suit a wrench (FIG. 2-4A). Drill for it, and start it with a blow from a hammer.

Screws are made in at least as many different metals as nails, and you can buy them with various protective coatings. Galvanizing tends to be rough, which might be an advantage because of its increased grip if you are dealing with large sections of rough wood, such as posts.

Bolts are obtainable in many forms and sizes. In general, if you ask for a bolt, it is threaded to take a nut only part of its length. If you want it threaded almost to the head, you must ask for a screw. General-purpose machine bolts have square or hexagonal heads and nuts (FIG. 2-4B). Stove bolts are long and thin with screwdriver heads (FIG. 2-4C).

The bolts most useful in small buildings are coach or carriage bolts (FIG. 2-4D). Under the shallow-domed head is a square neck that pulls into the wood and prevents the bolt from turning as you tighten the nut. It also retains the bolt in the wood, although you can knock it out if you have to. This characteristic is valuable if you want to disassemble occasionally. Always use a large washer under nuts on softwood.

For attaching wood to masonry, you have a choice of methods. This choice is particularly true on the foundations. The first way is to set special bolts in the concrete as you lay it, or even use an ordinary bolt with a large washer under its head to grip the concrete (FIG. 1-4C). The other way is to drill downwards, using a fastener or plug that will grip the concrete. With the first method, you have to care-

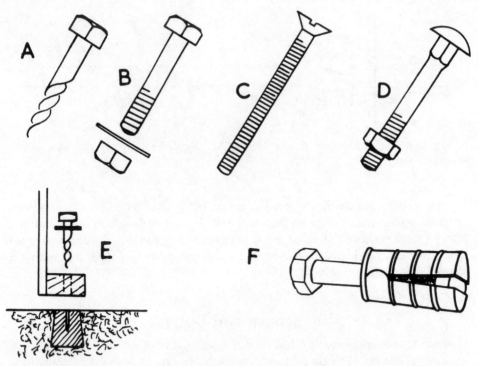

Fig. 2-4. You need large screws and bolts for joining parts of buildings and anchoring them to their foundations.

fully locate the wood over bolt ends already there. In the second method, you can drill downwards through the wood, so exact positioning is not so important.

Sometimes wooden blocks are let into the concrete (FIG. 2-4E), but they should be rot-resistant wood or you might find that the attachment to the foundation is negligible if the wood is weakened by rot.

Methods of attaching downward into concrete involve drilling fairly large holes, for which you will need special equipment. Several types of anchors are available. They have a part that goes into the hole which is then expanded by driving a bolt or screw into it. A typical anchor has a body in two parts. When you drive a bolt in, you force the parts outward (FIG. 2-4F).

Joints

In some frames it might be strong enough to simply nail joints where parts meet (FIG. 2-5A and B). If you cannot nail from outside, you could nail diagonally inside (FIG. 2-5C). To ensure exact location, you could nail a guide block at one or both sides of a nailed joint (FIG. 2-5D).

For more exact positioning when nailing, you could cut shallow notches at corners (FIG. 2-5E) or at intermediate positions (FIG. 2-5F). These aids to accuracy are important at doorways and at window openings.

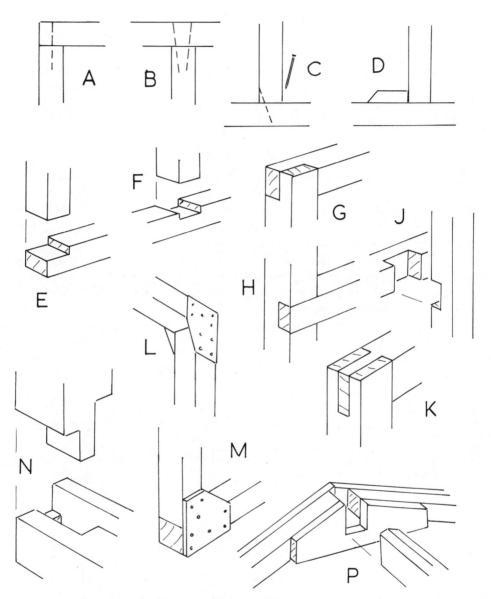

Fig. 2-5. *Nail joints in framing or hold them with cut joints.*

For stronger joints, you can halve the parts together, whether at corners (FIG. 2-5G), intermediately (FIG. 2-5H) or where parts cross (FIG. 2-5J).

All of these joints should be satisfactory when you can expect some strength from the covering, but if the framework has to be strong, you can use open mortise-and-tenon or bridle joints (FIG. 2-5K) at corners or intermediately. Nailed joints can be strengthened with sheet metal on both sides (FIG. 2-5L) or with a plywood gusset on the side away from the covering (FIG. 2-5M).

Corners of rabbeted frames, as in windows, are better joined with haunched mortise-and-tenon joints (FIG. 2-5N). For a three-way joint, as at the ridge, you can make a gusset for the third piece (FIG. 2-5P) or support it on a rail.

A framework clad with plywood contributes strength, and frame joints can be simple to result in a stiff assembly. With board covering, there is more risk of distortion, and stronger frame joints are advisable. A plywood lining, securely attached, will contribute more stiffness.

Sectional Construction

Even if the building you are making will never be taken apart and moved, you might find it advantageous to prefabricate some parts. This type of construction allows you to take whole sections to the site and have little to do except join them together. If you have the space to assemble sides and ends on the shop floor, you can do squaring, accurate laying out, and cutting joints more easily than in position while erecting the building. If size for transport is a problem, it might be possible to make a side in two parts and bolt them together at the job site.

You will have to use a little more wood when you are making prefabricated sections. For instance, if you make everything as you assemble on-site, one corner post will take the covering in both directions (FIG. 2-6A). If you wish to prefab-

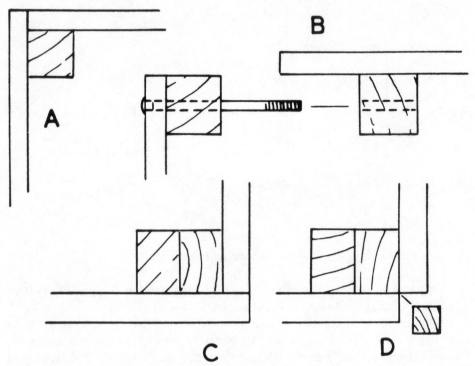

Fig. 2-6. For the simplest corners, nail them on one post. Others might bolt through two posts, with the skin overlapping or with a filler in the corner.

ricate, there must be an upright on both assemblies. They might nail together for a permanent assembly, or there could be carriage bolts (FIG. 2-6B). The extra strength from double corner posts might be worth having, but you could reduce sections and still have them as strong as a single post.

The covering boards could merely overlap at a corner (FIG. 2-6C), but you will protect end grain and improve the appearance when you nail in a covering strip (FIG. 2-6D).

If you have framed and boarded the roof, you might attach it in a sectional building with carriage bolts, if you arrange strips to come over the gable framing. Although you can drill holes for bolts in the roof framing or position bolts under the outer boarding, you might want to leave drilling the gables or trusses until the first assembly so that you can allow for slight variations, particularly with a ridged roof. Subsequent disassembly and re-erection will be easier if you mark all meeting parts.

When prefabricating, it is easy to accurately square door and window openings and make the fitting parts, but you might have to plane for accurate fitting after the building is in position. Even if you intend a door to reach the floor, it is advisable to make the side or end that will contain it with the bottom strip going across the opening, to keep the assembly free from twist. Cut through it after you attach the wood on each side to the floor or foundation.

3

Simple Storage Units

Several small buildings, or structures sometimes almost too small to be called buildings, might be useful on your property. A common need is for storage of garden tools, possibly some distance from your garage or main storage place, if your garden is extensive. Other items might not need much space, such as loose boating equipment near a dock or barbecue items that you prefer to keep apart from other things.

Construction is similar to any other small building, although some parts might be smaller and the work simpler. If your experience of constructing wooden buildings is slight or you are a beginning woodworker, one of these smaller assemblies will make a good introduction. It is unlikely you will go wrong, but if you do, you will not waste much material.

A very compact assembly is attractive, but make sure it will hold all you expect it to, and probably a little more. If you are preparing for garden hand tools, you do not want to have to force in something with a long handle diagonally, when you can plan for a few more inches to allow it to go in straight and cause less of an obstruction to other tools. Gather the equipment you plan to store and check to make sure you are allowing adequate internal measurements.

Upright Garden Tool Locker

You can make a storage unit quite simply with framed plywood. The locker shown in FIG. 3-1 is made mostly from 1/2-inch exterior plywood on 11/2-inch-square strips. It could fit against a fence or stand as an independent unit. As shown, it is assumed that it has a dirt floor, but a plywood bottom could rest on

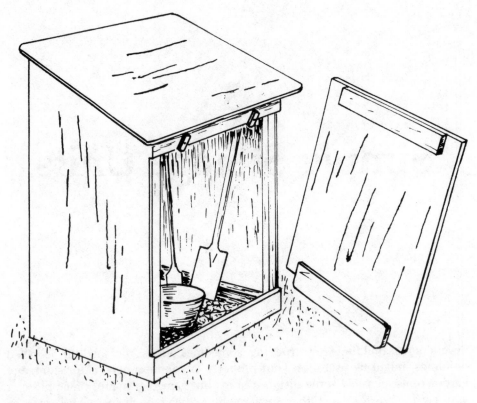

Fig. 3-1. This tool locker stores most tools upright.

Materials List for Upright Garden Tool Locker

2 sides	½- × -30- × -60 plywood
1 back	½- × -31- × -60 plywood
1 top	½- × -36- × -36 plywood
1 door	½- × -31- × -44 plywood
2 frames	1½ × 1½ × 60
2 frames	1½ × 1½ × 52
8 frames	1½ × 1½ × 30
2 front strips	½ × 3 × 32
2 door strips	½ × 3 × 29

the lower framing. The door lifts out, which allows the maximum access to the inside, but you could hinge it at one side.

Check the sizes of your equipment, but the locker shown in FIG. 3-2 should hold most gardening hand tools and lighter power tools.

Make the pair of sides first (FIG. 3-3A). Cut the plywood to shape and nail it to the framing strips. There is no need to cut joints between the framing parts. If you wish, allow extensions at the bottom to go into the ground (FIG. 3-3B). The

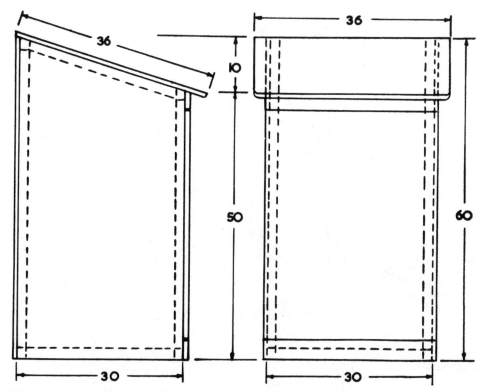

Fig. 3-2. Sizes of the upright garden-tool locker.

back goes over the sides and has stiffening pieces at top and bottom (FIG. 3-3C). Plane the top ply edge and its strip to match the shape of the roof.

At the front strips, go across above and below the door (FIG. 3-3D,E). They could be solid wood or plywood. Inside each put stiffening strips.

Check squareness in all directions, then add the roof. If the locker will come against a wall, stop the roof level with the back, but otherwise you can overlap it a small amount. Allow a good overlap on the other edges and around all corners.

Make the door to overlap the sides and fit easily between the front strips (FIG. 3-3F). Put a stiffening strip inside the top and one at the bottom to hook over the front piece (FIG. 3-3G). These strips should fit easily between the locker sides so you can put the door in or take it out without trouble.

You could drill two finger holes at the top of the door or cut a wooden block as a handle. Make two strip-wood turnbuttons to hold the door closed. Alternatively, fit a hasp and staple for a padlock or add an ordinary door lock.

Horizontal Garden Tool Locker

If there is no convenient wall to put an upright locker against, or if you want something less prominent in which to store tools, a horizontal locker might be

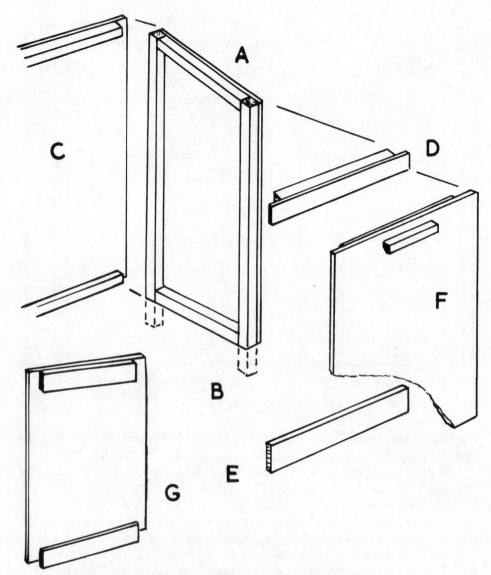

Fig. 3-3. Construction details of the upright garden-tool locker.

the answer. If you paint it green or allow it to weather to a natural color, it will be inconspicuous. The locker shown in FIG. 3-4 has a sloping lid to shed water, and part of the front opens for easy access to the tools inside. The bottom is raised clear of the ground.

You can use solid wood throughout, but these instructions assume the skin is made of 3/4-inch exterior plywood, with 1 1/2- or 2-inch-square framing. As with the first locker, check the space you need for your tools. The sizes suggested should suit most needs (FIG. 3-5).

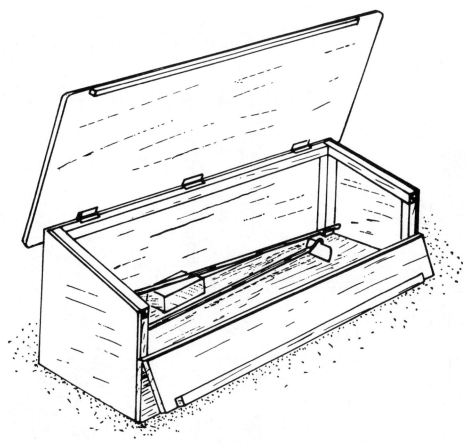

Fig. 3-4. *The horizontal tool locker has a lifting lid and a fall front for easy access.*

Materials List for Horizontal Garden Tool Locker

2 ends	¾- × -24-	× -24 plywood
1 back	¾- × -24-	× -60 plywood
2 fronts	¾- × - 9-	× -60 plywood
1 lid	¾- × -30-	× -65 plywood
1 bottom	¾- × -24-	× -60 plywood
6 frames	1½ × 1½ × 25	
2 frames	1½ × 1½ × 18	
4 frames	1½ × 1½ × 60	
1 lid edge	¾ × ¾ × 60	

Make the pair of ends (FIGS. 3-5A and 3-6A). Nail the plywood to the framing, preferably with the crosswise pieces overlapping the uprights. The back (FIG. 3-6B) overlaps the ends, and you should stiffen it at the top and the bottom with pieces which fit closely between the ends.

Form the front by hinging two pieces together (FIG. 3-5B). Make the lower part

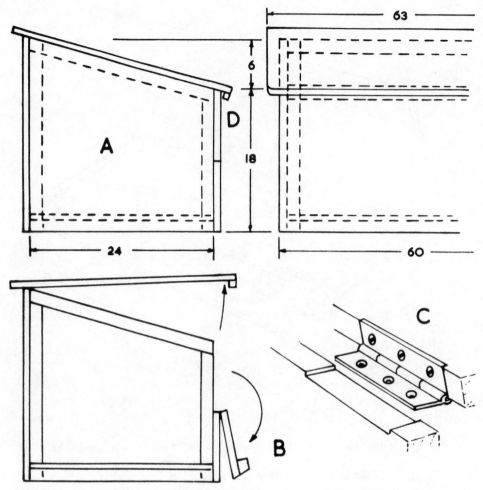

Fig. 3-5. *Sizes of the horizontal tool locker.*

with a stiffened bottom edge, in the same way as the back. Before nailing the lower part on, make the bottom to rest on the four bottom framing pieces, with notches around the uprights (FIG. 3-6C). Nail in the bottom and the front.

The meeting edges of the front (FIG. 3-6D) should be stiff enough to take three hinges (FIG. 3-5C). If you are doubtful about them holding their shape, put strips along their inner edges. Make the top part with framing along its upper edge to match the slope of the lid.

Make the lid with about 1½-inch overlap all around it. Round its corners and edges. If it is necessary to stiffen the lid, put pieces across inside so they clear the framing when you close it. The front strip (FIG. 3-5D) should hold that edge in shape. Hinge the lid to the back. Be sure it rests on the ends and the flap at the front. If necessary, plane these parts for a reasonably close fit, then there should

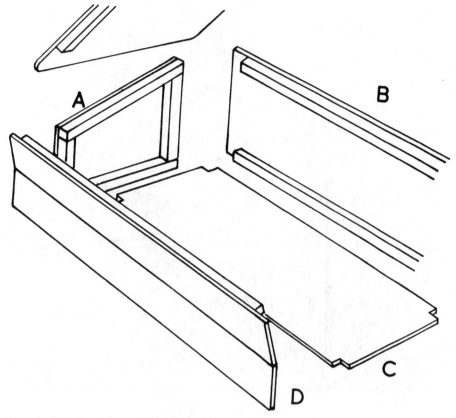

Fig. 3-6. The framed parts of the horizontal tool locker.

be no need for fasteners or handles. The weight of the lid will keep the flap closed, but a slight lift at the front allows you to pull open both hinged parts.

Walk-in Garden Shed

If a tool locker is too small for your storage needs, you can make a simple shed. It would be just big enough to walk in, but not large enough to work inside. It need not have windows and the head room might be minimal. If these are your needs, the shed in FIG. 3-7 is easy to make and the materials cost much less than for a larger building.

The suggested sizes shown in FIG. 3-8A are for a sectional building that you can make elsewhere and assemble in position, or you can disassemble it if you wish to move it. You can use plywood completely for the cladding, or you can board the walls and the roof or make the roof of plywood. In either case, cover the roof with roofing felt or other waterproof material. Framing might be nearly all 2-inch-square sections. Board the door or make it of plywood.

Fig. 3-7. The walk-in garden shed allows you to get into the storage unit.

Materials List for Walk-in Garden Shed

Ends

2 uprights	2	×	2	×	86
4 uprights	2	×	2	×	75
2 bottoms	2	×	2	×	56
2 tops	2	×	2	×	59
1 door rail	2	×	2	×	30

Back

4 uprights	2	×	2	×	75
2 rails	2	×	2	×	60

Front

4 uprights	2	×	2	×	86
2 rails	2	×	2	×	60

Roof

3 strips	2	×	2	×	54
2 panels	¾- × -35- × -66 plywood				

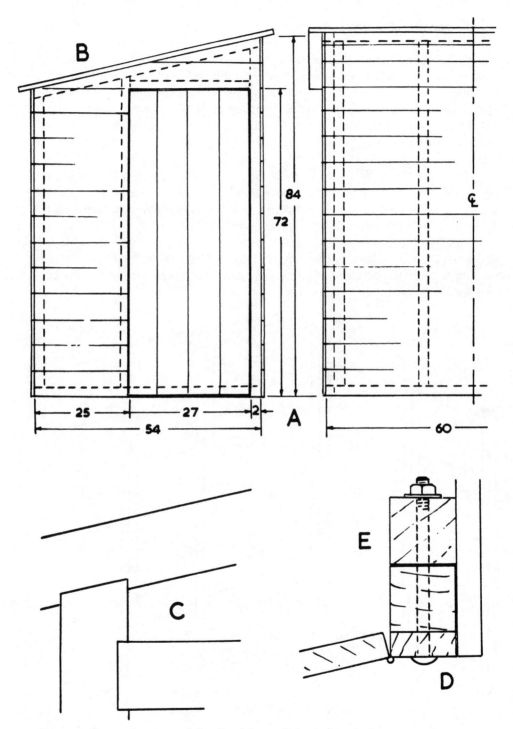

Fig. 3-8. Sizes and structural details of the walk-in garden shed.

The pair of ends control other sizes. Allow for the door in one end (FIGS. 3-8B and 3-9A). At the other end, the upright might be central. If the covering is plywood, it might provide sufficient strength at the corners for the framing pieces to abut against each other, but otherwise you should join them in one of the ways described in chapter 2. Locate all joints away from the corners with notches (FIG. 3-8C). Make sure the doorway will finish square. Horizontal boarding is shown in FIG. 3-8, but you could nail on vertical boards. At the high side of the door panel, put a vertical board (FIG. 3-8D). Finish the boards or plywood covering level with the framing all around.

Frame the back and front in the same way, with corner and intermediate joints similar to those of the ends. Use the ends as a guide to heights, and bevel the top members of both panels to match the slope of the ends. Two intermediate uprights should provide sufficient stiffness (FIG. 3-9B).

Allow for the boards on the back and the front to overlap the ends, so the end uprights are set back sufficiently (FIG. 3-8E). Drill for $^3/_8$-inch bolts. A bolt near the top and the bottom and two evenly spaced between the top and the bottom should be enough on each corner.

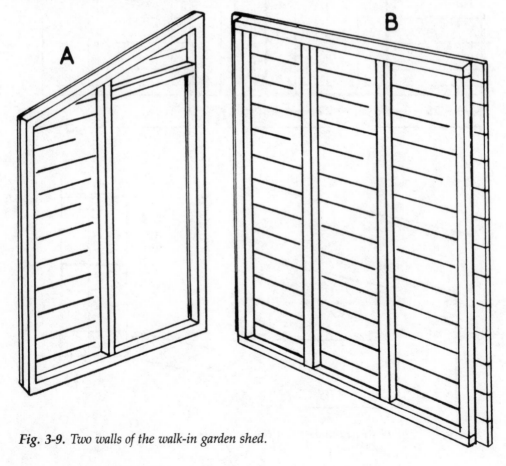

Fig. 3-9. Two walls of the walk-in garden shed.

For a boarded door (FIG. 3-10A), three ledgers should be level at the hinge side but set back a little at the other side. One brace should be enough to prevent sagging. Position the top and bottom ledgers so you can screw into them from the hinges, which might be T hinges on the surface, or you can let in ordinary hinges between the door and its post. A metal loop handle would be suitable, or you could make one out of wood or turn a knob on a lathe. The simplest fastener is a strip-wood turnbutton, but you could fit a lock on the door. The door will close against the bottom framing strip. That strip might be sufficient, but you could put a short stop piece near the top as well.

The roof is larger than you can make from a normal-size, single sheet of plywood. You can have a joint at the center (FIG. 3-10B). Make the size sufficient to give an overhang of about 3 inches all around. Three strips across should fit easily between the shed back and front. Those at the ends come inside the shed ends. They will hold the building square, and you should bolt them through in a similar way to the corners—three bolts on each end should be sufficient.

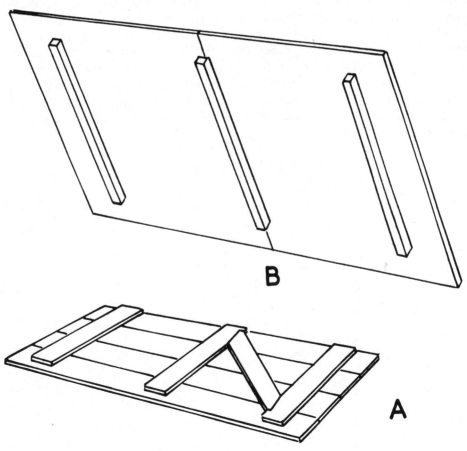

Fig. 3-10. Door and roof for the walk-in garden shed.

Although you could leave the plywood roof with just a paint finish, it would be better to cover it with a waterproof material. This covering should be the last job after you erect the building. Bolt it down to its foundation, and paint all the woodwork or treat it with preservative. For the best protection, paint inside the corners before bolting them together.

Lean-to Shed

If there is an existing high wall, fence, or side of a house, you might wish to make a small building as a lean-to attached to it. This construction means you already have a rigid support that will hold the building in shape and protect it from the effect of high winds. If it is upright and straight, it gives you a datum for squaring the building you are adding. If you check and find it is not true, do not make the new building to conform to its errors. The added shed should be upright and square or it will look wrong. Where the new shed meets the untrue wall, you should fair it in. You might be able to cut covering boards to conform, or you might have to attach shaped uprights to the wall, with their outer edges vertical. Treat the roof joint similarly. Obviously, the roof joint must be weathertight.

Consider the effect of the addition on its surroundings. Will you have to divert a path around it? Will it obstruct light or view through an existing window? When you put down foundations of whatever type make sure they cannot cause rainwater to run back into the house foundation. If you are joining onto a fence, is it in suitable condition for your purpose? You might be giving yourself more work in the future if you will have to replace the fence because of rot or for other reasons.

Materials List for Lean-to Shed

4 uprights	2	×	2	×	92
6 uprights	2	×	2	×	74
2 uprights	1	×	2	×	74
5 rails	2	×	2	×	96
2 rails	2	×	2	×	76
2 door rails	2	×	2	×	50
4 end rails	2	×	2	×	36
2 end rails	2	×	2	×	56
4 window posts	2	×	2	×	26
1 window sill	1	×	4	×	74
18 window frames	¾	×	¾	×	24
9 window frames	¾	×	3½	×	24
2 door frames	¾	×	3½	×	76
1 door frame	¾	×	3½	×	32
2 backs	1	×	6	×	100
4 roof frames	2	×	2	×	96
3 roof edges	1	×	1	×	108
Covering—tongue-and-groove ¾ × 6					

If you want to walk into it, a lean-to building must have enough height for a door. Slope the roof away from the existing wall. You can have a flat roof, but you should give it a slight slope so it sheds water. A steeper slope is usually better, particularly if you get heavy snowfalls. For a gardener's shed, the height at the outer wall can be less than 6 feet, if there is a worktop inside, so you do not walk right up to the wall. You may modify the sizes suggested to suit your situation.

The building shown in FIG. 3-11 is covered with vertical, matched boarding. For horizontal boarding, arrange the framing upright. For a plywood skin, the framing is satisfactory as shown. All of the parts are prefabricated—two ends and a front, with a roof that you can make in position.

Fig. 3-11. *This lean-to shed fits against a wall and has windows in its lower side.*

The ends settle the sizes of other parts. Make the door end first (FIG. 3-12). It is shown 72 inches wide with a height sloping from 90 inches to 72 inches, but this stage is where you make your modifications, if required. Assemble the frame with 2- inch-square strips, notching them into each other, and jointing the corners or using gussets (FIG. 2-5). The strip at the outer corner need only be 1 inch thick to fit inside the front piece (FIG. 3-12A).

At top and bottom of the high edge, notch the framing to take boards which you will use to screw the assembly to the supporting wall (FIG. 3-12B,C). Cover the framing with tongue-and-groove boards of about a 3/4-inch finished thickness and a 6-inch width. Allow for the overlap on the front (FIG. 3-12E).

Fit strips around the door sides and top to cover the boards and framing (FIG. 3-12D). Let these project forward with rounded edges. Leave the frame strip across the bottom of the door opening, either permanently or until after you have fastened down the walls.

Use this first end as a pattern for making the opposite end identical. Carry the rails right across. The boarding probably will provide adequate vertical stiffness, but if necessary, include some uprights between the rails. Cover that end with tongue-and-groove boards. If you wish, you can add another door or a window in the end. Arrange it as described for the front.

Make the door with upright boards similar to the covering. Put three ledges across and one or two diagonals. Put a strip as a stop on the side of the opening the door will close against. Arrange three hinges, a handle, and a lock or other fastener.

Make the front (FIG. 3-13) to match the height of the ends. You could bevel the top to match the slope of the roof, although you should get a close enough fit for most purposes by letting the roof rest on the front edge. Make all the framework with 2-inch-square strips, with joints similar to those in the ends. Corners fit inside the shed ends (FIG. 3-12F). Cover the framing with upright boards in the same way as the ends.

For the window openings, make a sill the full length, and notch it around the intermediate uprights (FIG. 3-13A). Put pieces of covering board over the two uprights, and frame around the window openings in a similar way to the doorway (FIG. 3-13B). Put strips around to make recesses for the glass (FIG. 13-3C).

Postpone fitting the glass until you have erected the shed. When you do fit it, putty the glass into the recesses or use more wooden strips.

As you erect the ends and front to the wall, screw or bolt the horizontal strips into their recesses at the back and fasten through them into the wall, taking care that their lengths match the front or you will be unable to square the assembly. If you do not expect to move the building, you can nail or screw the front corners; otherwise, use bolts. Fit square strips to cover the board edges.

The roof could be 3/4-inch plywood or tongue-and-groove boards laid with their smooth sides upwards. In both cases, use framing strips at about 18-inch intervals to fit inside the walls. Allow for an overlap of about 6 inches on the shed

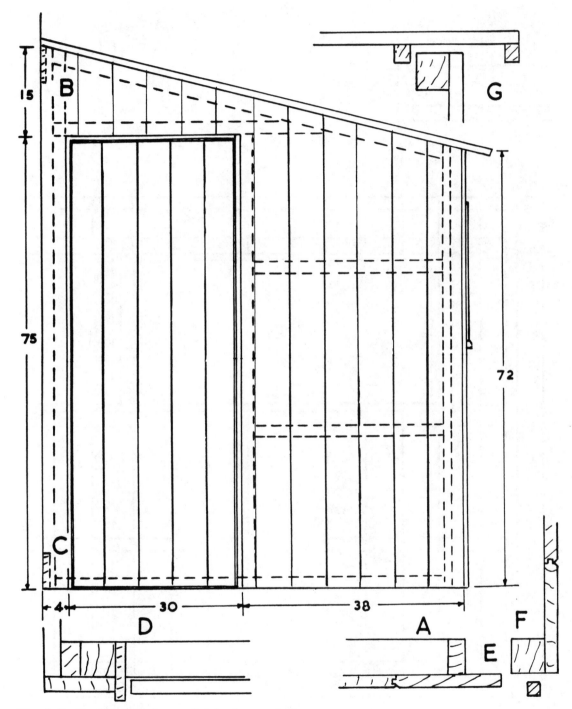

Fig. 3-12. Details of the door end of the lean-to shed.

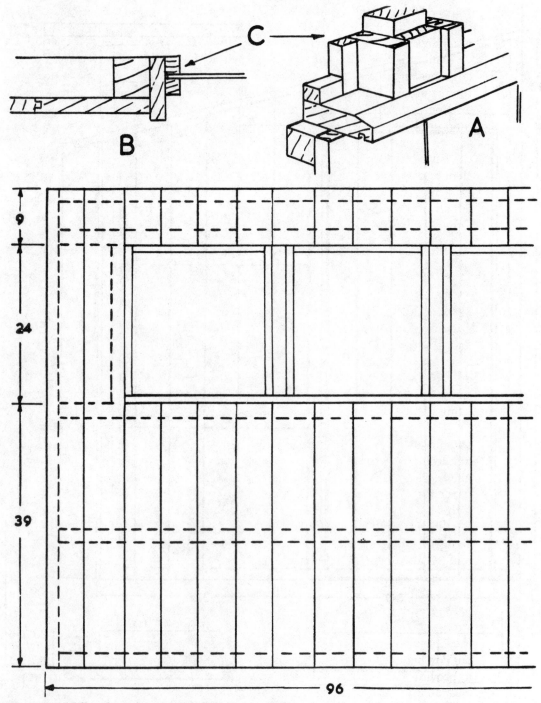

Fig. 3-13. Wall and window details of the lean-to shed.

walls. At the supporting wall, bevel to make a close fit and fair the edges if necessary. Edge the outer limits of the roof (FIG. 3-12G). More strips inside will help when locating places where other roof framing parts do not come.

Nail or screw on the roof. Cover it with tarred felt or other material. At the edges, wrap around the border pieces. At the top edge, the joint will depend on the material of the fence or wall. If possible, carry the covering material up so existing clapboards or other projections will shed water over the cover rather than under it. Screw strips through the covering to secure it. It might be necessary to use a jointing compound or mastic to ensure complete waterproofing.

For storing and preparing garden plants and equipment, it might be sufficient to paint the building and leave it as it is. For a neater inside and to provide some insulation, line the walls with hardboard or plywood. A broad shelf the full length under the windows will serve as a bench and also will brace the walls. Other shelves and storage arrangements attached to two or three walls also will provide stiffness.

Stressed-skin Gardener's Shed

Plywood has considerable strength. Obviously, it is stable compared with a covering of many independent boards. It holds framing and other parts in shape and is strong in itself. Much more strength comes from the skin than does an assembly with other covering. This fact applies if the plywood is on one side only, but if it is on both sides, a very rigid structure results. Even if there is only air between the skins, that provides some insulation. If you fill spaces with insulating batting or other materials, a good, all-weather building results.

The building shown in FIG. 3-14 is intended to have plywood inside as well as outside. Its sizes are arranged to cut standard sheets of 4-×-8-foot plywood economically. Two windows are suggested, but you can arrange others to suit your needs. The end door is far enough from one side to allow wide shelves there or a bench for a gardener's use. A bench for a hobby could go under the end window. If this is to be a year-round shed a wooden floor is advisable.

Overall sizes are shown in FIG. 3-15A. For sides and ends, use the plywood along the sheets vertically. Arrange roof sheets similarly, with joints along the roof (FIG. 3-16C). All of the framing is 2-inch-square wood.

Begin construction with the closed end (FIG. 3-16A). Mark out and cut the slopes of the roof (FIG. 3-15B). Fit framing all around. You do not need to cut joints between the strips. Nail through the plywood at about 6-inch intervals; for the strongest construction, use glue, too. Add a central upright and strips across at the eave's level and midway between that and the floor. If you are planning to build in benches or shelves, there may be other pieces included in suitable places to provide secure fixing points. Cut away to take a 2-inch-×-3-inch ridge piece (FIG. 3-15C). Before adding the inner skin, use this assembly as a guide when making the other end.

Fig. 3-14. This small gardener's shed has a skin made of plywood.

Make the door end the same way, but allow for the door opening and a window opening by putting framing strips in suitable places (FIG. 3-15D). Add additional framing where needed for shelves or benches. Arrange the bottom of the window to come a few inches above your bench, and allow head room in the doorway by keeping the cross member above eaves level.

When you are satisfied with the framing of both ends and the inner plywood, level the edges (FIG. 3-15E). At window and door openings, use strips to cover the plywood and extend them forward (FIG. 3-15F). Include strips at the inner edges to act as stops and to provide draft-proofing (FIG. 3-15G).

The sides (FIGS. 3-15H and 3-16B) are plain, rectangular assemblies on two pairs of upright sheets of plywood. Mark the height from the ends and bevel the tops to match the roof slope.

For a plain side, framing the edges should provide sufficient strength. Use a strip as a cover piece centrally and put a central, horizontal strip the other way.

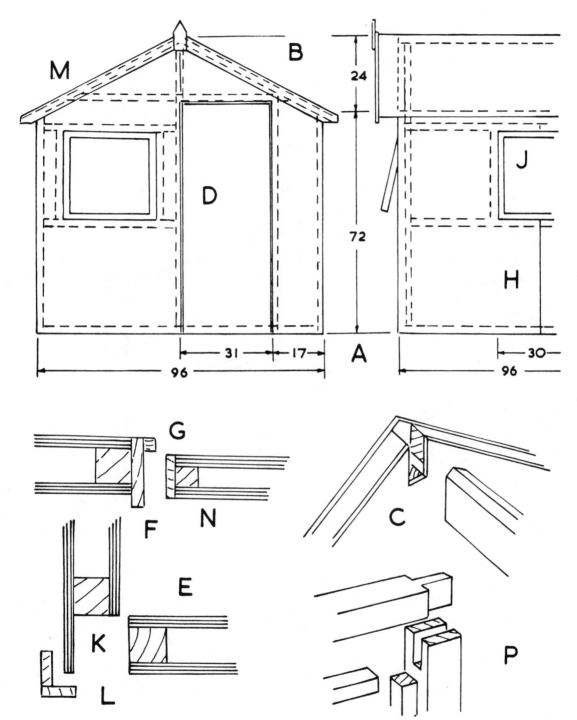

Fig. 3-15. Sizes and details of the stressed-skin gardener's shed.

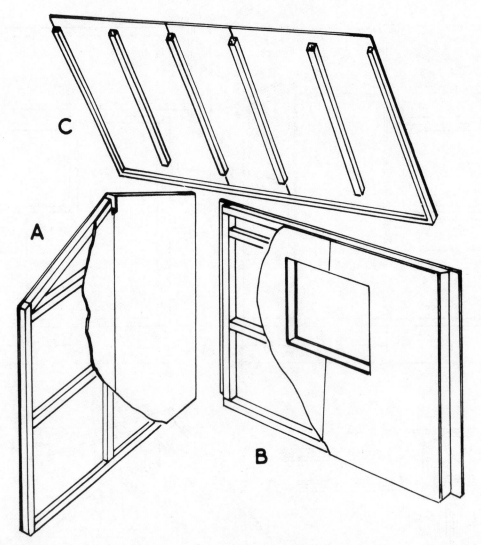

Fig. 3-16. Wall and roof details of the stressed-skin gardener's shed.

You might need other strips to provide places for benches or shelves. It is a good idea to put a window, the same size and height as the one in the end, in one side (FIG. 3-15J). Arrange horizontal framing to suit, with suitable uprights. Cover the sides inside and out in the same way as the ends, except at the corners, allow the outer plywood to extend over the end assemblies (FIG. 3-15K). When you put the building together, the corners will look neat, and you will protect the edge grain of the plywood if you nail on thin, wooden strips (FIG. 3-15L).

If you make the roof to finish flush with the ends, you will only need central joints. It will look better if it extends about 6 inches at each end and if you use

Materials List for Stressed-skin Gardener's Shed

2 end uprights	2	×	2	×	96
5 end uprights	2	×	2	×	74
5 end rails	2	×	2	×	96
5 side uprights	2	×	2	×	74
7 side rails	2	×	2	×	96
7 short rails	2	×	2	×	48
4 end slopes	2	×	2	×	60
2 door frames	¾	×	3½	×	75
1 door frame	¾	×	3½	×	32
8 window frames	¾	×	3½	×	30
8 window frames	⅝	×	⅝	×	30
1 ridge	2	×	3	×	96
8 roof frames	2	×	2	×	52
2 roof edges	1	×	1	×	96
4 roof edges	1	×	1	×	60
4 bargeboards	1	×	5	×	60
8 windows	1¼	×	1¼	×	30
8 windows	⅝	×	⅝	×	30
2 doors	1¼	×	1¼	×	75
4 doors	1¼	×	1¼	×	30
8 corners	½	×	2	×	72

Covering from 22 sheets ½- × -48- × -96 plywood

sheets 48 inches wide; there will have to be pieces 12 inches wide as well. Allow a 6-inch overhang at the eaves.

Erect the building without its roof, and cut the top plywood to suit. There should be sufficient stiffness from the edge supports, plus intermediate strips (FIG. 3-16C). Put strips around the projecting edges. Cover with tarred felt or other material, wrapping it over the edges and nailing underneath. You can improve appearance by nailing on bargeboards. Arrange them to stand slightly above the roof surface, and cut off the lower corners (FIG. 3-15M). Upright, pointed pieces at the center will finish the decoration.

Make the door with plywood on both sides and 1¼-inch-square framing. Include at least two cross members for stiffness (FIG. 3-17A). If there is to be a lock, put a block inside. Do the same to take screws from hinges, if you will be using T or other hinges that extend. Make the door an easy fit in its opening, allowing for covering strips around the edges (FIG. 3-15N).

For fixed windows, you can put glass against the inner strips and either putty to them or add other strips, as described for the last project. Alternatively, you can make one or both windows to open. In any case, it is better to have a wider, sloping sill at the bottom, to shed water (FIG. 3-13A).

You can make a window that opens with molding and mortise-and-tenon joints, in the same way as for a house. You can simplify the construction for this

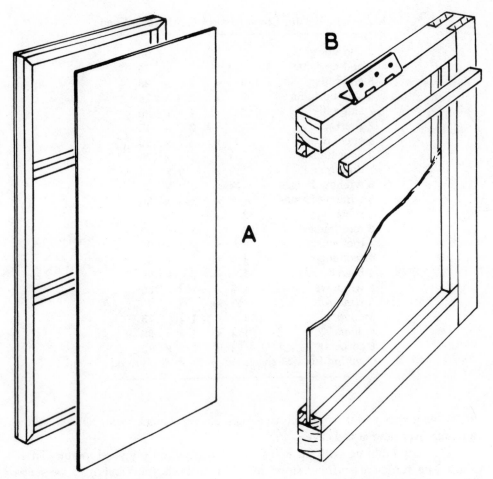

Fig. 3-17. Door and window construction for the stressed-skin gardener's shed.

shed, however, by using bridle joints and separate strips to make rabbets for the glass (FIGS. 3-15P and 3-17B). Use putty or second strips to hold the glass. Hinge each window at the top and have a locking strut at the bottom.

Exterior-grade plywood should have quite a long life if left untreated, but cover the edges to prevent the entry of water, preferably by bedding the covering strips in waterproof glue. You will improve appearance and increase durability if you thoroughly paint the building. A green finish under a black roof and barge-boards should look smart and blend in with most surroundings.

Curved-roof Plywood Unit

Plywood has considerable strength in itself, so a building made from it needs less framing because the panels contribute plenty of stiffness. The standard 4-×-

8-foot plywood sheets are large enough for you to complete your project with few joints. Of course, any plywood that will be exposed to the weather should be exterior grade. The quality plywood you choose depends on its purpose.

You can make a covered unit with a few sheets. The simplest unit would be with a sloping roof, but you will obtain an increase in strength and rigidity by curving the plywood. You can make the assembly in FIG. 3-18 from four sheets of $1/2$-inch or thinner plywood, with framing of 2-inch-square strips. Of course, you will not be able to walk into this building, as the doorway is only 27 inches high. You could use it for sheltering tools, equipment, or for animals. If you want to treat it like a small tent, it would be possible to sleep inside!

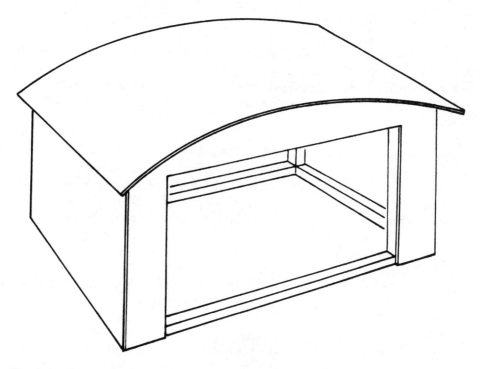

Fig. 3-18. A curved-roof unit made from sheets of plywood.

Materials List for Curved-roof Plywood Unit

3 sheets plywood	48	× 96	×	$1/2$
3 rails	2	× 2	×	92
6 uprights	2	× 2	×	30
7 rails	2	× 2	×	44

The roof is a full sheet without cuts. The front and back are full width, but reduced in length. The ends are made from half sheets. You can complete construction quickly if you need the unit in a hurry. Making this shelter is probably quicker than any other building in this book. If you are able to spend more time on it, you can give it a better finish.

Mark out the front (FIG. 3-19A). Cut the piece to length and mark a centerline on it. You can obtain the curve of the top by bending a batten around and penciling against it, but you will get a better curve, which is part of a circle, by using an improvised compass. Have a strip of wood just over 11 feet long. At 11 feet from one end, push through an awl. Extend the centerline from the sheet and position the awl in the floor on this line so the end of the "compass" is on the edge of the center of the sheet. Pull this compass around to draw the curve with a pencil against the end. Cut the curve and use the front to mark a matching back.

When you have assembled the parts, remember to place a beveled strip across the end to take the roof (FIG. 3-19B,C). Mark where this strip goes on the front, using the actual piece of wood as a guide to size. Put a strip of wood across immediately below this beveled strip, and mark the height of the doorway (FIG. 3-19D,E). Cut out the plywood to this height and 12 inches in from the ends (FIG. 3-19F).

Put a rail across the bottom of the opening and another across the top, with uprights at the ends and at each edge of the doorway. You can nail these parts through the plywood, but for a better construction, use waterproof glue as well.

At the back, put strips at the ends and across the bottom, leaving gaps at the top corners for the beveled strips that you will put across there. Cut the end plywood pieces to match the heights of the back and front and 42 inches across (FIG. 3-19G). Nail the ends to the back and front (FIG. 3-19H). Put beveled pieces across the top edges and square pieces across the bottom edges.

Stand the assembly on a level surface and check for squareness. Put three more pieces across to hold the roof in shape (FIG. 3-19J), nailing them through the back and front and leveling them so their upper surfaces are level with the curved edges.

See that the assembly is still square, then bend the roof sheet around, with help if necessary, to check the amount of overlap at its sides and each end. Mark on it where the walls come as a guide to nailing. Start at one end to nail the roof sheet down. Progress from there, nailing to each of the crosspieces in turn, until you finally nail to the beveled piece at the other end. It is the nails at the ends that are important. If you have very stiff plywood, it might be advisable to alternate screws with the nails at the ends.

You should bevel or round the corners of the roof to prevent splintering. For a better shelter, you might take off sharp edges all around. As designed, the unit goes directly on the ground. You could nail a piece of plywood to the underside of the walls to make a floor, but plywood is a better floor placed on top of the bottom-edge framing. The plywood will be easier to fit on top before you put the roof on.

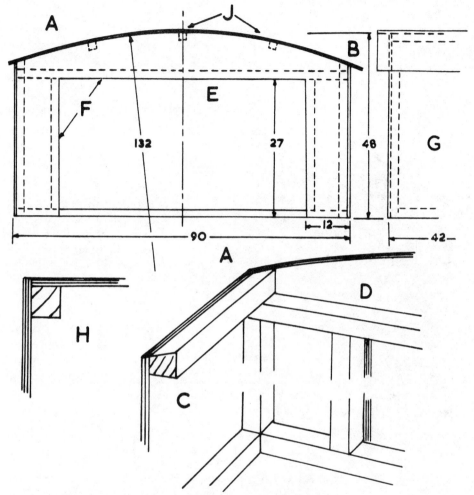

Fig. 3-19. Size and construction of the curved-roof plywood unit.

Mobile Toolbox

Most hand gardening tools are long and narrow. This box (FIG. 3-20) is intended to take what you need to a more distant part of your garden. The box will hold the tools protected from the weather, and you might find it a suitable seat as you rest from your labors.

Most parts are cut from 1-inch-×-12-inch boards. The suggested wheels are 8 inches in diameter on a 1/2-inch-diameter axle, which you should get before making the wooden parts, in case you have to modify sizes to suit. A softwood box would be lighter, but hardwood is more durable. Painted softwood should have a reasonably long life. Check your tool lengths and make the box to suit—60 inches is suggested (FIG. 3-21A).

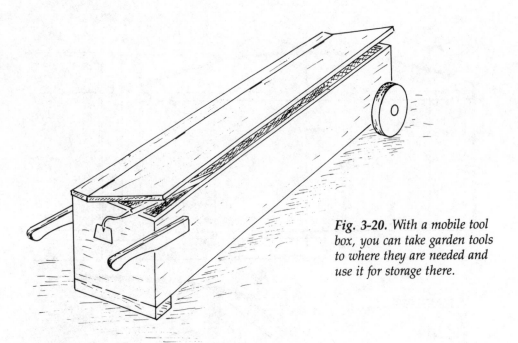

Fig. 3-20. With a mobile tool box, you can take garden tools to where they are needed and use it for storage there.

Materials List for Mobile Toolbox

1 back	1	×	12 × 62
1 front	1	×	11 × 62
1 bottom	1	×	12 × 60
2 ends	1	×	12 × 15
1 top	1	×	12 × 62
1 top	1	×	3 × 62
2 handles	1	×	3 × 24
1 block	2	×	3 × 15
2 pads	1/2	×	4 × 4

Make a pair of ends (FIG. 3-21B). The width matches the board to be used for the bottom, and the height suits the rear board. Allow a 1-inch slope on the top. Cut the back and front and make the bottom to fit inside them and the ends.

Corners could be joined with nails or screws, but cut joints would be stronger. A simple way of making stronger use of nails or screws is with a rabbet so you can drive nails both ways (FIG. 3-22A). A strong way is to cut broad fingers and nail through them (FIG. 3-22B). Best joints are dovetails with waterproof glue (FIG. 3-22C). Nail or screw the bottom inside the other parts.

Put 4-inch-square pads each side where the wheels will come (FIG. 3-21C), and drill through for the axle (FIG. 3-21D). Put washers between the wheels and the wood pads.

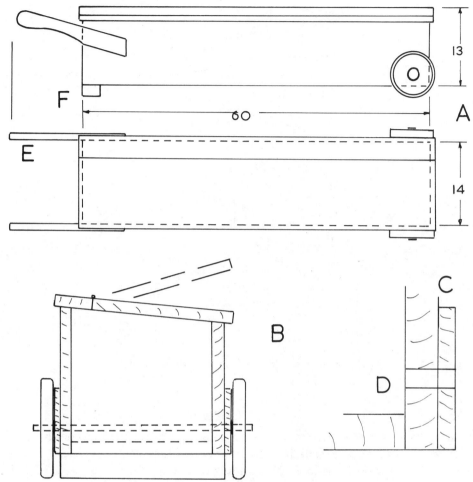

Fig. 3-21. *Suggested sizes for the mobile tool box.*

The handles (FIG. 3-21E) are shown at 15° to horizontal, but the angle is not critical, providing both handles are the same. Cut the wood to shape (FIG. 3-22D), and well round the extending parts that will be gripped. Bolts about 1/4 inch in diameter would be preferable to screws for attaching the handles to the box.

Make the top in two parts to overhang about 1/2 inch all around. The flap can be 12 inches wide, and the other piece can be cut to make up the width. Screw the narrow piece in place, and join the flap to it with three or four 3-inch hinges, which could be let into the edges for the neatest finish, or they could go on the surface.

Put a block under the handled end of the box to make up the height to the same as the wheeled end (FIG. 3-21F). Check the fit of the axle and wheels. Take sharpness off exposed edges and corners, then paint the wood before finally fitting the wheels.

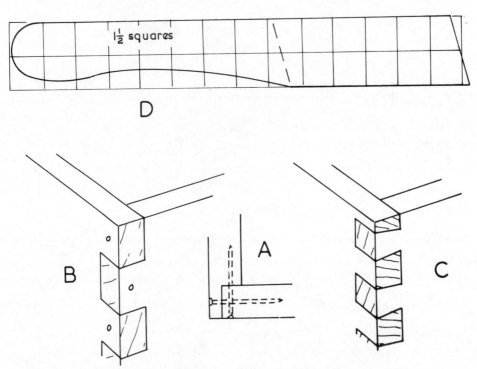

Fig. 3-22. Handle shape for the mobile tool box and alternative corner joints.

Tool Locker

If you want to store garden tools or yard games equipment and do not have the space or need for a large walk-in shed or other building, you might make a locker in the form of a weatherproof little building (FIG. 3-23). You could just get into it, but it is not intended to be more than a place to put a fairly large number of garden tools or such things as equipment for badminton, volleyball, or croquet. The locker has a sloping roof and a door that can be fitted to take smaller items. The floor is raised from the ground and the door is above the ground with its top sheltered by the overhanging top wall, as well as the roof.

The sizes suggested (FIG. 3-24) are intended to suit construction with 1/2-inch exterior plywood, framed around inside with strips of 1-inch-×-2-inch section. All joints should be made with waterproof glue and plenty of nails or screws. There should be no need for fitted joints, except you might use finger joints or dovetails at the corners of the door. You could cut joints at the ends of the shelves and rails inside the door, but it should be satisfactory to just screw them from outside.

The key parts, which control many other sizes, are the pair of sides (FIGS. 3-24A and 3-25A). Cut them to match each other. Frame them all around inside with 1-inch-×-2-inch strips arranged with the 2-inch width against the surface.

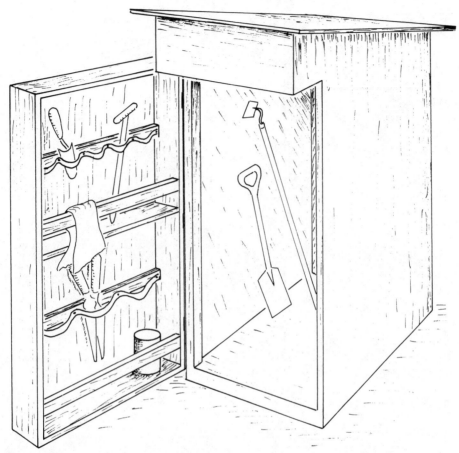

Fig. 3-23. *This tool locker is large enough to get into, but it is mainly useful for storing hand tools, with smaller ones in racks in the doors.*

Materials List for Tool Locker

2 sides	36	× 84 ×	½	plywood
1 back	30	× 72 ×	½	plywood
1 front	12	× 30 ×	½	plywood
1 top	34	× 40 ×	½	plywood
1 bottom	30	× 36 ×	½	plywood
4 side frames	1	× 2 × 84		
4 side frames	1	× 2 × 37		
5 crosspieces	1	× 2 × 32		
2 door sides	¾	× 6 × 72		
2 door ends	¾	× 6 × 32		
1 door front	30	× 72 ×	½	plywood
2 door shelves	½	× 6 × 30		
4 door strips	1	× 2 × 30		

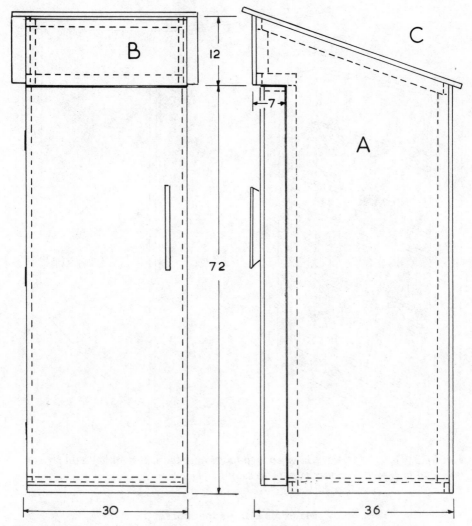

Fig. 3-24. Sizes of the tool locker.

At each external corner allow notches for the strips that will go across between them (FIG. 3-25B and C). See that all edges are level and the corner notches allow the crosspieces to fit level.

Make all the crosspieces the same length. Have the back (FIG. 3-25D) and the front (FIG. 3-24B) cut a little oversize, but ready to joint to the other parts when they are assembled, to hold the assembly in shape.

Join the two sides with all the crosspieces, glued and screwed into their notches. Glue and nail on the front and back to keep the assembly square. Make the bottom (FIG. 3-25E) to fit closely inside and notch around the corner pieces.

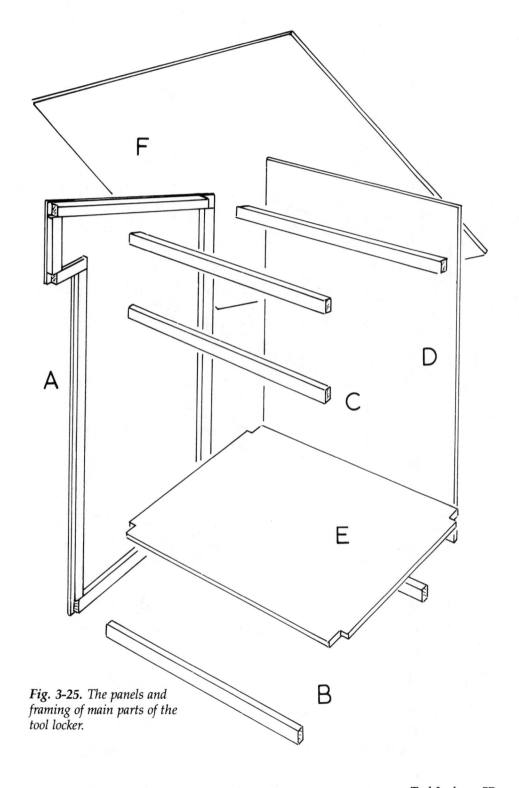

Fig. 3-25. *The panels and framing of main parts of the tool locker.*

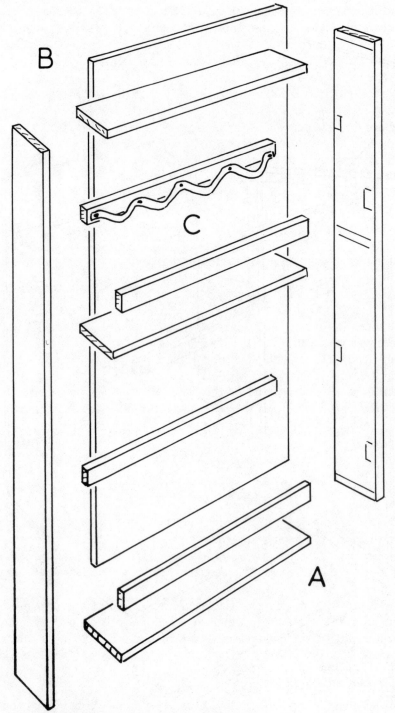

Fig. 3-26. Parts of the fitted door of the tool locker.

Glue and nail it in place. Stand the locker on a level surface to check for twist, and compare diagonal measurements at the top to see that part is square.

Cut the top large enough to overhang 2 inches all around (FIGS. 3-24C and 3-25F). Glue and nail it in place. After painting all of the locker, you could cover the top with felt, turned under and tacked.

Make the door as a shallow box. Arrange its depth back to front about 1 inch less than the space under the locker front, so it will be sheltered. Have its bottom 1 inch above the ground. Make the door from solid wood with a plywood front. You might find it satisfactory to just glue and screw the corners, but it would be better to use one of the corner joints suggested for the last project (FIG. 3-22). Mark out and cut the door framing parts (FIG. 3-26A) and the plywood (FIG. 3-26B). You can arrange shelves and fittings inside to suit your needs. The drawings show a shelf across the center, two restraining rails, then two strips with webbing or leather belting loops to hold tools (FIG. 3-26C). Make all these parts. Cut dado joints if you wish; otherwise, cut the parts to length and drill for screws through the door sides. Use the plywood as a template as you assemble the door. Try it against the locker. If there are slight discrepancies, allow for them, as you should fit the door so its outline matches the locker.

Assemble the door and see that it fits against the locker. There is no need for a precise finish for the locker, but take off sharp edges and corners, and smooth any excessive roughness before painting.

Hinge the door at one side. Three 3-inch hinges would be suitable. Arrange a handle at the other side. A long vertical type would be appropriate. Arrange a side fastener to keep the door closed. If you fit webbing pieces inside, allow loops of ample size and attach with roundhead screws through large washers. Finish the locker with several coats of paint. The lower part would benefit by being treated with preservative, especially if the locker is to stand on bare earth. A lighter color paint inside would make the contents easier to see.

Pegged Plywood Shelter

If you need a shelter occasionally, but for much of the time you wish to store it, there is an attraction in having something that packs absolutely flat. It is possible to make such a shelter from sheets of exterior-grade plywood. If the shelter is made of four pieces of 1/2-inch plywood, they can be put together for storage so they are no more than 2 inches thick.

If you use whole sheets for the larger parts, you can make an open-fronted shelter about 4 feet wide by 4 feet high by 8 feet long—suitable for smaller animals, produce that has to be kept dry, or anything that does not necessitate you walking into the shelter. If you need a more upright shelter, it can be about 4 feet square and high enough to walk into (FIG. 3-27).

Assembly is with pegged lugs or tenons, fitting through slots or mortises (FIG. 3-28A). The pegs are made from pieces of 5/8-inch dowel rod. Driving a peg in makes a very rigid joint, and an assembled shelter will be strong enough for

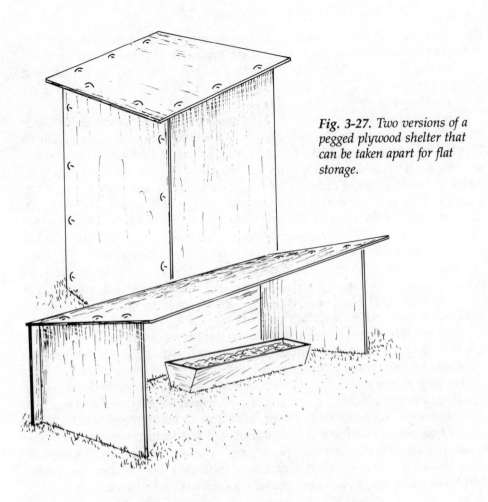

Fig. 3-27. Two versions of a pegged plywood shelter that can be taken apart for flat storage.

Materials List for Pegged Plywood Shelter

Cut from exterior plywood, 3 sheets (low) or 4 sheets (high) 48 inches by 96 inches by 1/2 inch.

temporary use. There is no need for these joints to be close-fitting. Allow at least 1/8-inch clearance all around in a slot (FIG. 3-28B). Drill a 5/8-inch hole so its lower edge comes 1/8 inch below the level of the slotted plywood (FIG. 3-28C). Pegs may be 3 inches long. You will have to experiment with the amount of taper to plane off (FIG. 3-28D), but it will help if you make a thin plywood template of a lug and its hole so you can mark and drill all lugs the same and tapered pegs will be interchangeable.

For the lower shelter, start by marking out and cutting a pair of ends (FIG.

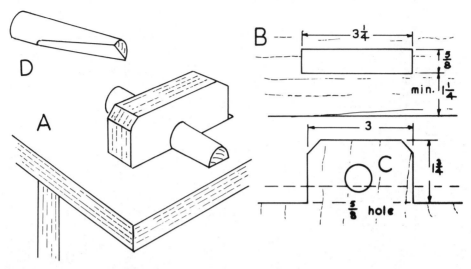

Fig. 3-28. The method of joining parts of the pegged plywood shelter.

3-29A), which can be fitted against each other in a standard sheet with a diagonal cut. With each side cut down to the width shown, the roof will overhang about 3 inches back and front. The 3-inch lugs on the rear and top edges are 4 inches from the corners (FIG. 3-29B), with another midway. Cut and shape the ends to match each other.

The roof or top is a full 48-inch-×-96-inch sheet (FIG. 3-30A). The back is also a full-length sheet, but its width is cut down to suit the height of the rear edges of the ends, plus the top lugs (FIG. 3-30B).

Mark and cut slots 3 inches from both ends of the back at positions to match the lugs on the ends (FIG. 3-30C). Arrange lugs along the top edge. Four should be sufficient (FIG. 3-30D), but if you have very flexible plywood you could add another.

Mark and cut slots 3 inches from both ends of the top (FIG. 3-30E) to match those on the tops of the ends and allow the same amount of overhang on both edges.

Cut slots along the rear edge to match the lugs on the back (FIG. 3-30F). Make a trial assembly without pegs to see that all parts fit. You might have to ease some slots. Try changing over ends and turning around the back. It will help in future assemblies if the parts can be brought together any way. It will not matter if you have to cut a little more out of some slots to allow this. You might want to round exposed edges and corners. Cut sufficient pegs and taper them. Try a rigid assembly with driven pegs on a flat floor, to guard against twist. Paint the parts or treat the plywood with preservative.

If you want to make an upright shelter, it will have to be about 4 feet square at

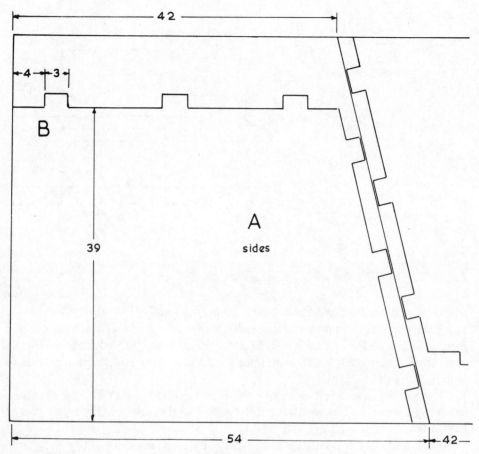

Fig. 3-29. How to mark out sides of the pegged plywood shelter.

the base, but you can make the height to suit your needs. It is unlikely that you will want the full 8-foot height. The drawing of parts (FIG. 3-31) suggests 7 feet, 6 inches at the front, but you can adjust this without altering the method of construction.

This upright shelter is made in the same way as the low shelter. Start by marking out a pair of sides (FIG. 3-31A). The arrangement of lugs on the top edge is the same as for the ends of the low shelter. Four lugs should be sufficient at the rear edge.

Make the back (FIG. 3-31B). The slots for the side lugs need only be 1¹/₂ inches from the edges, as the roof length will not be restricted to 48 inches.

The top has a 3-inch overhang at back and front, but it is drawn with a greater overhang at the sides (FIG. 3-31C).

As with the low shelter, make a trial assembly, then do any adjusting. Make a rigid assembly with pegs, then finish the parts with paint or preservative.

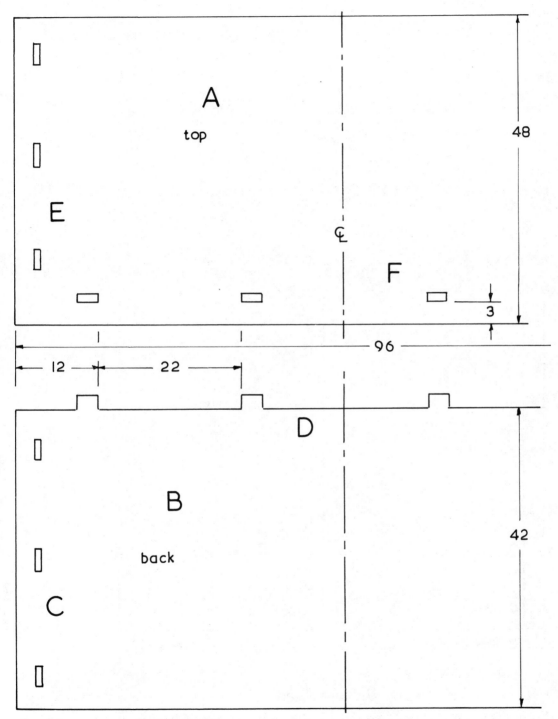

Fig. 3-30. Sizes of top and back of the pegged plywood shelter.

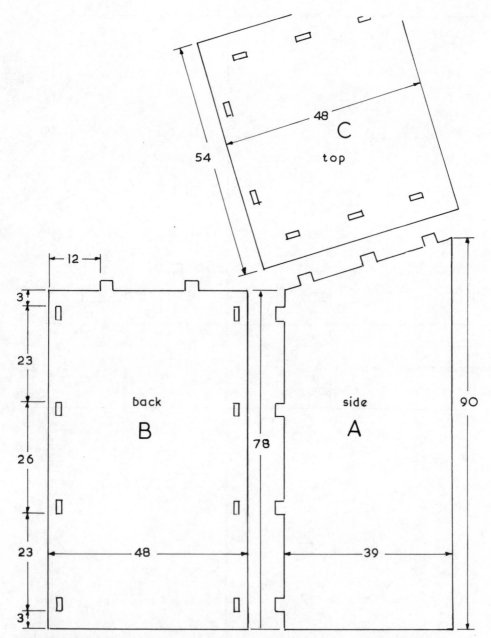

Fig. 3-31. Sizes of parts for an upright version of the pegged plywood shelter.

Bicycle Shed

This small building (FIG. 3-32) is a suitable size for storing several bicycles, but it could have many other uses, such as housing gardening and games equipment.

Fig. 3-32. *This small shed is a suitable size for storing several bicycles, but it could have other uses, too.*

The size allows you to make the roof from a single sheet of plywood. The base size is 7 feet long with a width of half this. The greatest height is also 7 feet (FIG. 3-33A). The shed is meant for storage rather than for working in, but there is sufficient head room and a window to provide light. The shed is best fastened down to a concrete base, but you could stand it elsewhere and put a wood floor inside.

Most of the framing is 2-inch-square wood. The covering could be plywood, but shiplap or other boards about 6 inches wide are suggested. No lining is

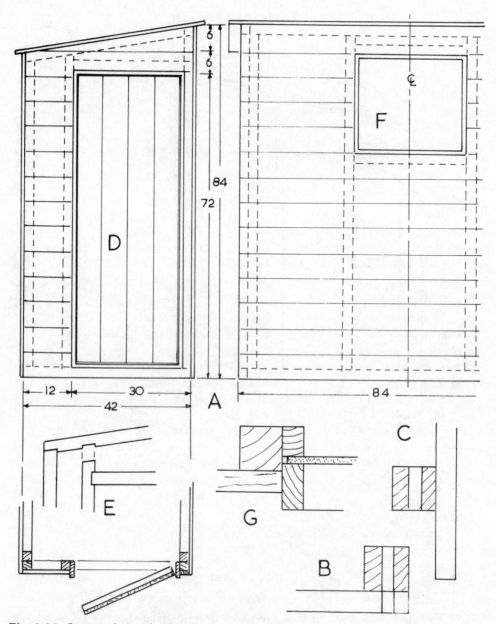

Fig. 3-33. Suggested sizes for the bicycle shed and some constructional details.

shown, but if the use you intend would be better with some insulation, plywood could be added to the inside of the framing. You can prefabricate all the parts before assembling on site. If you ever wish to move the shed, it should be possible to take the units apart with very little damage. The ends are covered with

Materials List for Bicycle Shed

6 uprights	2 ×	2	×	84
6 uprights	2 ×	2	×	78
1 door upright	2 ×	2	×	80
1 door top	2 ×	2	×	32
4 wall rails	2 ×	2	×	86
4 wall rails	2 ×	2	×	44
2 window rails	2 ×	2	×	30
4 window frames	1 ×	2	×	30
4 window frames	1 ×	1 1/2	×	30
2 door frames	1 ×	3 1/2	×	74
2 door frames	1 ×	3 1/2	×	32
3 door ledgers	1 ×	6	×	32
2 door diagonals	1 ×	6	×	36
1 roof	48 ×	96	×	1/2 or 3/4 plywood
4 roof rails	2 ×	2	×	44

Covering: 1/2 plywood or shiplap boards 3/4 × 6

boards or plywood level with the uprights (FIG. 3-33B), then the sides are made with the covering extended (FIG. 3-33C) and the corners bolted together.

Start by making the end with the doorway (FIGS. 3-33D and 3-34A). Framing can be nailed, but it helps in locating parts and preventing movement if you cut shallow notches (FIG. 3-33E). Check squareness and cover with boards or plywood so all edges are level, including around the doorway. At the narrow edge beside the doorway, put a strip to make up the level of the boards.

Make the opposite end to be a pair in overall size, but use one central upright.

Assemble the frame for the front to match the height of the ends (FIGS. 3-33F and 3-34B). The top edge could be beveled to suit the slope of the roof, but the angle is slight and it might not matter if you leave this edge square. Divide the length into three equal parts for the uprights, unless you prefer a different width of window opening. Notch and nail all frame parts. Check squareness and cover the framing, allowing enough projection to fit over the end walls.

Make the back in a similar way. Compare its length with the front and its height with the lower edges of the ends. It is unlikely that you will need a window in the back, but you could put one there or in the end if that will suit the intended use.

Edge the window opening with strips that project about 1/2 inch (FIG. 3-33G), leaving space for the glass and strips inside to hold it. It will be wisest to leave fitting the glass until after the shed has been erected. Edge the door opening with strips that project a little in a similar way. The bottom edge could be extended further with a supporting block underneath to form a step.

Make the door (FIG. 3-34C) to be an easy fit in the doorway. Use vertical boards or plywood and three ledgers with two diagonals sloping upwards from the hinged side. The door could be hinged either way to suit your preference.

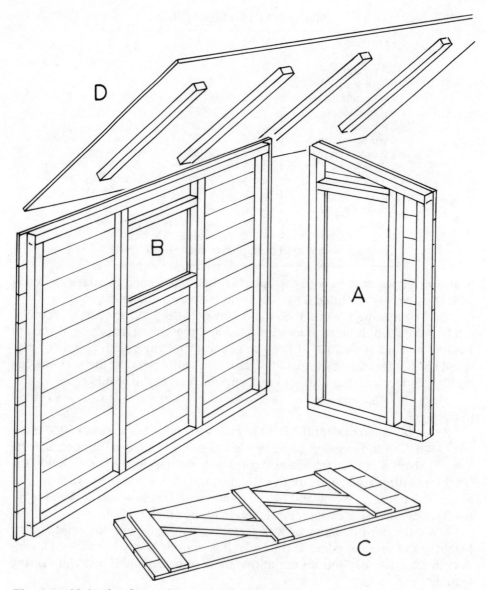

Fig. 3-34. Units that fit together to make a bicycle shed.

Use plenty of nails to reduce the risk of wood movement or warping later. It should be sufficient to use two 4-inch hinges at the upper and lower ledger positions. Arrange a handle and fastener at the other edge. Put a stop strip for the door to close against.

Drill the corner uprights for bolts. It should be sufficient to use $3/8$-inch bolts, with washers and nuts at about 18-inch intervals. Drill the bottom edges for holding-down bolts or other fasteners to the concrete. Assemble the four walls in position. Check squareness by comparing diagonal measurements at top and bottom.

Try a sheet of plywood in position as a roof. Mark on it the positions of the walls and the amount of overhang. Put strips across to fit inside the walls (FIG. 3-34D). Arrange the end strips to come close to the end walls. You will then be able to drill through for securing bolts. These bolts will ensure rigidity of the structure, but in the final assembly you should nail (or screw if you expect to have to disassemble later) at close enough intervals along the tops of front and back walls to hold the roof joints tight.

You could leave the plywood top uncovered and protect it with paint, but it would be better covered with tarred felt. If you do this, stiffen the edges before assembly, and add battens to the covering when you fit it.

Finish the wood with paint or preservative. You might decide to leave the inside untreated, but in this small shed visibility inside is improved if you use a light color paint.

Equipment Shed

This shed is intended to provide shelter for garden equipment, such as mowers and tillers (FIG. 3-35). There is space for hand tools and fuel cans, or you could use the building to shelter bicycles, games equipment, or anything else that needs protection from the weather. The overall size is small enough to be accommodated in a corner of the yard.

As drawn, the building can have a roof made from a single sheet of exterior-grade plywood (FIG. 3-36). This allows a floor plan 3 feet 6 inches by 6 feet 6 inches. There is a clear drive-in. Check the sizes of equipment you wish to store, and you might find you have to adjust some sizes. The height is not intended to give standing head room inside, but you can deal with stored items without stooping much.

The instructions are for a building covered with exterior-grade plywood. You could board the walls and door in a similar way to the last project, if you wish. It is possible to cover the sides first and use offcuts on the back, if you do not mind joints in the sheets showing there.

The sides control the sizes of other parts and should be made first. Allow for joints between the sheets on uprights or the central rails. Lay out the framing parts on the plywood. There will be no need for joints between the framing parts around the edges, as the plywood will provide strength. Allow space for the crossbar at the top front corners (FIGS. 3-36A and 3-37A) and notch the uprights for the lower crossbar (FIGS. 3-36B and 3-37B). Where the uprights cross the central rail, cut halving joints (FIG. 3-37C). It should be sufficient to securely nail the plywood to the framing, but you could also use waterproof glue for additional strength. The plywood comes level with the framing at the door end, but allow it to extend enough to cover the edges of the back (FIGS. 3-36C and 3-37D). You could leave a little extra there to plane level after assembly.

Fig. 3-35. *You can make an equipment shed a suitable size for storing such things as mowers and tillers, as well as hand tools.*

Materials List for Equipment Shed

14 side strips	2 ×	2	× 80	
3 back uprights	2 ×	2	× 68	
3 back rails	2 ×	2	× 44	
2 crossbars	2 ×	2	× 44	
2 door uprights	2 ×	2	× 68	
2 door crossbars	2 ×	2	× 44	
1 roof	48 ×	96	×	1/2 plywood
1 front	12 ×	48	×	1/2 plywood
1 door	42 ×	66	×	1/2 plywood
sides and back covering	1/2 plywood			

Make the back in a similar way to the sides (FIG. 3-36D). Its height must match the sides. You could bevel the top rail to suit the slope of the roof, but as this is slight, you might decide it does not matter if it is left square. Drill the uprights for 3/8-inch bolts at about 18-inch intervals.

Cut the two front crossbars to lengths that will hold the assembly with the sides parallel. Prepare the ground or a concrete base. Drill the bottom rails for bolts or other fasteners into the concrete, or take spikes into the ground if you will be mounting the shed directly on soil.

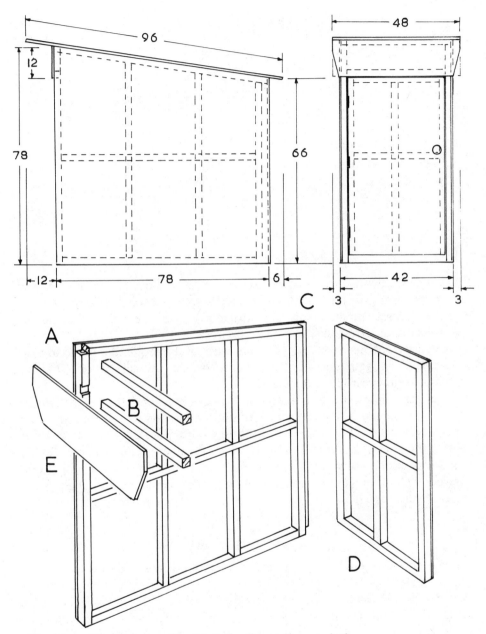

Fig. 3-36. *Sizes and assembly details for the equipment shed.*

Assemble the units to each other. Nail on the crossbars. Check squareness by comparing diagonal measurements. It will help to put a temporary crosspiece at the front to hold the sides parallel until the shed is fastened down.

Try the roof in position. Allow 3 inches overhang at the sides and 6 inches at

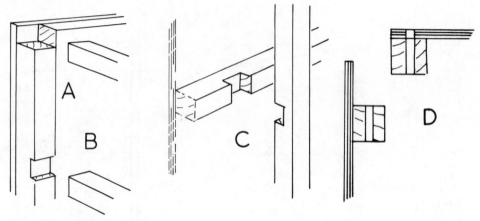

Fig. 3-37. Methods of joining parts of the equipment shed.

the back, with about 12 inches over the door. If you will be covering it with tarred felt, stiffen around its edges. If it will be painted, there is no need to do anything else to it. Unless you are using very flexible plywood, there should be no need for any stiffening strips inside. Nail on the roof.

Cut the front piece (FIG. 3-36E) to the width of the roof and tapered to match the sides. Check squareness of the doorway before you nail this on. The structure should now be rigid and square.

Make the door to fit easily between the sides of its opening. Allow at least 1 inch ground clearance at its bottom. Cut plywood to this size and frame it in the same way as the back. Use two or three 4-inch hinges. Put a latch or other fastener at the other side. Arrange a stop strip for the door to close against. Treat the woodwork with preservative, or paint inside and out. Seal exposed edges of the plywood to prevent water creeping in. A light color paint inside will help you see the contents.

Gabled Shed

There is something more visually attractive about a roof with a ridge than one with a single slope, although the single slope, or lean-to, might be just as effective at shedding water. This shed has a gabled front with a door, but it is quite shallow back-to-front (FIG. 3-38). It is particularly suitable for storing folding yard chairs and tables, as well as a great many other items. It is high enough to stand in and could serve as a shelter during a storm.

Its size would permit it being positioned on a narrow border, probably not big enough for most types of small building (FIG. 3-39). Located along a flower border, its gable front could be regarded as part of the decorative scene in your garden. It would make an attractive backing to tables and chairs for a garden meal, with useful storage for reserves of food and equipment.

Fig. 3-38. This garden shed is designed for a place where there is more space available for width than depth.

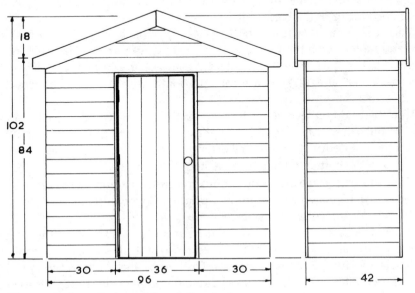

Fig. 3-39. Overall sizes of the garden shed.

Materials List for Gabled Shed

2 front uprights	2	× 2	× 84		
2 front uprights	2	× 2	× 94		
1 front rail	2	× 2	× 92		
2 front rafters	2	× 2	× 48		
5 front rails	2	× 2	× 36		
2 back uprights	2	× 2	× 84		
2 back uprights	2	× 2	× 94		
4 back rails	2	× 2	× 92		
2 back rafters	2	× 2	× 48		
6 side uprights	2	× 2	× 84		
6 side rails	2	× 2	× 42		
2 doorway edges	1	× 3 1/2	× 80		
2 doorway edges	1	× 3 1/2	× 36		
3 door ledgers	1	× 6	× 36		
2 door braces	1	× 6	× 42		
2 roofs	48	× 60	×	1/2 plywood	
4 roof edges	1	× 3	× 60		
2 roof edges	1	× 2	× 48		
4 bargeboards	1	× 5	× 48		

Cladding 3/4 or 1 × 6 shiplap boards or 1/2 or 3/4 plywood

The gabled shed is shown with shiplap boarding and a covered plywood roof. You could cover with plywood all around, but the pattern of boarding adds to the attractive appearance. The roof is shown with bargeboards both ends, but you might prefer to omit them at the back. There are no windows because enough light should come through the doorway, but you could put a small window at one side or in the back wall.

Make the front door frame (FIG. 3-40A). Position each part with a shallow notch and nails. Notch the rafters to take the ends of purlins. Have two reasonably close to the apex (FIGS. 3-40B and 3-41A), and others each side halfway to the eaves (FIGS. 3-40C and 3-41B). Cover the apex joints with a notched plywood gusset (FIG. 3-41C).

Trim the cladding level with the edge of the doorway and with the slope of the roof, but allow it to extend sufficiently to cover the sides (FIGS. 3-40D and 3-41D). Line the doorway with strips extending 1/2 inch forward (FIG. 3-41E). You could widen the bottom edge to form a step, if you wish.

Make the back a matching outline to the front. Extend the horizontal rails right across, using halving joints at the uprights. Cover with boards right across, with extensions to overlap the sides.

The two sides are simple rectangular frames (FIG. 3-40E). Make the height to match the front and back. Bevel the top edges to suit the slope of the roof. Trim cladding level with the edges all around. Drill for 3/8-inch bolts in the uprights at about 18-inch intervals. When you assemble the units, drill through these holes into the matching uprights.

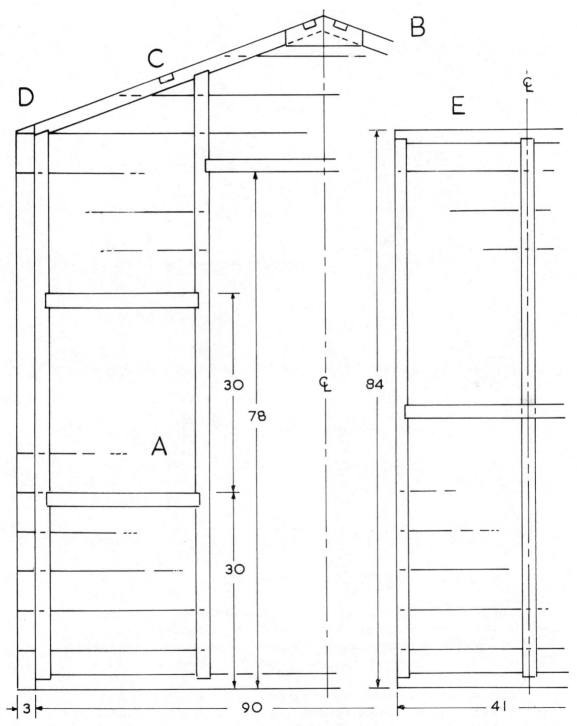

Fig. 3-40. Layout and sizes of front and sides of the garden shed.

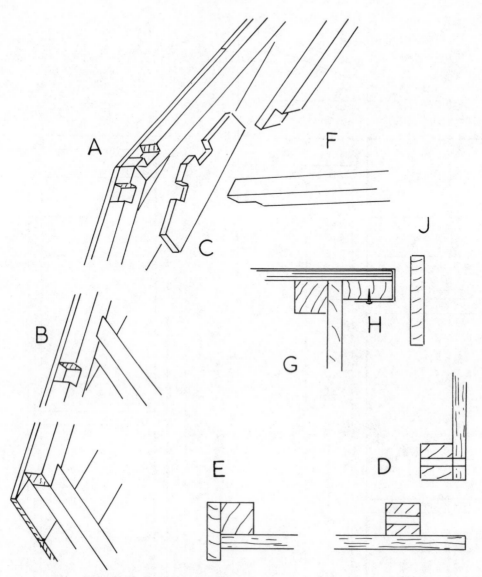

Fig. 3-41. Constructional details of the garden shed.

Join the four walls. Check squareness of the bottom edges before you fasten down to a concrete or a wood base. Cut purlins (FIG. 3-41F) to fit the notches, and nail them in position. See that the top of the assembly remains square as you do this. The corner of a plywood sheet laid on the slope at one side can be used as a check.

You can use the full 48-inch width of a plywood sheet at each side, cut to overhang the eaves about 3 inches. Bevel top edges to fit close to each other on the ridge. Stiffen the extending plywood edges. At back and front these pieces can fill the space against the cladding (FIG. 3-41G). You could use narrower pieces at the bottom edges.

Nail the roof panels in place. There is no need for stiffening along the ridge, but you could put a 6-inch-wide piece of tarred felt along it as extra proofing before covering the whole roof. Take the tarred asphalt underneath the edges and nail closely there (FIG. 3-41H). One central batten on top each side should be sufficient stiffening.

Although you could use the shed without bargeboards, they vastly improve appearance and direct rainwater down the slopes of the roof. Miter the boards at the apex, and trim their lower ends. Arrange them to stand 1 inch above the surface of the roof (FIG. 3-41J). Nail closely to prevent water dripping through the joints.

Make the door with three ledgers and two diagonal braces sloping upwards from the side you decide to fit the hinges (FIG. 3-34C). Trim the outline to be an easy fit in the opening and with adequate ground clearance. Use two or three 4-inch hinges, or you could put T hinges on the surface. Add a handle and latch or lock on the other edge. Arrange a stop strip inside.

The gabled shed will look attractive with the bargeboards a different color from the rest of the structure. The roof could be black or a dark color. Use a light color inside.

Split-door Shed

If you need access into a building for something big or wide, you must have a wide doorway. If the approach is directly from the front, you could arrange double doors, hinged at each side. If the approach has to be from one side, there might be one wide door hinged at the other side. However, large doors are cumbersome and heavy, so they are difficult to handle, need a wide area to swing, and might develop sags. An alternative is to make the door in two parts, with one hinged on the other. This way, as the door is opened, the parts can be folded on each other, then they swing over a more limited area and take up less space when swung back. This shed has a doorway 5 feet wide and split doors that will swing clear (FIG. 3-42).

Sizes are suggested, but could be modified without altering the method of construction (FIG. 3-43A). The drawings show shiplap board siding, but you could use plywood or other covering. All of the framing is made from 2-inch-square strips, except around the doorway there are 2-inch-×-3-inch pieces for extra strength. The roof is plywood, although it could be boarded. Assembly is similar to other sheds described in this chapter, with the subassemblies joined with bolts. You should be able to prefabricate the walls and doors before you take them to the site.

Make the front wall first (FIG. 3-44A). Allow for the boarding extending enough to cover the sides (FIGS. 3-44B and 3-45A). Framing parts can be notched and nailed. Assemble squarely, paying particular attention to the shape of the doorway. Line the doorway with strips at sides and top (FIG. 3-45B).

Fig. 3-42. This shed has a split door that is particularly suitable where a wide doorway is needed, but space to swing a large door is limited.

Materials List for Split-door Shed

4 front strips	2	×	2	× 86
4 front strips	2	×	2	× 14
1 front strip	2	×	3	× 86
2 front strips	2	×	3	× 74
7 back strips	2	×	2	× 86
2 end strips	2	×	2	× 86
4 end strips	2	×	2	× 80
6 door ledgers	1	×	6	× 32
4 door braces	1	×	6	× 36
2 doorway liners	1	×	4	× 74
1 doorway liner	1	×	4	× 62
1 roof	60	× 96	×	3/4 plywood
2 roof edges	1	×	2	× 96
2 roof edges	1	×	2	× 60

The pair of ends (FIG. 3-43B) are made to the same height as the front. Cut boarding level all around. Drill the uprights at about 18-inch intervals for 3/8-inch bolts (FIG. 3-45C). When you assemble the shed, use these holes as guides for drilling through the matching uprights.

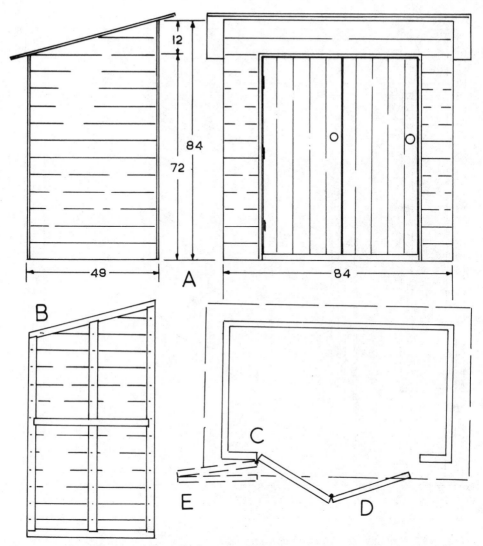

Fig. 3-43. Overall sizes of the split-door shed and the method of hanging the doors.

Make the back (FIG. 3-44C) the same length as the front, but with a height to match the sides. Frame as shown and board fully across with similar overlaps at the sides as allowed at the front.

Drill bottom edges of frames for bolts or other fasteners to a concrete or other base. Assemble the four walls squarely. Check for twist.

If you will be boarding the roof, you can nail the boards on following the slope. If you will be using plywood, cut two or more pieces that will make a roof with up to 6 inches overhang. The plywood might be stiff enough in itself. If you are doubtful about it remaining flat, put 2-inch-square strips inside following the

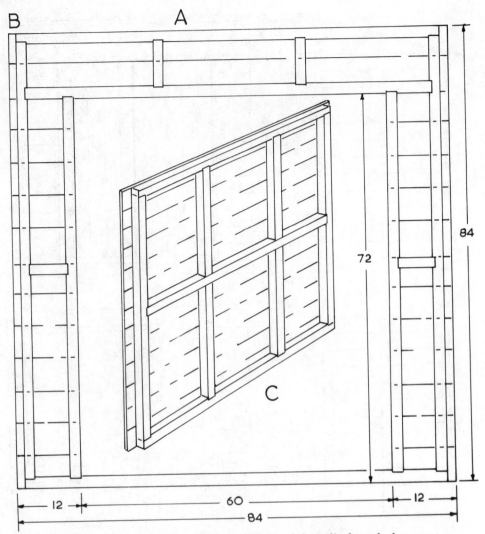

Fig. 3-44. Sizes and construction of front and back of the split-door shed.

slope and arranged at about 2-foot intervals (FIG. 3-44D). Cut these strips to come between the back and front walls, but they need not be attached to them. Even if you do not fit stiffeners, put lighter strips under any plywood joints. Stiffen around the edges of the plywood and nail tarred asphalt in place. Put battens on top, about 18 inches apart. The assembled shed should now be rigid, with no risk of distorting and spoiling the fit of the doors.

Even if you have made the doors in advance, allow for a little trimming of the edges as you fit them. They should fit easily in the opening and have enough ground clearance, but the bottoms should be left long enough to overlap the bottom rail. The pair of doors are the same and should be made with three ledgers

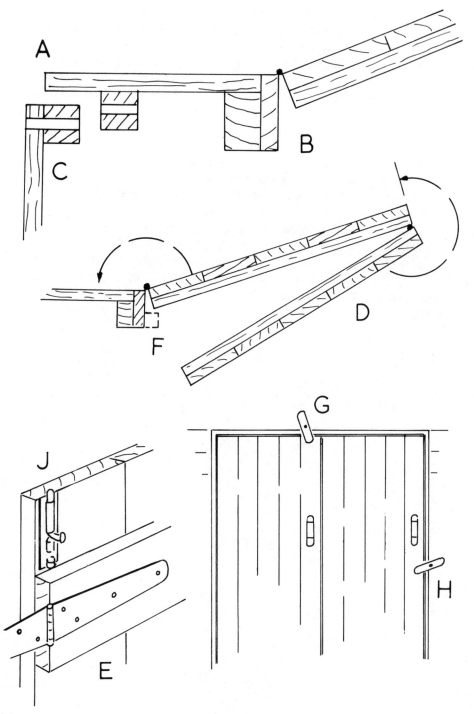

Fig. 3-45. *Sections of front and door. Method of hanging and securing the doors.*

and two diagonal braces. Note the action: One door swings outwards on its post (FIG. 3-43C); as it is opened the second door will swing inwards on it (FIGS. 3-43D and 3-45D), so when fully opened the doors are flat against each other (FIG. 3-43E).

This means the knuckles of the hinges to the post have to be outside and the knuckles of the hinges between the doors inside. You can use ordinary butt hinges or T hinges at the door posts. It would be better to use strap hinges on the ledgers between the doors (FIG. 3-45E). Cut the doors to size and hinge them to try their movement. You might have to unscrew them to trim edges to get a neat fit.

Put a stop strip inside at the opening side (FIG. 3-45F), and arrange handles or knobs on both doors for pulling open. If it is not important to lock the shed, the simplest fasteners are two strip wood turnbuttons; one to hold the first door closed (FIG. 3-45G) and one to hold its partner (FIG. 3-45H).

If you want a more secure fastening, put a bolt inside the first door (FIG. 3-45J), with a matching hole in the top rail. Choose a bolt that is no thicker than the ledger below it, so it does not interfere with folding the doors. You might decide a similar bolt is advisable at the bottom. Put a lock at the side of the second door, either inside with a keyhole or outside with a hasp and staple for a padlock.

4
Shelters

People need shelters for many occasions. The shelters I am referring to are not fully enclosed buildings with doors. They usually have one or more sides open. In a garden or yard, such a shelter might be all you need for storing yard furniture. You can add seating to the shelter so you can rest from your labors or sit and admire the flowers growing. Anyone collecting admission money at an event can use a simple shelter, possibly of portable construction. Something similar might provide shelter for children waiting for the school bus.

A more advanced shelter could have an enclosed part with door and windows towards the back and a broad, more open part, large enough for chairs and table, at the front. You might call this type of shelter a summerhouse or a gazebo. If made large enough, it almost could become a second home. It is difficult to decide on the dividing line between a shelter and a building.

Construction might be very similar to some of the buildings described in chapter 3, but if the front is open, there is a problem of providing stiffness there. If you provide the open front by just leaving out what would be the front of the building, there is no crosswise stiffness, and a hard push or even a strong wind on one side could distort or even collapse the shelter.

Take-down Shelter

The take-down shelter is a basic, open-fronted shelter, that you can make a permanent structure, but which is also suitable for disassembling into flat sections by removing a few bolts. It has a wooden floor, which keeps the assembly square. As shown in FIG. 4-1, this structure is intended to be a one-person shelter

Fig. 4-1. You can take apart this open-fronted shelter.

Materials List for Take-down Shelter

2 uprights	2	×	2	×	86		
4 uprights	2	×	2	×	74		
8 rails	2	×	2	×	36		
2 diagonals	2	×	2	×	40		
2 fronts	¾	×	2¾	×	76		
1 front	10-	×	-38-	×	-¾-exterior plywood		
1 floor	36-	×	-36-	×	-¾-exterior plywood		
1 roof	42-	×	-48-	×	-¾-exterior plywood		

Covering: about 40 pieces shiplap boards ¾ × 6 × 38 or equivalent

for a ticket seller or money taker at an event. It would also provide shelter from a storm or a storage place for a few garden tools. The sizes suggested in FIG. 4-2A are for a shelter of this type, but you can use the same method for a shelter of many different sizes.

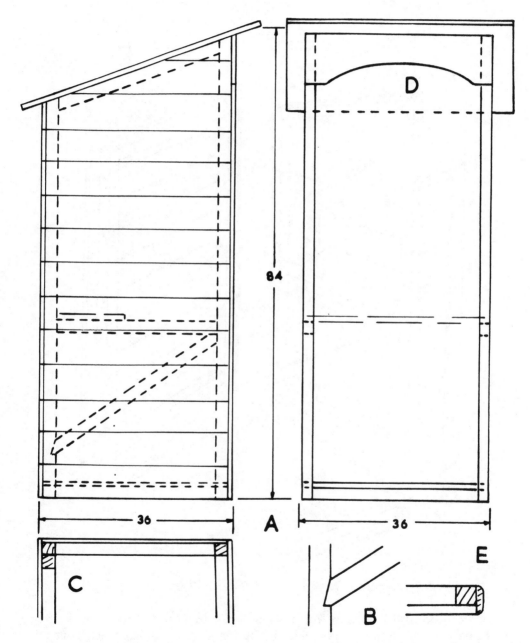

Fig. 4-2. Sizes and construction details of the take-down shelter.

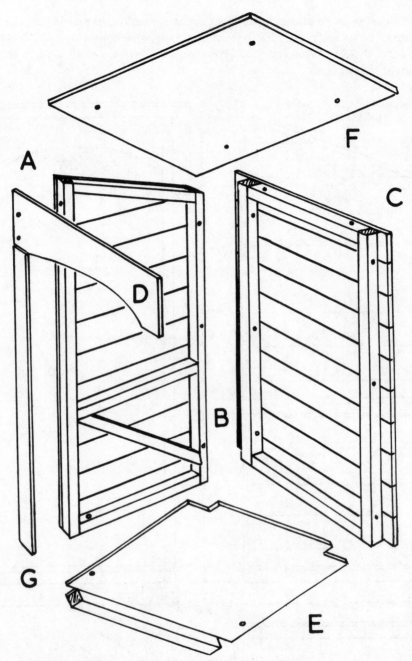

Fig. 4-3. Assembly of the parts of the take-down shelter.

You can board the walls on 2-inch-square strip frames. The roof and floor might be ³/₄-inch plywood. Assemble the building with ³/₈-inch coach bolts, which might be left in the outer parts when you take down the shelter.

Start with the pair of sides (FIG. 4-3A). The nailed boards might not be enough to keep the sides square, so include crossmembers and diagonals (FIG. 4-3B). If the crosspieces are about 30 inches from the ground, they can support a board across to act as a temporary high seat or somewhere to put boxes of tickets or other items. So you do not interfere with fitting or removing the floor, notch the diagonals into the rear uprights a few inches up (FIG. 4-2B).

Make the back to fit between the sides (FIG. 4-2C), with the covering boards extending to overlap the side boards (FIG. 4-3C). This assembly should hold its shape, but include a diagonal brace if you think it is necessary. Bevel the top to match the slope of the roof.

For the top of the front, make a piece of plywood to bolt onto the sides (FIGS. 4-2D and 4-3D). Round the edges of the hollow. Make a plywood floor (FIG. 4-3E); notch it around the uprights to rest on the bottom rails of the sides and back. Make up the thickness with a strip at the front. Cut a plywood roof to overlap about 3 inches all around (FIG. 4-3F). Cover the front edges of the sides with a strip (FIG. 4-2E) to fit against the plywood front (FIG. 4-3G).

Three bolts at each corner between the walls should be sufficient. Put two bolts through each end of the plywood front. For the floor, there might be two bolts upwards near the front. If the floor is a close fit, you might not need any other bolts through the floor. For a temporary assembly, you can drop the floor onto the bolts without using nuts. It will be best to make a temporary assembly, then mark the roof-bolt holes with the roof in position. When you are satisfied with the first assembly, round all exposed edges and separate the parts for painting.

Sun Shelter

Something with a more decorative appearance than the rather basic take-down shelter will look better in a yard or garden if you intend to sit in it, sheltered from wind and sun. You can also use it to store outdoor furniture or garden tools.

As shown in FIG. 4-4, the back and the front are parallel and upright, but the side walls slope inwards. Curve the top and back of the door opening, and give the front bargeboards shaped edges to avoid an austere appearance. This design includes a wooden floor, so the shelter could be self-contained and not attached to the ground, making it easier to move it to a different location. With the usual softwood construction, it should be possible for two men to carry the whole assembly for a short distance.

The sizes suggested in FIG. 4-5A allow for occupying a ground area about 48 inches × 60 inches, but you can modify the sizes to suit your needs, providing you do not increase the size excessively. The skin suggested is shiplap boarding, but you can use plywood or other sheet material. You can use boards or plywood for the roof, then cover it with roofing felt or other material. Nail the bargeboards on after you have covered the roof. You can build in any seating or you can rely on separate chairs.

The key assembly is the back (FIG. 4-6A). Set this part of the building out sym-

Fig. 4-4. The sun shelter has sloping sides and decorative bargeboards.

metrically about a centerline. With the usual covering, one central upright should be all that you need to supplement the outside framing, which you can halve together (FIG. 4-6B). Cover the back with boarding, working from the bottom up.

Use the back as a pattern for getting the shape of the front (FIG. 4-6C). Arrange uprights for the doorway sides. Cover with boarding. At the top of the opening, nail stiffening pieces inside and cut the curve through them and the boarding, preferably with a jigsaw. Round all edges of the doorway.

You can make the two sides as separate units, with bolts into the back and the front, if you want to prefabricate the shelter or arrange it to take apart for removal to another site, but it is compact enough for you to move it bodily by truck. Consequently, you might find it simpler to assemble it completely and

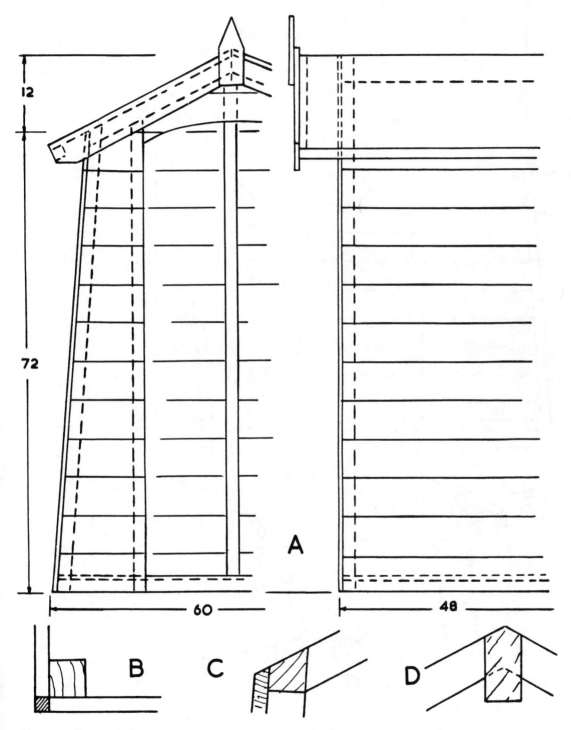

Fig. 4-5. Sizes and corner joints of the sun shelter.

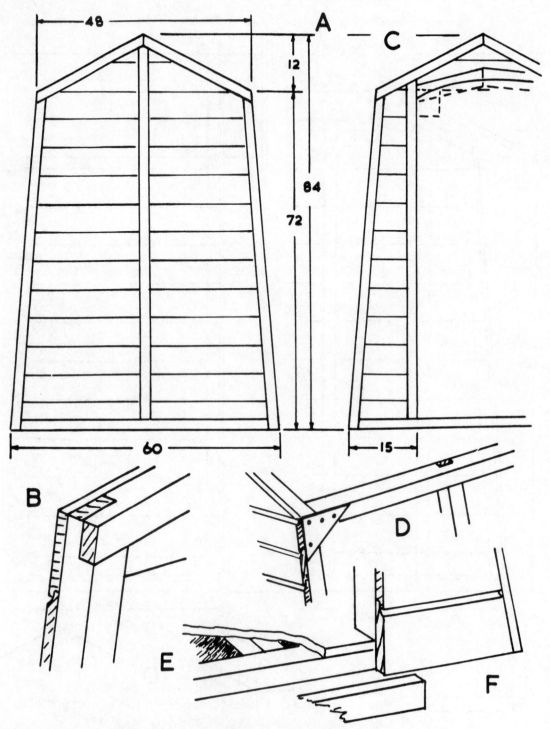

Fig. 4-6. Back, front, and constructional details of the sun shelter.

permanently. If so, put pieces across at top and bottom and central uprights at each side (FIG. 4-6D).

The easiest way to join to the front and back is with sheet-metal gussets. When you have nailed the side boarding on, you will strengthen the joints further. For the neatest corners, stop the board ends at the uprights and fill the corners with square strips (FIG. 4-5B).

You might consider it satisfactory for your purpose for the eaves strips to be left with square edges, but it will be better to plane them to the slope of the roof (FIG. 4-5C) and make a ridge piece with matching slopes (FIG. 4-5D).

Square the assembly as you fit the floor. What stiffening you provide depends on the materials. Two pieces from back to front should be sufficient (FIG. 4-6E). Over these strips might come particleboard, plywood, or 6-inch-wide boards. Cover the front edge with a strip to match the thickness of the shiplap boarding (FIG. 4-6F).

Allow for a 6-inch roof overhang all around. You can use plywood or arrange boards from back to front. Stiffen all edges with strips below (FIG. 4-7A). Take the roof-covering material over the top without joints. Turn in the edges and tack underneath (FIG. 4-7B). Use more large-head nails elsewhere on the roof, if necessary.

Make the bargeboards to stand about $1/2$ inch above the roof covering and to project at least 1 inch at the eaves. Leave the lower edges straight, or give them a regular pattern of deckle edges. The pattern shown is distinctive (FIG. 4-7C), and you can cut it with a portable jigsaw. Cut one and use it as a pattern for marking the others. The central piece can have a simple point, or it can be curved to match the other decoration.

Materials List for Sun Shelter

8 uprights	2	× 2	× 75
1 upright	2	× 2	× 86
4 tops	2	× 2	× 30
2 bottoms	2	× 2	× 62
2 bottoms	2	× 2	× 50
2 bottom supports	2	× 2	× 50
2 top rails	2	× 2	× 50
4 corners	1	× 1	× 75
2 roofs	36- × -72- x-$\frac{3}{4}$ plywood (or boards)		
4 roof edges	$1\frac{1}{2}$ × $1\frac{1}{2}$ × 36		
2 roof edges	$1\frac{1}{2}$ × $1\frac{1}{2}$ × 74		
1 ridge	2	× 4	× 50
4 bargeboards	$\frac{3}{4}$ × 5	× 36	
2 bargeboard ends	$\frac{3}{4}$ × 4	× 15	
1 floor	48- × -60- x -$\frac{3}{4}$ plywood or particle board (or boards)		
Covering: shiplap boards about $\frac{3}{4}$ × 6			

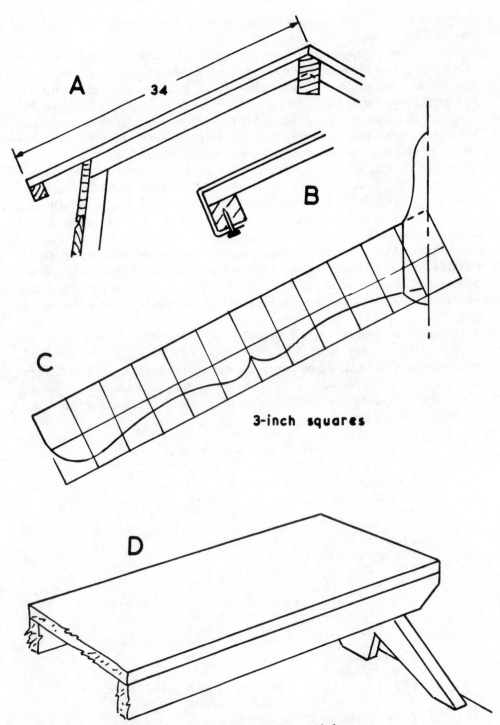

Fig. 4-7. Roof, bargeboard, and seat details for the sun shelter.

If you put strips across the sides at seat height, you can place one or more boards across as a seat and move them to stand on end if you want to use the shelter as a store. Another idea would be to make a bench with its feet arranged to come between the sides (FIG. 4-7D); then you can lift outside when you prefer the open air.

If the sun shelter is to stand on soil or grass, soak the lower parts (at least) with preservative. For a permanent position, you should place it on a concrete base. You can leave the inside untreated, but it would look best if you finished it in a light-color paint, even if you paint the outside in a dark color.

Canopied Shelter

If there is driving rain or if the sun is very hot, it is advantageous to extend the roof forward on your shelter. If you can extend the sides also, you can provide a wind break, as well as improve the appearance of the shelter.

The previously listed designs are for shelters used in a garden or yard, and anyone selling or collecting tickets at an event will appreciate them. The shelter shown in FIG. 4-8 is large enough for many purposes, but it is small enough for a single-sloped roof. This type of shelter is simple, but if you want a much larger shelter, it would be better to have a ridged roof, which I will describe later.

This shelter is shown on a wooden base that extends all around, with extra width at the front, so you can bring a chair forward while still benefiting from the shade of the structure. You can make a base of concrete, or you can place the

Materials List for Canopied Shelter

10 side frames	2	× 2	× 90	
2 side frames	2	× 2	× 62	
4 front frame	2	× 2	× 86	
3 front frames	2	× 2	× 66	
3 back frames	2	× 2	× 74	
2 back frames	2	× 2	× 66	
1 front bar	2	× 2	× 66	
2 corners	1	× 1	× 74	
2 cover strips	¾	× 3	× 90	
2 cover strips	¾	× 3	× 80	
1 front board	1	× 8	× 80	
2 roof panels	40- × -90- × -¾ or 1 plywood			
1 roof-joint cover	2	× 2	× 66	
1 roof-joint cover	2	× 2	× 30	
2 base frames	2	× 2	× 80	
6 base frames	2	× 2	× 90	
2 base covers	1	× 3	× 90	
Baseboards	1	× 6	(approximately)	
Shiplap boards	1	× 6	(approximately)	

Fig. 4-8. This shelter has its sides and roof extended to make a canopy.

shelter directly on the ground, if you are locating it only temporarily. Construction is done by bolting sections together, so you can do most of the work on the parts before erecting them on a site.

As shown, most of the framing is 2-inch-square wood, and the covering is shiplap boards. You also can use plywood or other covering material. You can board the roof, but stout, exterior plywood is strong and simple. Figure 4-8 is shown with the front board decorated with a deckle edge, but if you use a plain board, it could carry announcements if you are using the shelter at an event. Nail, halve, tenon, or hold framing joints, including those on the base, with sheet-metal gussets.

The sizes suggested in FIG. 4-9A will make a shelter of reasonable proportions. If you alter sizes, make sure the roof has enough slope to allow water to run off. If you get heavy snowfalls, it might be advisable to make it steeper. Do

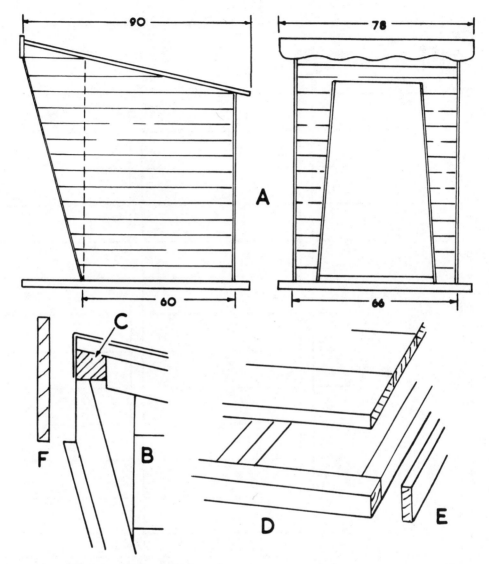

Fig. 4-9. *Sizes and details of the canopied shelter.*

not lengthen the canopy too much if you do not anchor down the shelter, otherwise it might tend to fall forward.

Start by making a pair of sides (FIG. 4-10A). Keep three uprights square to the bottom. Bevel the sloping front pieces and nail them at the bottom (FIG. 4-10B). At the top, place a 6-inch upright part to take the front board. When you cut that corner to shape, reinforce it with another piece inside (FIG. 4-9B). Cover the framing with shiplap boards, starting from the bottom. Cut the board ends, back and front, level with the framing. On the front edges only, put on cover strips with rounded, outer corners (FIG. 4-10C).

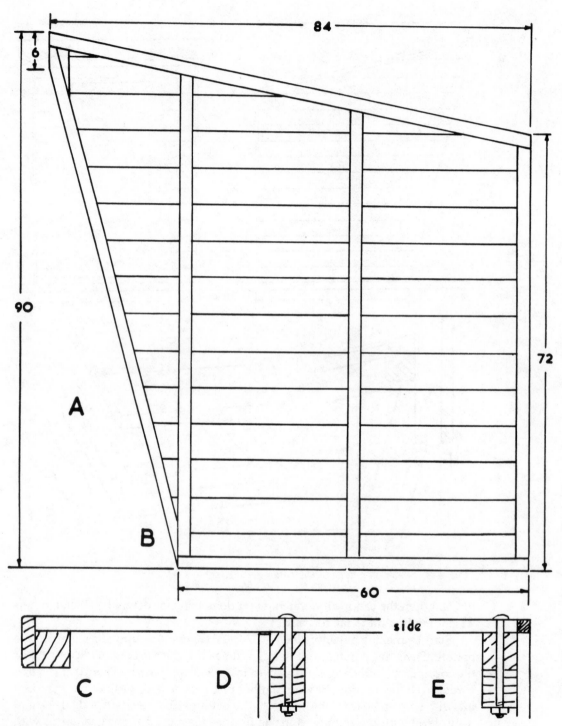

Fig. 4-10. Side and joint details of the canopied shelter.

The upright front (FIG. 4-11A) fits between the sides. The doorway is shown with sloping sides to match the design of the shelter sides. Make the overall height to match the sides, and bevel the top to match the roof slope. Arrange a crossbar to give sufficient head room (FIG. 4-11B).

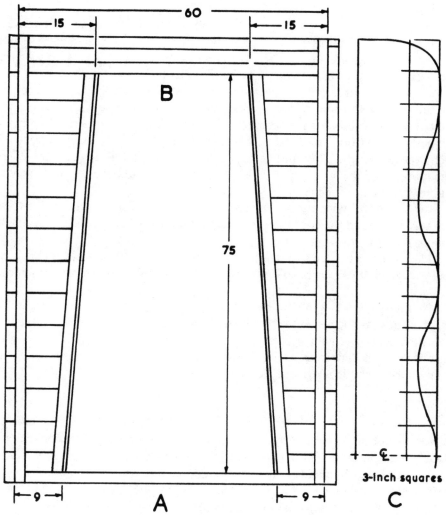

Fig. 4-11. Front and bargeboard details for the sun shelter.

When you have assembled the shelter, bolt the front and side uprights together (FIG. 4-10D). Extend the covering boards far enough to go over the second upright, without being so long as to prevent complete tightening. When you cover the front with boards, see that the assembly is without twist.

The back is a simple, boarded frame, with strips around the outside and one central upright. Make its height to match the sides, and bevel the top to suit the roof. In a similar way to the front, the boarding has to overlap a second upright when you bolt the parts together. Allow for this overlap (FIG. 4-10E), but you will get the neatest appearance by fitting a square piece in the corner.

When you assemble the shelter, put a bar across the front (FIG. 4-9C). This bar holds the sides at the correct distance and provides a place to attach the roof covering.

If you make a base, allow it to project about 6 inches outside the back and sides. At the front, it might go as far as the canopy. The suggested construction has a framework with supports across at about 18 inches (FIG. 4-9D), close boarding over that, and a strip covering the board ends (FIG. 4-9E).

If you use stout, exterior plywood for the roof, there will have to be a central joint from back to front, if you cut standard sheets. Arrange a strip under the joint. If the plywood does not seem stiff enough, add additional strips to provide support. At the front, cut the roof sheets level with the bar, but allow about a 6-inch overhang at the sides and back. It might be satisfactory to leave the edges unsupported, but you can place 1-inch-square strips underneath for strength and to give a more substantial appearance when covered.

Cover the roof with any of the usual covering materials. Nail to the front bar and turn in around the edges so you can nail underneath. If necessary, nail light battens over the covering on top.

Make the front board so it overhangs a little at its ends and projects above the roof (FIG. 4-9F). If you wish, shape its lower edge (FIG. 4-11C), then nail or screw it in place.

No internal work is shown, but you could build in seating or arrange removable benches, as suggested for the previous shelter.

After treating it with preservative or paint, bolt or screw the shelter to its base. If you will want to move the shelter and base, use a few blocks or battens to keep the bottom edges correctly located on the base.

Ridge-canopied Shelter

A ridged roof has a more attractive appearance than a lean-to or single slope. Both look better than a horizontal roof. Over a certain size, a ridged roof is preferable, as it sheds rain and snow easier and offers less wind resistance. A shelter with a ridge from back to front and extending canopy or porch has good access, provides maximum shelter, and looks good.

The shelter in FIG. 4-12 has a floor area of about 60 inches by 84 inches, with a lengthwise canopy of approximately another 24 inches. Good clearance is provided through the doorway, and the shelter has ample head room inside. No base or floor is shown, but you could add a wooden or concrete platform, or you might build in a wooden floor. Construction is sectional, so you can prefabricate most parts and bolt them together on-site.

Shiplap boarding is suggested for the covering, but you can use other materials. The sizes given in FIG. 4-13A allow for economical cutting of standard ply-

Fig. 4-12. This canopied shelter has a ridged roof.

Materials List for Ridged Canopied Shelter

14 uprights	2	× 2	×	80
2 uprights	2	× 2	×	104
5 rails	2	× 2	×	92
4 rails	2	× 2	×	56
4 edge covers	1	× 3	×	80
2 corners	1	× 1	×	80
10 roof frames	1½	× 1½	×	60
2 roof frames	1½	× 1½	×	90
2 bargeboards	1	× 6	×	60
8 roof battens	½	× 1½	×	60

Shiplap boards for walls 1 × 6 (approximately)
Roof: 1- × -10 boards or ¾ plywood

wood sheets. Arrange internal framing of some panels to suit joints between plywood sheets. Join framing parts to each other by halving, tenoning, or by using sheet-metal gussets. Many parts will be satisfactory if you notch and nail them.

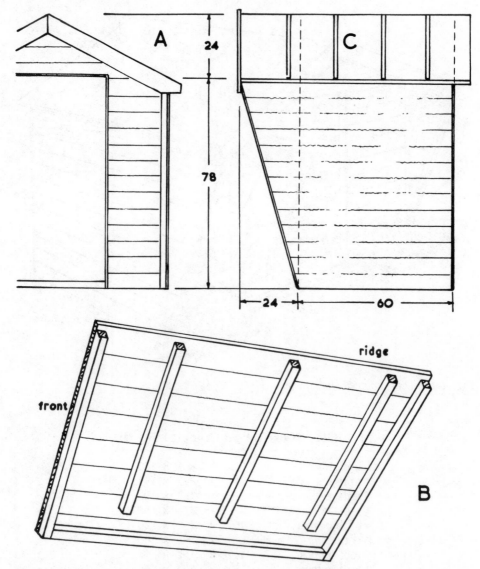

Fig. 4-13. Sizes and roof details for the ridged-canopied shelter.

Start by making the front (FIG. 4-14A). Fit this piece between the sides as previously done in FIG. 4-10D. Allow the covering boards to extend to overlap the side uprights. The doorway is shown 48 inches wide, but you can alter that. If you want good protection for articles stored inside, make it narrower. If you want to let in plenty of sunlight while you sit inside, make it wider.

At the top, cut away for a 2-inch-×-4-inch ridge piece to pass through and put a supporting piece across, below the gap (FIG. 4-14B). After covering with boards, put rounded-edge pieces at each side of the doorway (FIG. 4-14C).

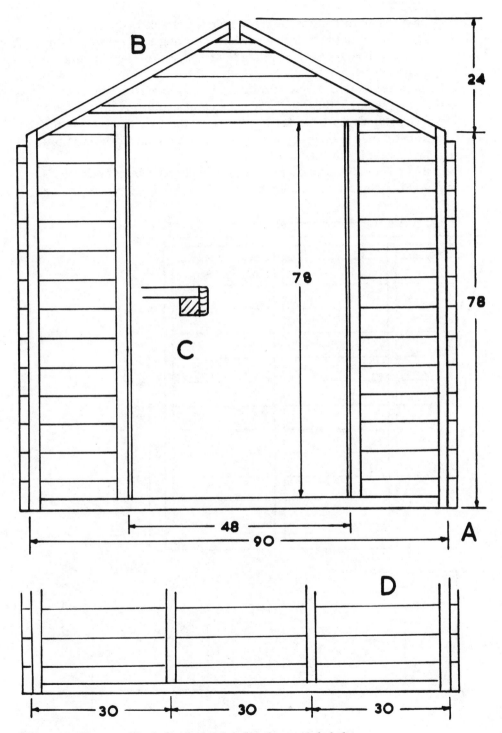

Fig. 4-14. Front and back details for the ridged-canopied shelter.

The back has the same outline as the front. Bolt its uprights to the uprights at the rear of the sides, and cut the boarding to allow for fitting a square strip in the corner (FIG. 4-10E). To allow for fully boarding the back, arrange two uprights to the full height intermediately (FIG. 4-14D).

Make the pair of sides (FIG. 4-15A), cutting the boards level with the framing. Allow a 4-inch vertical part at the front to take the bargeboards. Reinforce with a block inside (FIG. 4-15B). Check the side heights against the matching parts of the front and back. Bevel the top edges to suit the slope of the roof. Cover the front sloping edges for a neat finish (FIG. 4-15C).

For assembly, it should be satisfactory to use $^3/_8$-inch coach bolts at about 18-inch intervals. Drill holes for these bolts in the sides. Do not continue drilling

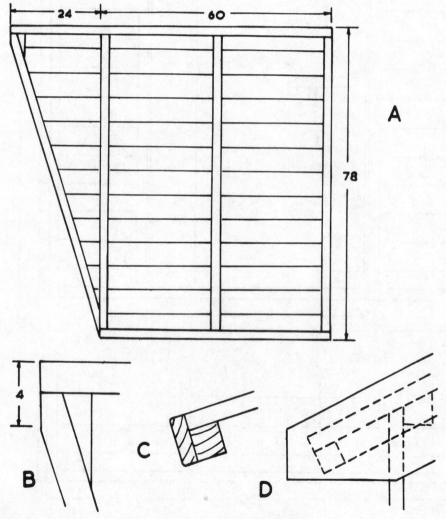

Fig. 4-15. Side and roof details for the ridged-canopied shelter.

into the front and back uprights until you bring them together on-site, to ensure exact mating of holes.

Make a 2-inch-×-4-inch ridge piece to go right through the full length of the roof. Bevel its top edge to match the slope on each side. At the front, match the extension with the shelter sides. At the back, an overhang of about 5 inches should be enough.

You can make the two halves of the roof of thick plywood or wide boards (FIG. 4-13B). Bevel the top edges so they meet along the ridge. Make the sections wide enough to allow for a 5-inch overhang at the sides. Frame at back, front, and eaves. Arrange a strip to fit inside the shelter front and another to fit inside the back. These strips will hold the whole assembly square. The number of other pieces will depend on the stiffness of the roof, but there will have to be at least one more.

Cover the roof from eaves to eaves, with tarred felt allowing a good overlap. Turn under and fix with large-head nails at the eaves and the ends. To hold down the fairly large area on top, nail light battens at about 18-inch intervals (FIG. 4-13C).

Fit bargeboards at the front only, or at both ends. Cut so the boards stand about 1 inch above the roof surface and overlap about 1 inch at the corners of the roof (FIG. 4-15D). Nail into the roof end and into the shelter's sides. No central, decorative piece is shown at the apex of the bargeboards, but you can use one similar to those used on roofs discussed previously, or you might wish to cut and mount a badge or personal emblem there.

Small Barbecue Shelter

The weather is not always as kind as you would wish when you want to use your barbecue. If there is no rain, the sun might be uncomfortably hot or the wind too strong. You also might have the problem of crowds, particularly children who might get burned if they get too close. A shelter that has a roof, but is basically open all around except for barrier walls, allows the cook to work uninterrupted. He can have his equipment and food nearby and is able to serve hamburgers, sausages, or whatever through the open front or sides.

The shelter shown in FIG. 4-16 is designed with this purpose in mind. It also has possibilities as a booth for selling or collecting almost anything. Although you could erect it as a permanent shelter, it is designed with portable sections, so you can use it anywhere. Assembly and disassembly should not take more than 30 minutes. Construction is plywood on 2-inch-square strip framing, but you could use shiplap boards, if you wish. For a portable shelter, the roof is plywood without extra protection. For a permanent shelter, you could stiffen its edges and cover the roof with roofing felt or other material.

The suggested sizes are based on 30-inch-wide bays (FIG. 4-17A). The height allows normal clearance through the doorway at the back. The barrier-wall edges are 36 inches from the ground, which is a convenient height for serving and

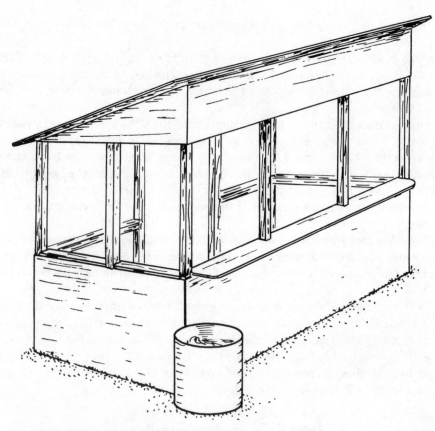

Fig. 4-16. *This barbecue shelter has a roof and barrier walls, but there is plenty of open space for ventilation.*

Materials List for Small Barbecue Shelter

6 upright	2 × 2 × 98
8 uprights	2 × 2 × 80
6 rails	2 × 2 × 62
7 rails	2 × 2 × 92
2 rails	2 × 2 × 36
2 top rails	2 × 2 × 70
3 roof stiffeners	2 × 2 × 62
2 roof panels	50- × -72- × -½ plywood
1 roof-joint cover	6- × -72- × -½ plywood
2 end panels	36- × -62- × -½ plywood
2 end panels	18- × -62- × -½ plywood
1 front panel	36- × -92- × -½ plywood
1 front panel	18- × -92- × -½ plywood
2 back panels	32- × -36- × -½ plywood

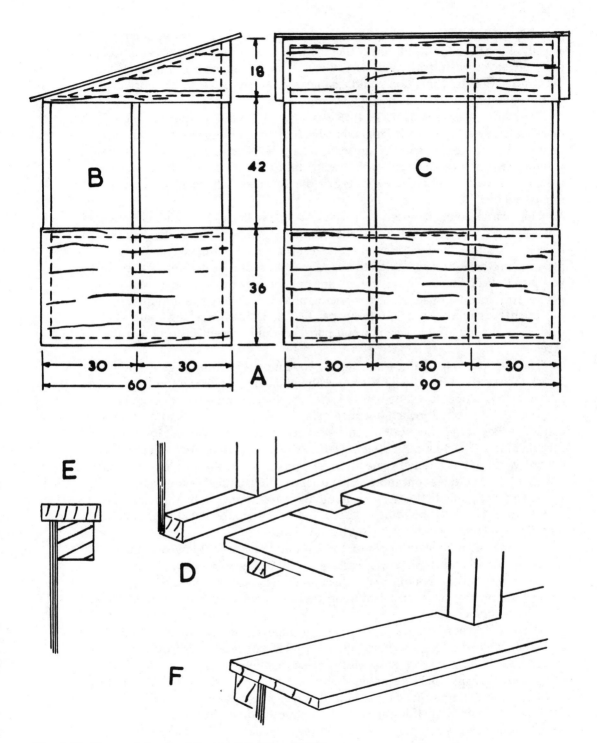

Fig. 4-17. Sizes and details of the small barbecue shelter.

probably enough height to keep most wind off the barbecue surface. Boarding directly above the barrier walls is not included, but you could fully enclose any of the walls, if you wish, particularly if you have to contend with a strong, prevailing wind in one direction. You could arrange removable panels to fit in or hang on the open framing, if your needs will vary.

Start with a pair of ends (FIGS. 4-17B and 4-18A). With the complete structure, make sure the parts of the uprights that edge the openings are smooth and with lightly rounded edges, so they are safe if anyone holds on to them. Halve together the uprights and rails, which cross at the middle. You can make any of the other usual joints elsewhere. Nailing on the plywood skin will give rigidity to the assemblies.

Hold corner joints between walls with 3/8-inch bolts at about 18-inch intervals, similar to the other shelters described earlier. For a portable shelter, you can finish the covering panels level with the edges. For a more permanent shelter, the plywood on the ends can overlap the back and front for a neater appearance. If you plan to keep the shelter in sections for transport by truck to anywhere you need it, you might damage the overhanging plywood, so it is better to omit it.

The back is a simple frame, mostly open (FIG. 4-18B), so use strong joints, particularly at the top. The lower plywood panels should prevent distortion of the assembly.

The front (FIGS. 4-17C and 4-18C) has plywood top and bottom to give rigidity. Check the back and front heights against the ends, and bevel the top edges to match the roof slope. It will be best to locate bolt holes during a trial assembly.

The roof can be 72 inches down the slope and in two pieces to overhang about 6 inches at the ends. Put a 6-inch-wide cover strip on one half to overlap the other piece (FIG. 4-18D). A stiffening strip under the lapped piece will prevent distortion. If this will be a permanent shelter, you can screw the roof into place as it is, but if it is portable, put more strips underneath to fit inside the walls (FIG. 4-18E). With the portable shelter, you should use a few screws or bolts to hold the roof down and keep the building in shape. It is best to do the detail work on the roof during a temporary assembly of the other parts.

You can use the shelter directly on the ground, but you could make a floor to fit inside, probably in three parts, each about 30 inches × 60 inches. Arrange boards to overlap the bottom wall edges, with notches around uprights and strips underneath (FIG. 4-17D). Dropping these sections in place will hold the other parts square.

What you do at the edges of the openings depends on your needs. You can leave the plywood edges uncovered, but it would be better to add cover strips. Where you do not need any extra width, make them with a slight overlap (FIG. 4-17E). You also could make a serving shelf or countertop, just at the center (FIG. 4-18F) or along the front, notched around the uprights (FIG. 4-17F).

Almost certainly, anything inside will be freestanding, so you can move it around. A few ledges between uprights, however, would allow you to put boards across to serve as seats, shelves, or tables. Use the space above the front opening

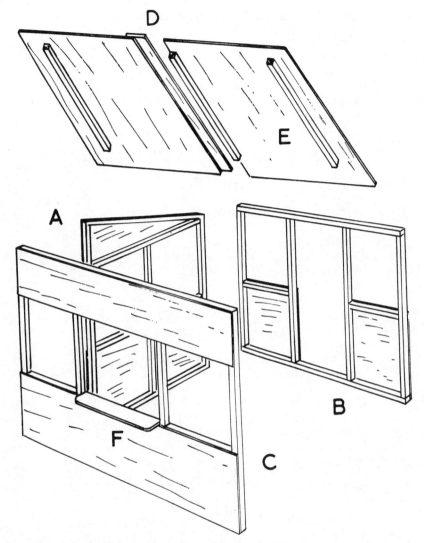

Fig. 4-18. Assembly arrangements of the small barbecue shelter.

in this way for a shelf, particularly if you plan to use the shelter for selling or serving from a large stock of food or drink.

Large Barbecue Shelter

A large shelter that will accommodate many people during a barbecue, picnic, or other outdoor gathering when the weather turns sour or when there is an urge to congregate more closely, needs to be an adequate size. It should be a permanent structure and should be built in position, although you might prefabricate some parts.

Materials List for Large Barbecue Shelter

Gables

4 uprights	2	× 3	×	86
4 uprights	2	× 3	×	120
4 rails	2	× 3	×	98
2 rails	2	× 6	×	98
4 uprights	2	× 3	×	44
4 uprights	2	× 3	×	24

Sides

3 rails	2	× 3	×	146
2 rails	2	× 3	×	50
2 wall plates	2	× 6	×	146
8 uprights	2	× 3	×	86
6 uprights	2	× 3	×	44
4 blocks	2	× 6	×	12

Roof

1 ridge	2	× 6	×	158
2 purlins	2	× 4	×	158
4 truss rafters	2	× 3	×	60
2 truss ties	2	× 3	×	86
46 roof boards	1	× 6	×	64
4 roof edges	1½	× 1½	×	64
2 roof edges	1½	× 1½	×	158
16 roof battens	½	× 1	×	64
4 bargeboards	1	× 6	×	68

Walls

Shiplap boards 1-×-6 or ¾ plywood (approximately)

Ventilator

4 ends	1	× 5	×	24
2 battens	1	× 2	×	30
6 tops	1	× 6	×	24

The shelter shown in FIG. 4-19 has a ridge roof and a doorway at one side, although you can place these items elsewhere without difficulty. Closed walls reach 42 inches high, and there are open spaces above that. Spacing allows for seating to be built in, or you might prefer to use separate chairs or benches. The framework has to be stouter than in previous shelters and is mostly 2 inches × 3

Fig. 4-19. *The large barbecue shelter has space inside for several people as well as the barbecue.*

inches. The cover might be shiplap boards, although you can use plywood or other covering.

The sizes suggested in FIG. 4-20 would allow you to use a single, standard plywood sheet in the width and one and a half sheets in the length. The roof is boarded and covered with tarred felt or other roofing material. The pair of gables settle the shape, but two trusses to support the ridge and purlins are under the roof. You should install this type of building on a concrete base. A wooden floor would be inappropriate. In a suitable situation, compacted earth might be satisfactory.

Start with the two gables, which are the same (FIG. 4-21A). All of the framing is 2-inch-×-3-inch strips, except the piece across below the eaves, which is a 2-inch-×-6-inch section. All pieces have their 2-inch faces towards the outside. You can halve corners (FIG. 4-22A) and the central upright where it crosses the rails. At the top, put cheek pieces so you have a space for the ridge (FIG. 4-21B). Notch the other uprights and nail them to the rails. Notch the ends of the 6-inch piece (FIG. 4-22B). Check squareness of the framework and see that the opposite ends match as a pair. Board the outsides level with the openings and edges.

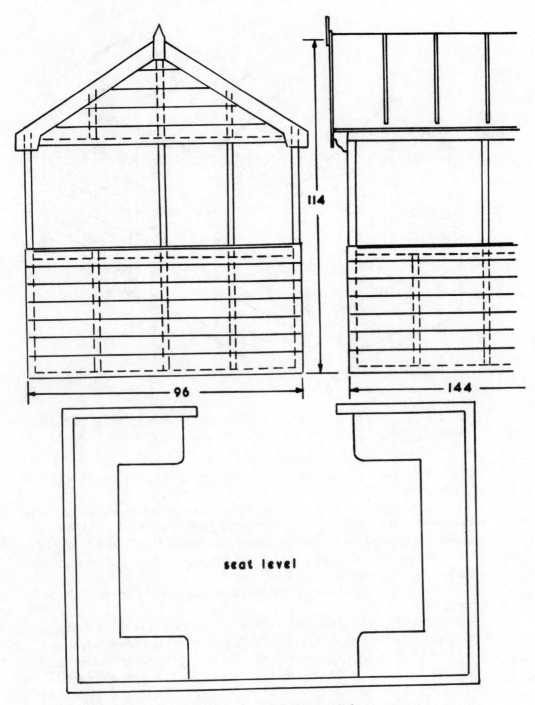

Fig. 4-20. Sizes and suggested layout of the large barbecue shelter.

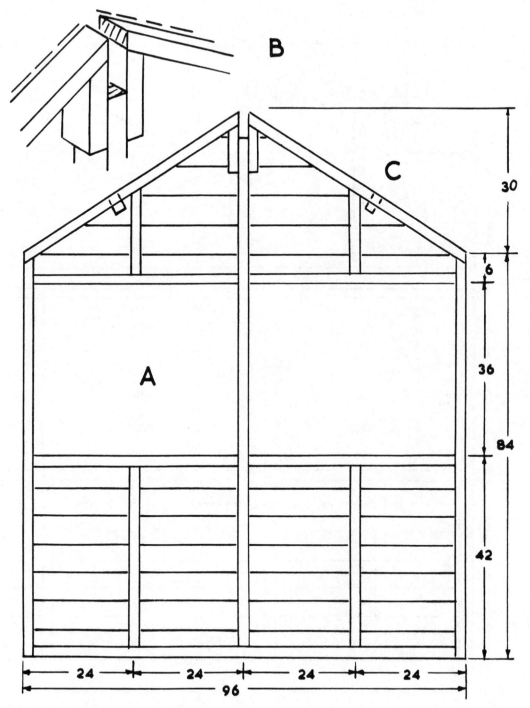

Fig. 4-21. An end of the large barbecue shelter.

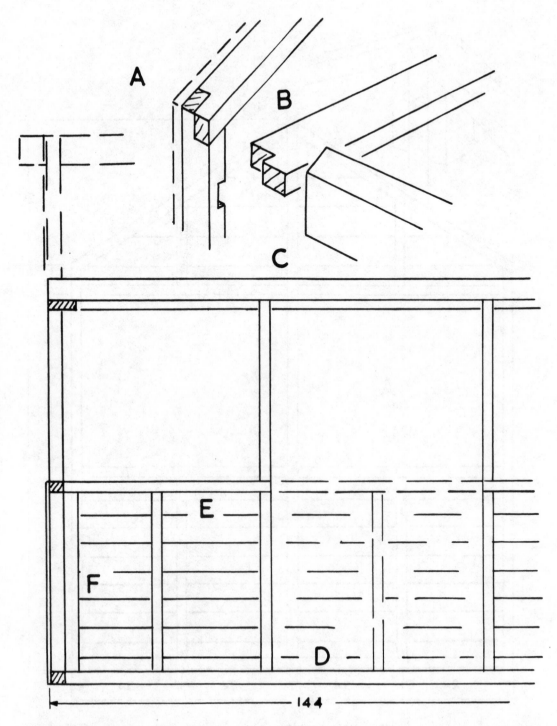

Fig. 4-22. Side arrangements of the large barbecue shelter.

The lengthwise supports for the roof are the ridge, which fits into the apex slots of the gables; two wall plates (FIG. 4-22C), which rest on the horizontal piece across each gable; and two purlins. Notch the purlins into the gables below where the uprights come (FIG. 4-21C).

When setting up the building on-site, start by joining the gables with the bottom members of the sides (FIG. 4-22D). Notch for the uprights at 24-inch intervals, and join to the gables with sheet-metal gussets. Use struts or other temporary supports to hold the gables vertical until you fit other lengthwise parts. Make and fit the intermediate rails on the closed side (FIG. 4-22E), with notches for uprights to match the bottom members. Include uprights at the ends (FIG. 4-22F) for additional stiffness.

Bevel the top edges of the wall plates to match the slope of the roof. Notch the wall plates where the uprights come, then fit both wall plates to the gables and the uprights that connect to them. Treat the side where there will be a doorway in the same way, but leave a central space.

Check that the assembly is symmetrical by comparing diagonals, particularly on the sides. When you are satisfied that the assembly is square, board up to the intermediate rails and cover the wall plates with similar boards.

At this length, there is a risk of an inadequately supported roof sagging after it has been in position for some time. To prevent this sagging, use two trusses, equally spaced, placing one over each full-depth wall upright. Obviously, the whole roof assembly must be kept in line. It is advisable to partially make the ridge and purlins, then have the parts of the trusses ready (FIG. 4-23A) so you can cut joints by testing where pieces cross, and you will maintain the line of the roof.

At the apex of each truss, allow for the ridge piece and put a supporting strip across (FIG. 4-23B). At the purlin crossings, notch the parts together, but take out less of the truss than the purlin (FIG. 4-23C). At the eaves, cut the trusses against the wall plates and nail each part to a block (FIG. 4-23D). Sight along a temporary assembly to see that the roofline is straight. Check on the slope of the roof in several places with a board resting on ridge, purlin, and wall plates at each side. When you are satisfied, nail all the roof structure parts in place. Let the ridge extend about 5 inches at each end. At the corners of the gables, make blocks that extend the same amount and have sloped tops to match the roof (FIG. 4-23E).

Cover the roof with boards from the ridge to overhang the eaves by about 6 inches. You can use plain boards, although tongue-and-groove edges would be better. Thicken under the edges (FIG. 4-23F). Turn the roof covering under and nail all around. Nail thin battens at about 18-inch intervals from the ridge to the eaves to prevent the covering material from lifting (FIG. 4-23G).

Make bargeboards for the ends, with central decoration, if you wish (FIG. 4-23H). Nail the bargeboards to the roof, to project about 1 inch above its level.

If you are using the shelter for a barbecue, it would be advisable to arrange a central ventilator in the roof. Fit the ventilator in during boarding of the roof. A

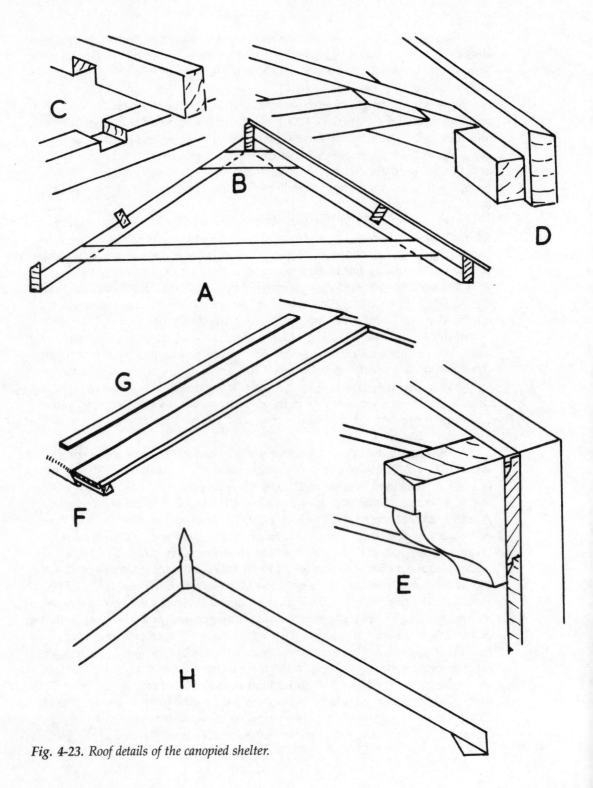

Fig. 4-23. *Roof details of the canopied shelter.*

simple type is shown in FIG. 4-24. Cut the opening as you lay the boards (FIG. 4-24A). Support cut ends with battens underneath, extending lengthwise on each side of the shortened boards (FIG. 4-24B). Nail on strips at each end of the opening to raise the ventilator roof about 5 inches, then board lengthwise over them (FIG. 4- 24C). Do not cut or alter the ridge piece below the opening. When you cover the roof, carry the covering material up the ventilator ends and put more over its

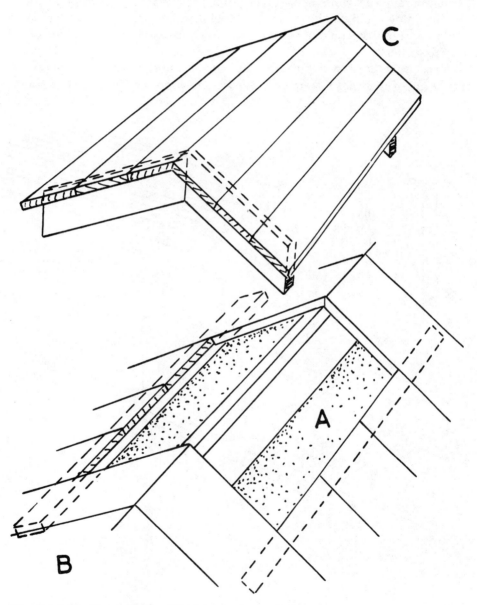

Fig. 4-24. Ventilator details of the large barbecue shelter.

roof. The ventilator does not have to be central; you can position it to suit where you will put the barbecue fire.

What you do inside the shelter depends on its intended uses. You can leave it as it is, which might be satisfactory for varied and occasional uses. A lining inside the closed walls would improve appearance, add to strength, and reduce drafts (FIG. 4- 25A). Put a capping over the edges, preferably with a groove below to prevent rainwater running back and inside the cladding (FIG. 4-25B).

The lining could be plywood or particleboard. You might use oil-tempered hardboard, but that would not stand up to rough use, particularly if animals will use the shelter.

Bench seats are easy to build in. Put battens where the seats are to come. A seat height of 16 inches is suitable. Make framed supports. Put a strong support

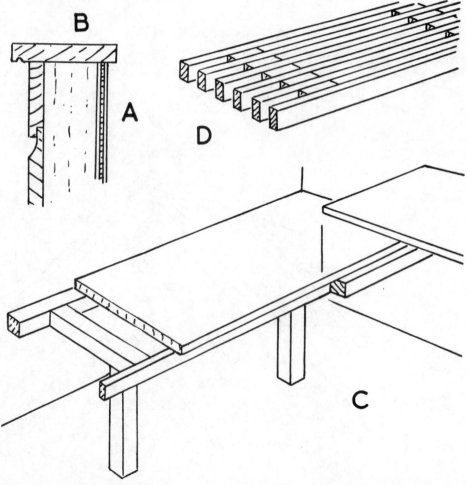

Fig. 4-25. Wall section and suggested seat construction for the large barbecue shelter.

underneath if you carry the seating around a corner (FIG. 4-25C). The simplest seat top is made from thick, exterior-grade plywood. Boards can make up the width. A neat top, which does not trap water or leaves that blow in, is made with 1-inch-×-2-inch strips on edge (FIG. 4-25D).

Arrange seats as lockers for storage. Complete them as boxes, nailing down with a few inches at the back of the top and arranging the rest to hinge up. Fit shelves inside the roof at the ends or along each wall plate.

Lifting-door Building

In some situations, there is an advantage in having a building with a large door that can be swung up to form an awning or canopy, but at other times it seals the building, giving protection from animals or interlopers. This might be on a recreation field, where teams can shelter, clothing can be left, or refreshments served. You might have a need for such a building on your property, possibly where only occasional use will be made of the shelter.

This small building has a front door that swings up to cover an area over 6 feet square, while leaving an opening of similar size to give access to the inside (FIG. 4-26). There are sloping end walls with upright windows and a roof with a good overhang. This arrangement gives interest and character to the building.

Fig. 4-26. *The door of this building is hinged at the top and can be swung up to form a canopy. End walls slope and have upright windows.*

Materials List for Lifting-door Building

2 front uprights	2	× 2	×	86
2 door uprights	2	× 2	×	82
2 front rails	2	× 2	×	124
2 front rafters	2	× 2	×	52
2 rear uprights	2	× 2	×	86
4 rear uprights	2	× 2	×	92
2 rear rails	2	× 2	×	124
2 rear rafters	2	× 2	×	52
8 side uprights	2	× 2	×	86
8 side rails	2	× 2	×	72
4 side rails	2	× 2	×	24
1 ridge piece	2	× 6	×	86
4 intermediate rafters	2	× 2	×	52
4 bargeboards	1	× 4	×	60
4 window sides	1	× 7	×	42
2 window frames	1 1/2	× 1 1/2	×	24
2 window frames	1 1/2	× 1 1/2	×	42
4 window fillets	3/4	× 3/4	×	24
4 window fillets	3/4	× 3/4	×	40
2 doorway trims	1	× 4	×	80
2 door tops	1	× 1	×	80
1 door trim	1	× 5	×	74
8 door rails	1 1/2	× 1 1/2	×	78
2 door legs	1 1/2	× 1 1/2	×	80
10 roof battens	3/8	× 2	×	48
Skin and roof	1/2 or 3/4 plywood			
Roof edges	3/4 × 1 1/2 or 1 × 2			

Covering with plywood is suggested, but you could board the walls if that would fit in better with surroundings.

The instructions assume plywood will be used. Sizes (FIG. 4-27A) are not critical. If you alter them, remember that there should be enough head room when the flap is up, and this controls the amount of sheltered area.

The framework is mostly 2-inch-square strips, and the covering can be 1/2-inch or 3/4-inch plywood. It might be satisfactory to merely butt framework parts of the walls together as the plywood skin adds strength to the joints and reinforces the assembly. For the best construction, crossing parts should be halved. All other joints could be halved or shallow notches used to reinforce nailing. It should be sufficient to nail on the plywood, but you could use waterproof glue as well.

The sizes of some other parts are controlled by the shape of the front assembly. Set out half or the whole front assembly full-size on the floor or plywood (FIGS. 4-27B and 4-28A). This will show you lengths and angles of the frame parts. The bottom rail (FIG. 4-28B) is necessary to keep the assembly in shape, but after

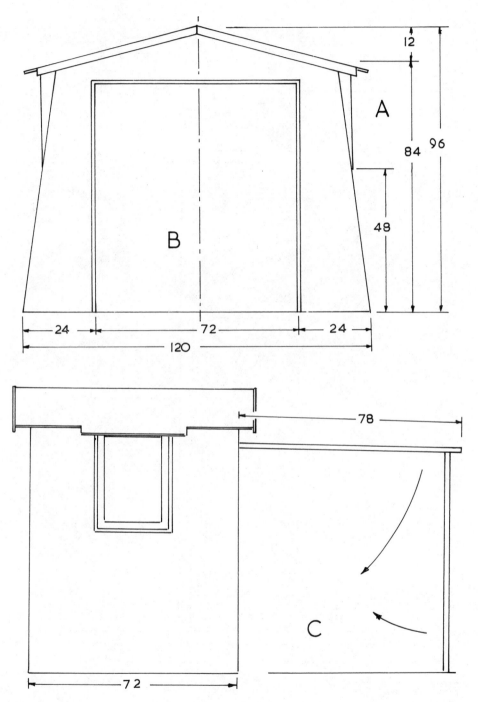

Fig. 4-27. Main sizes of the lifting-door building.

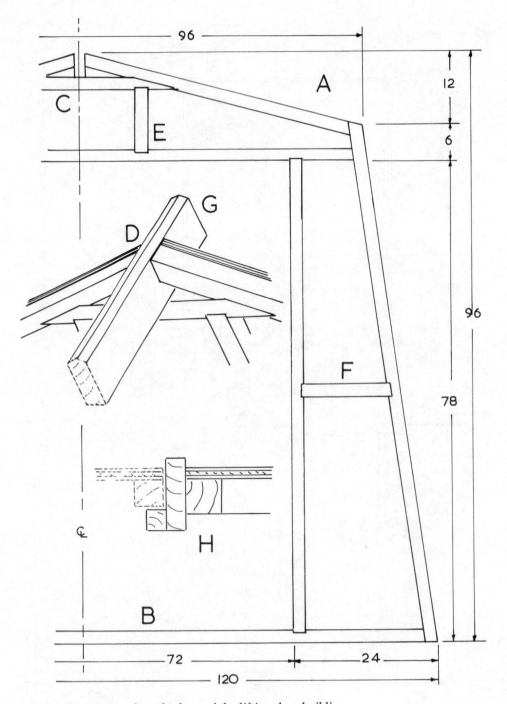

Fig. 4-28. Framework at the front of the lifting-door building.

the building has been erected and the sides fixed down, this rail can be cut at the width of the door opening. Make the front frame, and cover it with plywood. Leave a gap at the apex (FIG. 4-28C) where the ridge piece has to go through (FIG. 4-28D). Trim plywood level with the edges all round and at the door opening.

Make the back to the same outline, but without a doorway. Fit the same members as for the doorway at the front, but also carry the two top uprights (FIG. 4-28E) to the floor rail and the central short rails (FIG. 4-28F) right across. Cover completely with plywood, arranging joints over frame parts. Trim plywood level all round.

The end walls (FIG. 4-29A) are made so the side uprights fit inside the front and back uprights and the plywood extends far enough to cover them (FIG. 4-29B). The heights have to match the sloping ends of the front and back. For the simplest construction, you could leave the top and bottom rails square. The roof would then only make contact at the outer edge, and the bottom rail would have to be kept up a little to allow the building to rest flat on the ground. It would be better to bevel the rails. The bottom one (FIG. 4-29C) is not far out of square and you might decide not to shape it, but the top one needs a greater angle if it is to fit the roof closely (FIG. 4-29D).

Leave the window space open with the plywood cut level. Let the plywood extend enough at the edges—a small excess width can be trimmed during assembly. Bevel the plywood to match the frame angles at top and bottom edges.

You could fit the upright windows at this stage or wait until after the walls have been fitted together. If you make them before assembly, obtain the angle from the slope of the edge of the front. The windows should finish upright. Measure the length of the window opening, and see how far out you need to go to get an upright line. If you are working to the sizes given, this will be about 5 inches. You have to cut a pair of boards for the sides of each window. It will be advisable to mark and cut a template from scrap plywood or hardboard, and try it in position before using it to mark the boards. Cut the top to fit around the framing and continue the slope of the roof (FIG. 4-30A and FIG. 4-30B). Cut the bottom level inside, but let the window frame come 1/4 inch forward of the plywood (FIG. 4-30C), so water is unlikely to run into the joint. Nail these boards inside the window openings in the end walls.

Make window frames to fit between the boards. Use halving joints at the corners. The inner surfaces must be square, but you will get the best fit if top (FIG. 4-30D) and bottom (FIG. 4-30E) are beveled to fit closely into the opening.

Glass will be held between fillets, but it will be wisest to delay glazing until all other work on the building has been done. Have fillets inside and outside. The bottom outer fillet can be extended to make a sill (FIG. 4-30F).

Prepare the base. You may mount the building on a wooden floor or make a concrete slab. There could be bricks or concrete slabs let into the ground under the walls.

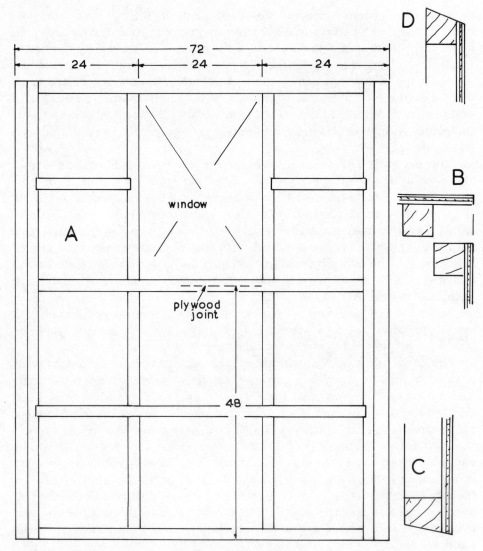

Fig. 4-29. Framework at the sides of the lifting-door building.

Assemble the walls to each other in position. You will nail the corners both ways, but it will help to get the joints tight if you use a few $3/8$-inch bolts to pull through the meeting uprights. Check squareness by comparing diagonal measurements on the floor and at eaves level. Fasten down through the bottom rails, but do not fasten through the rail at the bottom of the doorway, if you intend removing it after all other parts are securely fixed. Leave making the door until after the other parts of the building are completed.

Make and fit the ridge piece to fit in its slope and project 6 inches at back and

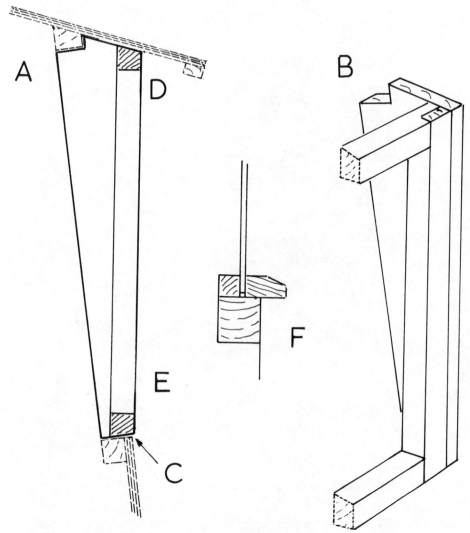

Fig. 4-30. Window frame details for the lifting-door building.

front. Bevel the top to match the slope of the roof (FIG. 4-28G). The roof is too big an area for the plywood to be unsupported. Arrange intermediate rafters on each slope to meet the eaves outside the window position (FIG. 4-31A). Notch the ridge piece (FIG. 4-31B) and eaves rails (FIG. 4-31C) to take the ends of the rafters. Fix the ridge piece and rafters in place. Check that they are in line by sighting across and testing with a straight board over them in all directions.

Make up the roof panels (FIG. 4-31D) with joints between sheets over the rafters. Allow for meeting on the ridge and an overhang of 6 inches all around, including the windows (FIG. 4-31E). Stiffen the overhanging edges with strips

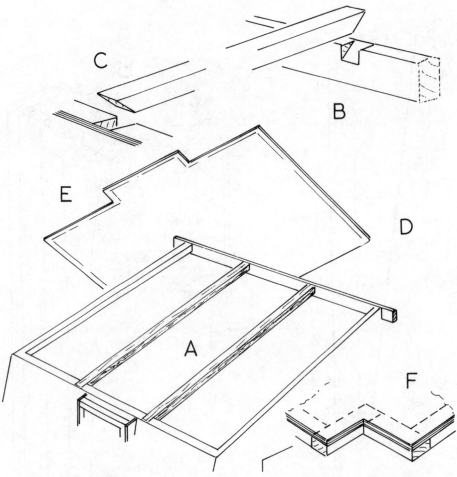

Fig. 4-31. Roofing arrangements for the lifting-door building.

underneath (FIG. 4- 31F) for nailing the covering tarred felt. Nail on the roof pan-els securely to all parts they cross.

Cover the roof with tarred felt, nailed under one eaves and taken over the ridge to nail to the other. Cover the ridge with a strip of felt and add battens down the slope at about 18-inch intervals, as described for several other projects (FIG. 4-23F and G). Turn the felt over at back and front, then you could cover with bargeboards, if you wish. In most situations very decorative bargeboards would be inappropriate. Parallel boards 4 inches wide could be used.

Line the sides of the doorway with strips that project $1/2$ inch forward and far enough behind to take door stops (FIG. 4-28H). Line under the top of the doorway with a strip that comes level with the side strips inside the building, but it can project further forward to throw rainwater clear (FIG. 4-32A). It does not have a door stop.

Frame the door (FIG. 4-32B) with 1½-inch square strips. Check the sizes of the opening it has to fit. Allow about 1-inch ground clearance. Side clearance could be ¼ inch. Use halving joints at all meeting places. Join the plywood on the central upright.

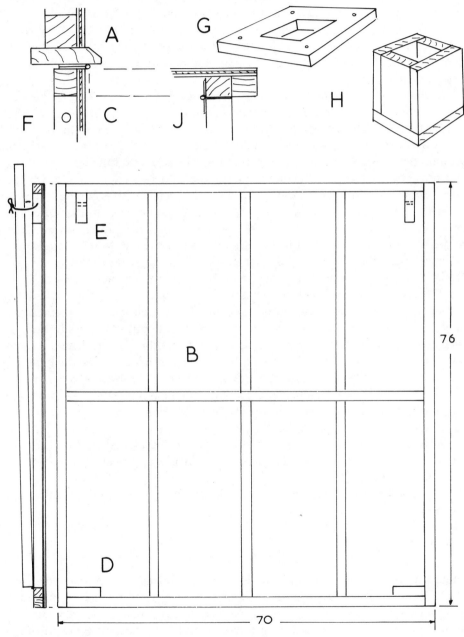

Fig. 4-32. *Details of the door for the lifting-door building.*

The door has to be supported by its hinges, and they should be strong enough and close enough. There could be five hinges, with one near the end of each upright. Choose butt hinges with enough width to put the screws into the framing and not the plywood when the knuckles are outside the front edge of the door. Stout 4-inch hinges would be suitable. Do not let the hinges in deeply, or that might restrict movement as the door is raised (FIG. 4-32C).

Fit 6-inch blocks at the corners, parallel at the bottom (FIG. 4-32D) and vertical at the top (FIG. 4-32E). Drill $1/2$-inch holes in the top ones. Legs hinge on the bottom ones and are secured by a cord through the hole in the raised position (FIG. 4-32F).

In the simplest arrangement, the door is raised to near horizontal, the legs swung down and allowed to rest on the ground (FIG. 4-27C). In some circumstances that might be satisfactory, but they are liable to be knocked out of place. You could make a baseplate with a hole to be pegged to the ground at each leg position (FIG. 4-32G). A better arrangement would be a box 3 inches deep to let into the ground (FIG. 4-32H) to take the bottom of a leg. Experiment with the raised door, and trim the leg lengths to suit. Allow a few inches of slope so rainwater will run away and not towards the building. Use hinges on the surface of leg and block and screw them so when the leg is supporting the door, pressure comes wood-to-wood and not just on the hinge knuckle (FIG. 4-32J). As legs will be longer than the height of the door, the cords through the holes in the top blocks will hold up the legs to clear the inside of the top of the doorway.

The door will hang closed, and that might be all you want, but in most situations it should be held in the closed position. The simplest way to prevent the door being opened by the wind or prying animals, is to put wood turnbuttons at each side near the bottom. If you need to fasten the door more securely, there could be a door lock near the bottom each side with each lock inside the building wall and its bolt going into a slot in the door or a catchplate attached to its inside, with keyholes in the walls. You could put locks on the other way, so keyholes are in the door. Much depends on the type of lock. Alternatively you could use hasps and staples with padlocks.

If security of the building is important, you could protect the window openings by making framed plywood shutters to fix inside, to prevent entry that way after breaking the glass.

A painted finish is advisable. Inside the building and under the door/flap might be light color.

Folding Shelter

One of the simplest and most adaptable shelters is formed by hinging two sheets of plywood together. The standard 4-foot-×-8-foot sheets of $1/2$-inch plywood will provide a useful covered area, but you could cut down the sheets, particularly if you find the combined weight too much to carry easily. Even cutting a sheet in half to make a shelter 4 feet long would still serve for many purposes.

Materials List for Folding Shelter

2 sheets	48 × 96 ×	¹/₂ plywood
2 strips	1 × 2 × 86	
2 handles	1 × 2 × 18	

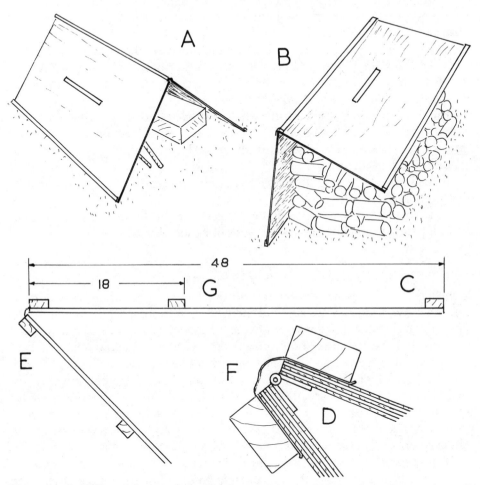

Fig. 4-33. *A folding shelter made by hinging two sheets of plywood together can be used to provide protection in several ways.*

For this project (FIG. 4-33), it is assumed you will use full sheets. Parts added are all 1- inch- × -2-inch strips of softwood.

For the simplest form of shelter, the sheets are opened to an inverted V (FIG. 4-33A). This will protect quite a lot of equipment, or it could be used by children as a play tent.

For easier access and greater convenience, you might prefer to use the shelter on edge, as when covering logs (FIG. 4-33B) where the pile will gradually be reduced. You could use this arrangement to protect yourself during a sudden downpour, putting a temporary prop on the open side.

Stiffen the lower edges with strips nailed or screwed on (FIG. 4-33C). Along the top edges allow for 3-inch hinges at about 24-inch intervals (FIG. 4-33D). There will be stiffening strips along these edges (FIG. 4-33E), but for the best protection you should include fabric, trapped under the strips (FIG. 4-33F). This could be any waterproof canvas, but plastic-impregnated canvas will be most durable. Arrange the fabric so when the sheets are close together it is fairly tight. To get the tension right, fasten the strip and fabric at one side, then add the hinges to that side. Close the hinges and plywood sheets together with the edges in line, and fix the fabric with its covering strip to the second edge. Open the assembly and put screws in the second sides of the hinges.

For convenience in carrying the shelter single-handed, put 18-inch strips centrally on each side (FIG. 4-33G). Check that the distance from the top suits your arm length. You should be able to put the top edge in your armpit and grip the handle with your fingers.

If used as a child's tent, the shelter should be pegged to the ground or suitably supported.

You could leave exterior plywood untreated, but this folding shelter will look better if painted, possibly green so it will not be too obtrusive.

Carport

A shelter for a car should have sufficient overhang to protect the vehicle from rain and snow, or sometimes sun, but there has to be a compromise or you could make it unduly large. Similarly, you need to be able to drive in and out without difficulty, but the structure should not be larger than will allow this. The best protection without excessive size will come by not having the roof too high above the vehicle, but high enough so that you can walk about. Keep in mind that you might want to park your car with a load on a roof rack. You also have to consider what happens if you change your car. A fairly close-fitting carport for your present car might not suit your next car if it is bigger. Only you can decide on the size of carport to suit your needs.

This carport (FIG. 4-34) is freestanding so you can position it away from the house. It is designed to stand on a concrete base, although you could take the columns into the ground, as suggested in previous projects. The structure is shown open at both ends, so you can drive a car through. If you will drive in and back out, you could close in the low end. You might decide to board in one side, either completely or partway. Much depends on the situation. You could have the carport without any siding, but this one is shown with boarding under the roof down to the level of the low end. Beside providing protection, boarding in this way helps to stiffen the assembly, so it is better able to withstand strong winds.

The sizes suggested (FIG. 4-35) are for a roof 10 feet by 20 feet, with a slope of 2

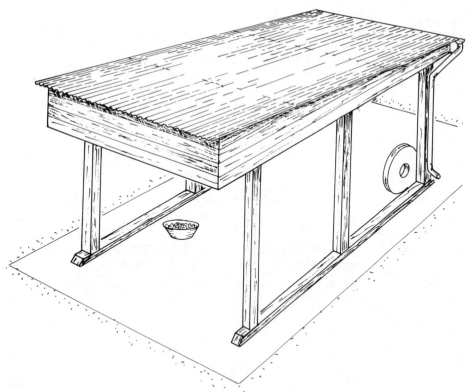

Fig. 4-34. An open-sided shelter with a sloping roof can serve as a carport.

feet and a minimum clearance of 7 feet. If you decide to modify sizes, this should not affect the method of construction. Corrugated translucent plastic sheet would make a good roof covering. The instructions assume this will be used, but you could use corrugated steel or aluminum or have plywood covered with felt or similar material. The roof is shown with sufficient slope to shed water. Not much snow would run off, but the roof should be strong enough to take the dead weight of a reasonable amount of it.

The roof assembly is made from 2-inch-×-6-inch and 2-inch-×-4-inch wood. The columns are 4 inches square, which should be solid wood of this size or you could screw together 2-inch-×-4-inch pieces. Parts of the roof assembly are notched together, then the tops of the columns fit into corners of these parts. All of the roof parts are first cut in advance, then assembled in position.

Start by setting out a side view of the main lines of the top of the assembly (FIG. 4-35A), preferably full-size on the floor, although you could work from a scale drawing. This will give you angles and the heights of columns.

Have the wood for the three rafters ready and mark them out together. The covering will project 3 inches at the ends. Purlins have to be positioned to suit joints in the sheets. You can cover the roof with three lengths of 7-foot sheets

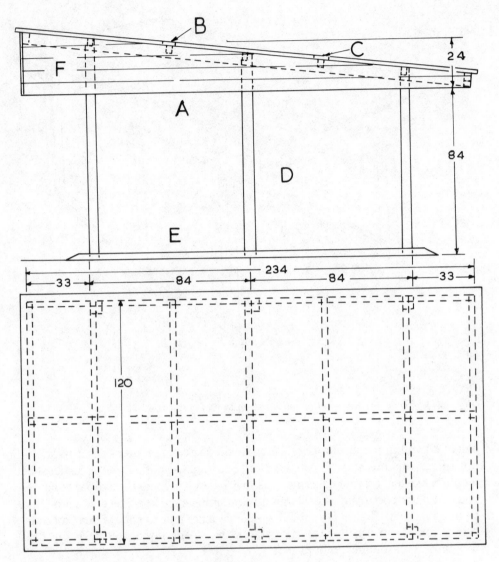

Fig. 4-35. Suggested sizes for the carport.

with 6-inch overlaps or 8-foot sheets with 12-inch overlaps. Mark purlin positions on the rafters to come centrally under these overlaps (FIG. 4-35B and C). Mark the positions of intermediate purlins. Position those towards the ends to suit the outer column positions and the middle one to suit the central columns (FIG. 4-35D). You might have to consider the convenience of opening car doors and column positions could be moved a little to suit.

Cut wood for the purlins. The end ones are 6 inches deep. The other five are 4 inches deep. Mark them together for the joints where they will cross rafters.

Cut halving joints in all these parts, with the end joints to half the thickness, but the intermediate cuts in the rafters 2 inches deep. Cut for close fits with top surfaces level (FIG. 4-36A).

If the columns are to be sunk into the ground, as in the previous projects, allow sufficient length at the bottom. If the carport is to be on a concrete base, allow for the columns being tenoned into base strips (FIG. 4-36B). Allow a little excess length at the tops.

Mark where the undersides of the side rafters will come on the columns.

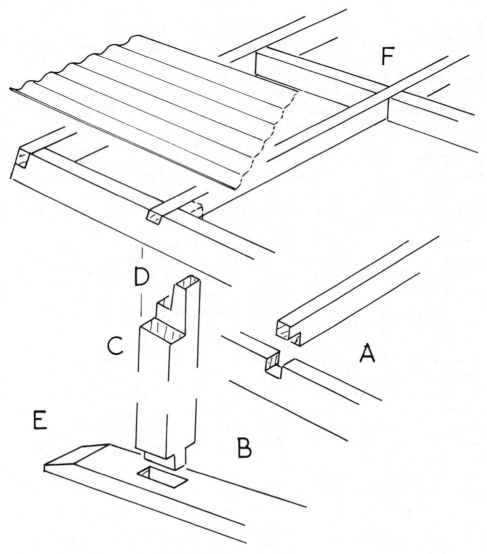

Fig. 4-36. *Constructional details for the carport.*

Materials List for Carport

2 columns	4	× 4	×	96
2 columns	4	× 4	×	108
2 columns	4	× 4	×	102
3 rafters	2	× 6	×	240
2 purlins	2	× 6	×	120
5 purlins	2	× 4	×	120
2 base strips	2	× 4	×	196
sidings	1	× 6	or plywood	

Notch the outsides of each column to fit around the rafter (FIG. 4-36C). Mark to suit the purlin, and cut this notch (FIG. 4-36D). You have to allow for the slight angle of the roof, but you should finish with a projecting piece about 2 inches square to trim level after assembly.

Make the pair of base strips (FIG. 4-35E). Mark the column positions so they will be upright when attached to the roof. Allow for these strips projecting about 12 inches to tapered ends (FIG. 4-36E). Cut tenons on the columns and matching mortises in the base strips. To allow for adjustments you could cut the mortises up to 1 inch too long. You can then move the columns during assembly to get them exactly upright, then the gaps in the mortises could be filled with wood.

Locate the base strips on the concrete. Use a purlin to check that they are the correct distance apart. Check squareness across the mortises. Fit the columns into the mortises. Put the outer rafters in place, and clamp them to the columns. Drop in some of the purlins to check spacing. Stand back and look at the assembly to check squareness and that the columns are upright and match each other.

If you are satisfied nail or bolt the tops of the columns to the rafters. Fit in the purlins and add the central rafter. Nail or screw these joints. Check that the top surfaces are level (FIG. 4-36F). If necessary, plane high spots to make a reasonably flat surface for the covering sheets.

Check that the columns are plumb. Move the base strips and adjust mortises to suit. When this is satisfactory join the strips to the ground with screws into plugs.

Siding could be exterior-grade plywood, but it will probably look better if you use 1-inch-×-6-inch boards along the sides (FIG. 4-35F) and across the high end. Put 2-inch-square upright pieces in the corners where the boards meet. You could fit shelving for storage in the high end, and this could be taken a short distance along each side.

You might find it convenient to paint the wood or treat it with colored preservative before adding the roof.

Follow the manufacturer's recommendations when fitting the roof sheets. Allow for about 3 inches overhang on the wood all around. Start at the lower end, and arrange upper sheets to overlap the lower ones. Nail or screw through, using the spacing recommended by the manufacturer.

Rainwater will run off at the lower end. It might not matter if it spreads on the ground, but you could fit a gutter and downpipe (FIG. 4-34) and direct the water into a drain or into a container if you want to use the water on a garden.

Lean-to Carport

In many situations, the best position for a car shelter is against the side of a house. The carport is then a lean-to roof supported by the house at one side and by columns at the free side. Besides sheltering the car, the roof will usually also provide covered access to a door and a place to protect smaller items.

This carport is drawn to cover an area 9 feet by 18 feet and with a minimum head room of 7 feet (FIGS. 4-37, 4-38, and 4-39). You will probably want to adapt these measurements to suit your needs and available space, but the method of construction can be the same. There are 2-inch-×-6-inch rafters and 2-inch-×-4-inch purlins, with 4-inch-square columns, which could be 2-inch-×-4-inch pieces screwed together. The suggested roof is translucent plastic corrugated sheeting, but you could use corrugated metal or fit plywood sheets to cover with felt.

Fig. 4-37. A lean-to carport can be built onto the side of a building or existing wall.

Start by drawing the main lines of the slope of the roof (FIG. 4-38A). This will give you the length of the rafters and the angle of some parts. The two beams (FIG. 4-38B and C) are best beveled on the top edges, but the slope is slight and you should find it satisfactory to leave these edges square. Cut the two beams to length, and mark on them the positions of the rafters (FIG. 4-39A). Make the seven rafters 6 inches deep. Allow for halving joints at their ends (FIG. 4-38D). Cut the

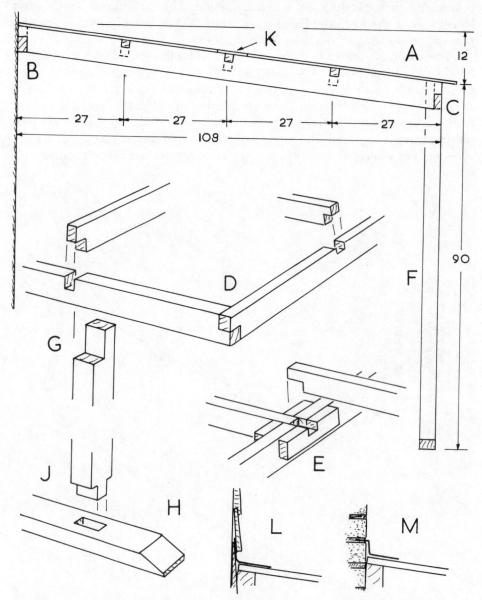

Fig. 4-38. End view and constructional details for the lean-to carport.

purlins to the same length as the beams (FIG. 4-39B) and mark on the positions of the rafters. If you have to use shorter lengths, allow for joints over rafters. Thicken the rafters where the joints will come, to permit a longer cut end of each purlin (FIG. 4-38E). If there are to be several of these joints, stagger them, so they come on different rafters.

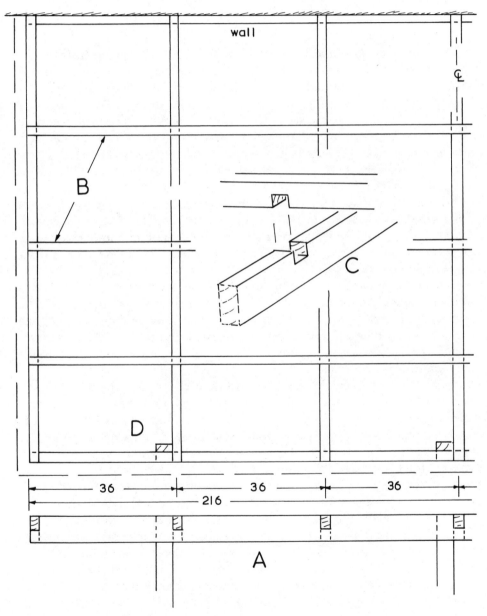

Fig. 4-39. *Roof details for the lean-to carport.*

**Materials List for
Lean-to Carport**

3 columns	4	× 4	×	92
2 beams	2	× 6	×	216
7 rafters	2	× 6	×	112
3 purlins	2	× 4	×	216
1 base strip	2	× 4	×	200

Cut halving joints where all roof parts cross (FIG. 4-39C), so top surfaces will come level. If you have not beveled the beams, make the joints so the rafters will finish level with the outer edges of the beams; then you will get the best fit of roofing material.

The three columns are the same. Cut them to length to reach the top surface of the beam (FIG. 4-38F). You will probably mount them on concrete or other hard surface, but they could be lengthened to go into the ground. Notch the tops to fit around the beam (FIG. 4-38G). When you assemble, the notches will be located on the outsides of the rafters (FIG. 4-39D).

Make a base strip to extend about 12 inches past the end columns (FIG. 4-38H) with beveled ends. Mark mortises for the columns and form tenons to match (FIG. 4-38J). To allow for adjustment to get the columns plumb during assembly, you could cut the mortises too long and fill any spaces with wood after satisfactory assembly.

The top beam has to be held to the side of the house securely. How this is done will depend on the house structure. With brick or stone, there should be plugs and long screws. For wood structure, you must locate the studs and take long screws into them. If there is any doubt about the strength of attachment, arrange vertical strips to the ground, possibly three pieces of 2-inch-×-4-inch wood opposite the columns.

Assemble the columns to the base strip and clamp the tops to the beam. Stand this in place and temporarily fit the end rafters. Use one or more intermediate rafters clamped in place for additional security. Square this assembly. You could compare diagonal measurements. Squareness is important, if the roof sheets are to fit properly. Move the base strip and the columns to get the width correct at the bottom and the columns upright. Stand well back and check that the assembly seems correct when viewed from different angles. Mark the position of the base piece on the concrete. Plug the concrete and screw it down.

Nail the rafters to the beams and the column tops in their corners. Add the purlins. Check that top surfaces are level. Plane off any high spots. Extreme precision is unnecessary. The whole assembly should now be rigid. You might wish to paint or treat the wood with preservative before adding the roofing.

Fit the roof sheets in the way recommended by the manufacturers. Allow for an overlap on the central purlin (FIG. 4-38K) . The sheets can overhang the woodwork by 3 inches at ends and front. Take the top edges close to the house wall.

How you waterproof the joint against the house wall depends on the wall. It might be sufficient to fill the space with mastic. Even if you do more, a putty-like jointing compound along this edge will be worthwhile. If the wall has wood siding, you could use stout flexible plastic sheeting, held under a board and allowed a good overlap on the roof sheeting (FIG. 4-38L). It could be held by adhesive and nails into the beam and rafters. If you have to deal with a brick wall, the best treatment is to pick out mortar, then let in the sheeting with new mortar (FIG. 4-38M). This sheeting could be plastic or thin lead, which can be made to conform to corrugations without adhesive.

Hip Roof Barn

There is something attractive about a hip roof, with the ends sloping at the same angle as the sides. There is also the practical advantage of a reduction in wind resistance compared with gable ends. In some parts of the country traditional barns have been built with only partial hip roofs, but there seem to be no advantages in that. For a small building, it is better to provide full hips at both ends.

There are some complications in construction, but in a small building these are only slight. A boarded or plywood roof covered with tarred felt or shingles can be fitted with little more difficulty than covering a roof with a gable end. Corrugated sheeting or tiles would be more difficult and should be avoided for your first hip roof.

This building (FIG. 4-40) is shown with double doors at one end and windows in one side (FIG. 4-41A). Several other configurations are possible. You could have a door and a different window arrangement in one side. Both ends could be closed or could have more windows. You might want a rear door. The barn is drawn 8 feet wide by 16 feet long and 8 feet to the eaves. The roof slopes at 45 degrees, so it is 4 feet high, making the total building height 12 feet. Variations in size to suit your needs should not make any difference to the method of construction.

The walls are framed, with the long sides divided into two. Although plywood covering is possible, shiplap boards or clapboards are suggested. It would be possible to use vertical tongue-and-groove boards. There are wallplates around the tops of the walls, and the roof is assembled on them. A boarded roof is described, but you could use plywood. In either case, weatherproofing is by tarred felt or shingles. A concrete base is advisable, although you could provide concrete or stone footings under the walls only, if you want to let the main area remain earthed.

Make and assemble walls first, then slight variations in sizes will not matter if you make the roof to match the actual dimensions.

Make four side wall sections (FIG. 4-42). See that they all have the same overall size. Corner frame joints could be halved or notched. Crossing parts must be halved. The layout allows for a window opening (FIG. 4-42A). This can be any size you wish, but as shown, the framing is divided into fairly even spaces. As

Fig. 4-40. *This barn has a hip roof and large double doors.*

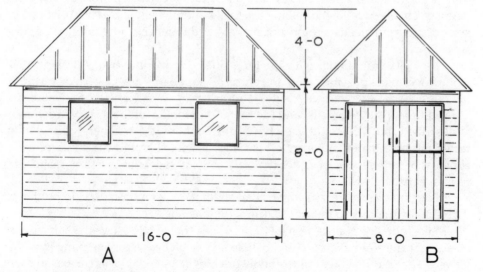

A

4-0

8-0

16-0

8-0

B

Fig. 4-41. *Suggested sizes for the hip roof barn.*

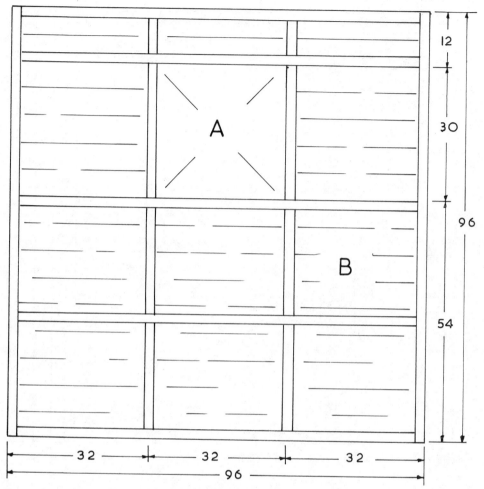

Fig. 4-42. Details of a side wall section of the hip roof barn.

designed, you need two sections with windows and two without. For those without, arrange the framing to divide the area into three equal divisions each way. Check squareness of the framing and cover with boards (FIG. 4-42B), trimming level on all edges.

The drawings allow for doors in one end (FIGS. 4-41B and 4-43A). You could arrange one narrower door centrally or to one side of the end. Assemble the framing in a similar way to the sides. Allow for the covering boards extending over the side sections (FIG. 4-43B) when assembled, so the uprights should be set in sufficiently. Board above and beside the doorway, trimming level at top and bottom and around the doorway, but you can leave a little extra on the overlapping edges, for trimming after assembly. For the closed end arrange the framing in a similar way to the closed sections, fitting the framing to divide the area into

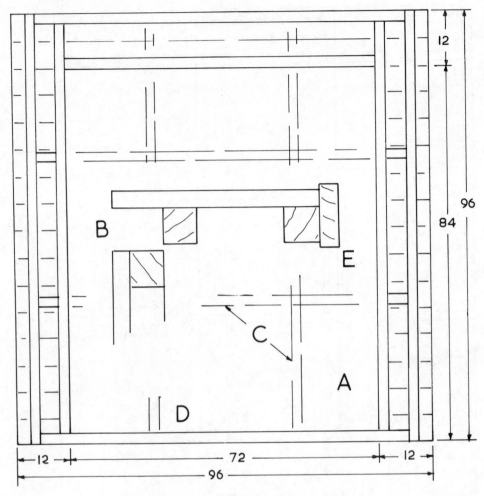

Fig. 4-43. Details of the end sections of the hip roof barn.

three both ways (FIG. 4-43C). Board all over that end, with extensions for the overlap at both upright edges. You will probably prefer not to have the framing strip across the bottom of the doorway (FIG. 4-43D) when the building is in use, but it must be left in place until the walls have been erected. When the framing each side of it has been fastened down you can saw it off.

Join the wall parts with ³/₈-inch or ¹/₂-inch bolts through meeting frame edges at about 18-inch intervals. You could also use nails through the overlapping boards. Join the two side sections to each other, then assemble to the ends. Check squareness of the assembly, then fasten down. Sight across the top edges to see that opposite sides are parallel and the building is without twist.

Fit wallplates (FIG. 4-44A) all round the tops of the walls. The roof could be made at any angle, but it is drawn as 45 degrees, which looks attractive in a hip

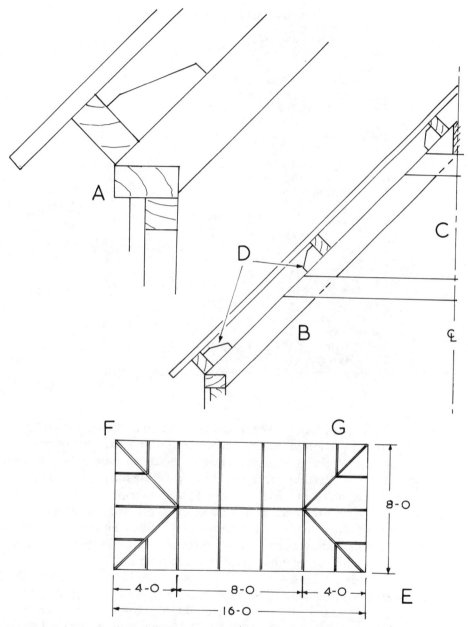

Fig. 4-44. *Roof layout and details for the hip roof barn.*

configuration when viewed from ground level. If the viewpoints are mostly higher, you could choose a shallower slope for an equally attractive effect. If the roof is at 45 degrees, its height will be half its span. Measure across the outsides of the wallplates and draw a line at right angles to the base the same height as half that width to get the slope of the rafter (FIG. 4-44B).

Materials List for Hip Roof Barn

51 wall frames	2	× 2 ×	98	
2 wallplates	2	× 4 ×	16-0	
2 wallplates	2	× 4 ×	8-0	
10 rafters	2	× 4 ×	72	
4 truss ties	2	× 4 ×	72	
4 truss ties	2	× 4 ×	26	
4 hip rafters	2	× 4 ×	9-0	
8 jack rafters	2	× 4 ×	56	
1 ridge	2	× 6 ×	98	
3 door trims	1	× 4 ×	86	
6 window trims	1	× 4 ×	33	
2 window trims	1	× 6 ×	33	
1 door stop	1	× 1 ×	74	
2 purlins	2	× 4 ×	108	
2 purlins	2	× 4 ×	13-0	
2 purlins	2	× 4 ×	16-0	
2 purlins	2	× 4 ×	96	
2 purlins	2	× 4 ×	70	
2 purlins	2	× 4 ×	24	
7 door ledgers	1	× 6 ×	38	
4 door braces	1	× 6 ×	48	
8 door edges	1	× 2 ×	42	
Wall covering	3/4	× 6 shiplap boards		
Roof covering	1	× 12 boards		
Door covering	3/4	× 6 tongue-and-groove boards		

Make four identical roof trusses (FIG. 4-44C). Notch to fit over the wallplates, and leave a gap at the top to take the ridge piece. Put a strip across below the ridge and another to act as a tie. Put cleats to hold the purlins in place (FIG. 4-44D). If a purlin is at the bottom of a rafter, it will close the gap above the wallplate. Position the end roof trusses on the wallplates so their outer surfaces are at the same distance from the ends as half the span over the wallplates (FIG. 4- 44E), then the roof end slopes will be the same as at the sides. Fit the ridge, with its top beveled and its ends level with the outsides of the trusses. Set the assembly upright and use temporary struts, if necessary, to hold the parts accurately.

Put end rafters (FIG. 4-45A) in place. They are similar to the truss rafters, notched over the end wallplates and cut to fit and nail against the ridge at the top (FIG. 4-45B). Fit hip rafters (FIG. 4-44F). Notch into the corners of the wallplates, and miter into the spaces at the top (FIG. 4-45C). Use a purlin or a straight piece of wood to put across the truss rafters to check the level of the roof. The line across the hip rafter might show it to be a little high, but that does not matter.

Fit jack rafters between the hip rafters and the wallplates (FIGS. 4-44G and 4-45D). Check that the slopes and levels match those of the truss rafters. Put cleats for purlins in matching positions on these short rafters. Ideally, purlins will run the full length of the building, but you could make joints over trusses.

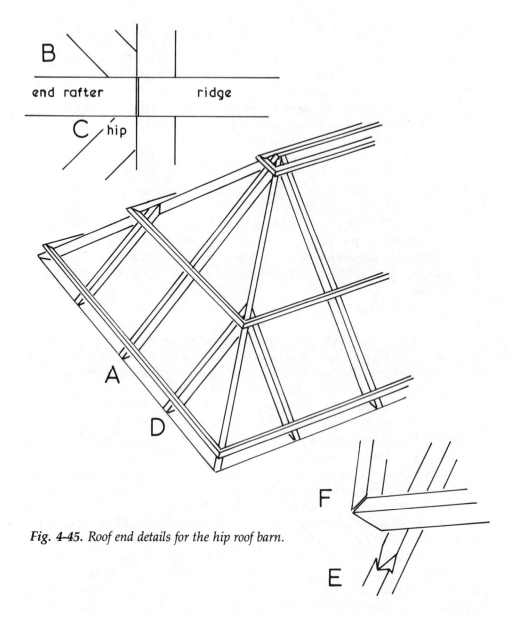

Fig. 4-45. Roof end details for the hip roof barn.

As you fit each purlin, check its level over a hip rafter. You might have to notch the rafter slightly (FIG. 4-45E). So far as possible, cut the ends of the purlins to miter over the hip rafters (FIG. 4-45F), but precision there is not important because boarding or plywood will cover any gaps which are not too large.

Boards or exterior plywood at least ³/₄ inch thick should be fitted all over the roof. Bevel meeting edges on the ridge and down the hip lines. Aim for a reasonably close fit, but if there are gaps they can be covered by strips of tarred felt laid along the joints under the final covering of felt or shingles.

Start by covering the central slopes of the roof with boards beveled where they meet along the ridge and an even overhang of 6 inches at the eaves. At a hip end it will probably be best to put a board central and square to the slope, cut to fit closely at the top, then work out from it, cutting upper ends of boards to meet those the other way over the centerline of the hip rafter. Work from the other way, as well, so boards can be fitted against each other. On this size roof, the covering might be stiff enough to support itself between purlins. If not, make supporting blocks to fit on the rafter under joints.

If the roof is to be covered with tarred felt, first nail strips between 6 inches and 12 inches wide along the ridge and down the hip joints. Cover the main parts of the roof with felt nailed under at one eaves, then taken over the ridge to be nailed under at the other eaves. Allow ample overlaps between pieces.

Continue with more pieces cut to the hip line one way, but from the other direction you can wrap over about 3 inches and nail down securely. You could add a 6-inch-wide strip of felt down each hip line and have a similar strip along the ridge, with a protective overlap at the end trusses. Put battens at about 18-inch intervals down all slopes.

If you use shingles, you could work directly on the boards or plywood, or lay felt first.

You could line the walls, either to the eaves or partially. This might just be plywood to provide a smooth interior or you could provide insulation with suitable foam in the gaps. Do this before framing the windows and doorway.

Windows may be made with glass between fillets, as described for several other buildings. Let the outer fillets extend about $1/2$ inch ahead of the boarding, and the bottom one could go further to form a sill (FIG. 4-46A). Put a similar edging around the doorway (FIG. 4-43E). Cut off the rail at the bottom of the doorway, if you have not already done so.

You could make a simple pair of ledged and braced doors with tongue-and-groove boards arranged vertically. One side might be arranged as a stable door so the top could be opened without the bottom. Much depends on your needs. If you line the walls, similar lining could be used for the doors. Each full door will be just under 36 inches by 84 inches and could be quite heavy.

Make a single door (FIG. 4-46B) with ledgers across 2 inches from each end and another ledger at the center, although appearance is better if it is above midway. Notch the diagonal braces into the ledgers. You could improve the doors by putting 2- inch-wide strips between the ledgers (FIG. 4-46C). If the opposite door will be a two-part stable door, you might consider putting the intermediate ledger on the single door at the same height as the top of the lower part of the other door, for a neat appearance.

If the other door is to be in two parts, make the parts in a similar way to the single door. You can arrange the upper door to close against the other with a sealing joint, if the ledger on the lower door stands up $3/4$ inch and the boarding on the other projects downwards to overlap it (FIG. 4-46D).

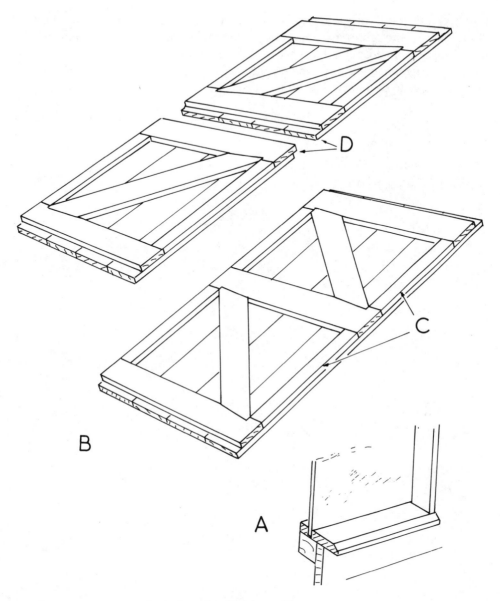

Fig. 4-46. Doors and windows for the hip roof barn.

Use strong 4-inch hinges at the ends of each ledger. Put a stop strip across the top of the doorway. You can arrange the top part of the stable door to hold the lower part with its overlap and have the other door held by a bolt to the top of the doorway. You might also arrange a bolt downwards into the floor on the same door. If you fit a lock inside the lower ledger of the top part of the stable door with a keyhole through to the front, both doors will be locked. Handles on each side will open and close the doors when they are not locked.

The finish applied will depend on your choice of wood and the surroundings that might have to be matched. Colored preservative would be a good treatment.

5

Workshops

A common small building need is a workshop. A workshop might be for any craftwork—from woodwork or metalwork to leatherwork or macrame to collecting and repairing all sorts of things. Whatever the craft or activity, the advantage of a separate workshop is that you can equip it as you wish, and then leave it ready for use next time. You do not have to clear things away, as is necessary in a room you need for other purposes as well.

If yours is a dirty or noisy activity, having a separate shop will keep you from annoying others in the house. If you need to keep bulky stock, as you might for woodworking, storage in the shop is tidy and away from other people. If you use machines, the separate building gives you scope to arrange them permanently so you can use them to their best advantage. The considerable noise you often create will be kept away from those who do not appreciate it, much more so than using a room in the house or basement.

Whether your craftwork is a hobby or a part-time or full-time business, consider the space you need and your probable future needs. Most experienced craftwork enthusiasts soon reach a stage where they wish they had more space. If it is a woodworking shop, consider any machines you have now and what you might get. A guiding size is a 48-inch-×-96-inch sheet of plywood or manufactured board. Ideally, you should be able to move it in any direction around a table saw. Practical considerations might dictate a building too small to permit this turning, but you should think about how you will deal with large and long pieces of wood. Allow for assembly space. Do not fill the shop with equipment so that you cannot put together a table or cabinet. If the weather is reasonable, you might have to manipulate large things through doors or windows.

Obviously, a shop should be strong and weatherproof, but besides standing up to anything that might happen outside, some activities require strength inside. Scrap wood or metal accidentally flying off a machine might hit a wall or roof with considerable force. Hardboard is unlikely to make a strong enough lining for your workshop. Strength in the building also is valuable when you want to brace something to it. If you lever against a wall, you do not want the wall to distort.

There should be plenty of light, both natural and artificial. Windows normally should be above bench and working level, to reduce the risk of them becoming broken too often. You do not want the shop to be a greenhouse, but make sure enough light gets in. It could be dangerous working in shadows. Windows in the roof can provide plenty of light, with a good spread, but they are not so easy to make watertight. In most shops, have some opening windows. Besides ventilation, you might need them to get long materials in and out of the shop.

If you live where there is a mild climate, a building with little or no insulation might be all you need, providing it is waterproof. Elsewhere, you should consider insulation, particularly if you suffer from extremes of climate and you want to be able to use the shop all year round. Windows are a source of heat loss, so do not make them any bigger than necessary. Double-glazing is possible, but unusual in this type of building. Curtains or sheets of hardboard over the glass will have a similar insulating effect when you are working by artificial light. Remember roof and floor insulation.

Although a concrete base is desirable as a firm foundation for a shop, its unprotected surface inside the building is undesirable. If you drop tools and other items on it, you might damage them. The surface is cold and uncomfortable to your feet. It might produce dust that you do not want in some activities. It would be better to have a wooden floor, preferably with an air gap over the concrete. If you cannot arrange that, provide some protection with boards or plywood directly on the concrete. Rubber mats will prevent much damage to dropped chisels or other edge tools.

You will need electricity in the building. Make sure you install this properly and adequately for your needs. A temporary cable from the house supply could be dangerous and almost certainly would not cope with all your needs. Have plenty of lamps. Individual lamps on adjustable arms are better than a few fixed, general lights. Do not rely too much on fluorescent lighting, particularly if it is close to machines because of the risk of the stroboscopic effect. You could meet a situation where light and machine frequency agree and you assume a part is not moving when actually it is. Individual filament lamps might be better. Install the necessary main switches, trip switches, fuses, etc., for more than your initial needs so there will be no problem when you add more load, as you certainly will.

It is easy to be so occupied with all the practical needs in your new workshop that its effect and appearance on other people not so enthusiastic on functional aspects might be lost. Don't forget to locate the building and arrange its external appearance so it is as attractive as possible.

Basic Workshop

The size and arrangement of a building you make for use as a hobby shop will depend on many factors, including the available space and the situation. You will have to consider the actual craft or occupation and its needs. However, a building with about an 8-foot-×-12-foot floor area with working head room and several windows will suit woodworking and metalworking, as well as many other crafts. The building shown in FIG. 5-1 is of basic, partly prefabricated construction. It has a door wide enough to pass most pieces of furniture or light machinery, and the suggested windows should give enough light if most activities are on a bench you arrange at one long side.

At the entrance end, a window is shown in the door. The wall alongside it

Fig. 5-1. A basic workshop with boarded walls and ample windows.

then would be available for shelves and racks. Two windows, which open, are shown over the long bench (FIG. 5-2A), and you might put another window which opens at the back (FIG. 5-2B). Besides providing ventilation, these windows allow long or awkward work to be extended outside, if that is the only way

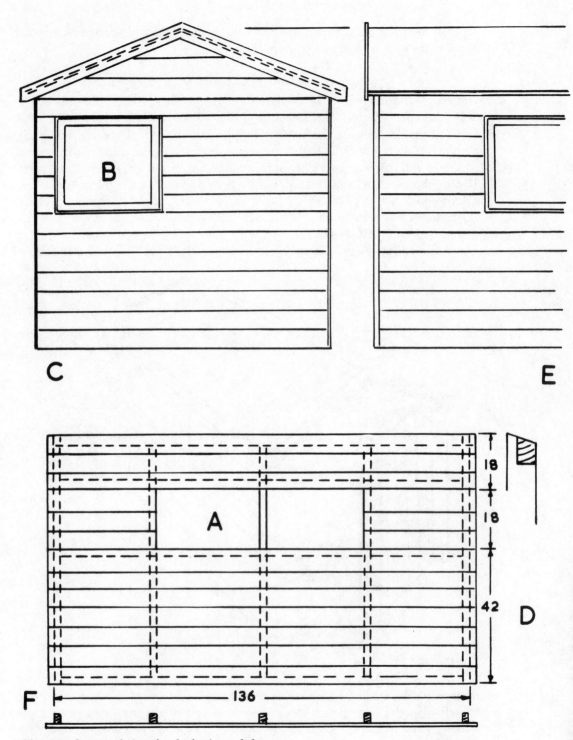

Fig. 5-2. Suggested sizes for the basic workshop.

to handle it. You might leave the other long side without windows, but that will depend on your needs. If you want to have a lathe or table saw near that wall, arrange more windows there, not necessarily ones which open.

This structure is not intended to be a portable building. It is not intended to be moved once you have assembled it fully. However, you can prefabricate much of it. You can make the four walls elsewhere, then assemble them to each other on-site and add the roof. Nearly all the framing is made from 2-inch-×-3-inch-section wood. The covering is shiplap boards about 6 inches wide, but you could use exterior plywood or other covering. As described, the building is not intended to be lined, but it would not be difficult to line and insulate the finished building. If you build in a full-length bench, it will give rigidity to the structure as well as help brace the building. Fix shelves, racks, and other storage arrangements directly to the walls.

Start by making one end (FIG. 5-3A). Halve or tenon external-frame joints. Halve or notch internal-meeting joints. Halve crossing parts. At the top, bevel the rafters to rest on the other parts and nail through. Check squareness by comparing diagonals—a door or window out of true will be very obvious.

Cover the end with shiplap boarding or other covering, starting at the bottom edge. Cut board ends level with the uprights. At the top, fit the covering under the roof (FIG. 5-3B). Leave some excess here for trimming to fit later. At the apex, leave space for the 2-inch-×-6-inch ridge piece, with a supporting member under it.

Make the opposite end (FIG. 5-2C) to match the overall size. Arrange uprights at about 24-inch intervals. Put pieces across at window height, to match the windows in the side (FIG. 5-2D). Cover this end in the same way, leaving a ridge notch and allowing for trimming of board ends later under the roof.

Make the side heights to match the ends, and bevel top edges to match the roof slope. Like the ends, all the side framing has the 2-inch width towards the outside, except for the top piece, which you arrange vertically (FIG. 5-2E). If the overall length is to be 12 feet, the constructed side length will be about 8 inches less (FIG. 5-2F) over uprights.

Make a side frame with rails for the windows. If one side is without windows, arrange two intermediate rails equally spaced. Uprights are shown about 32 inches apart, but you could alter uprights and rails to suit benches and shelves you might wish to build in. Do not have fewer framing parts than suggested. Use joints similar to those in the ends for the side frame parts.

Check squareness, then cover the framework. Where the sides meet the ends, carry the boarding over, so it will go far enough on the end uprights to allow you to put a filler piece in to cover the board ends (FIG. 5-3C).

Line the doorway sides, and top with strips level with the inside and outside (FIG. 5-3D). Do the same at the sides and tops of the window openings, but let the outside edges project up to 1/2 inch (FIG. 5-4A). You can treat the bottom in the same way, but it will be better to make it thicker and extend it further to make a sill (FIG. 5-4B).

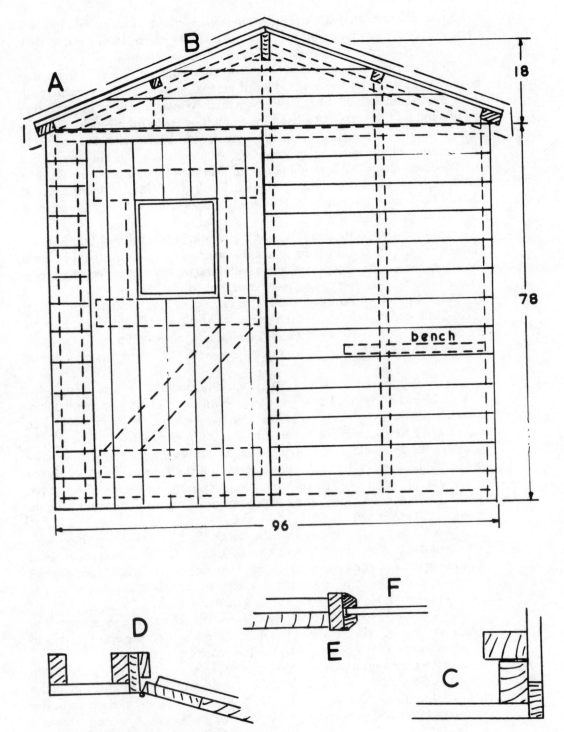

Fig. 5-3. *The door end of the workshop.*

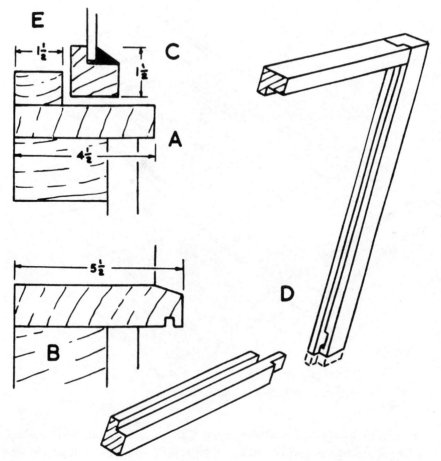

Fig. 5-4. Window details for the workshop.

Make a door to fit the opening, with its boards overlapping the bottom frame member, with 1/2-inch ground clearance. Three ledgers and one diagonal brace are shown in FIG. 5-5A. If there is to be a window, arrange it between the upper ledgers, and frame the sides with strips (FIG. 5-5B). After covering with vertical boards (preferably tongue-and-groove boards), line the opening with pieces that overhang a little (FIGS. 5-3E and 5-5C). You can make the window in the door by simply holding glass between strips (FIG. 5-3F). Cut the glass a little undersize, to reduce any risk of cracking. Waterproof the window by embedding the edges in putty or a jointing compound.

Put strips around the doorway sides and top to act as stops and draftproofing. Keep the ledgers on the door short enough to clear them. You can put hinges in the edge of the door, or you might fit T hinges across the surface. Fit an ordinary door lock with bolt and key, if you want to secure the shop; otherwise, a simple latch should be adequate.

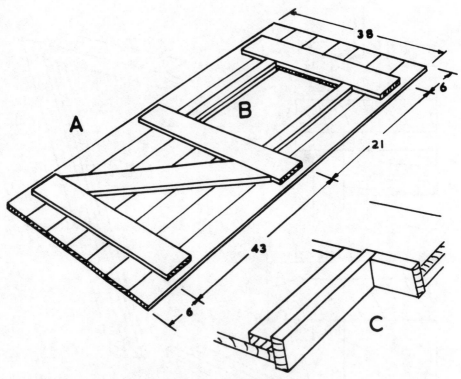

Fig. 5-5. The workshop door with a cutout for a window.

You can make the windows with standard molding, but these windows might be a much lighter section than the usual house windows. It would be better to prepare simple, rabbeted strips (FIG. 5-4C). If you use a standard window molding, you probably will have to increase the width of the pieces around the window openings.

Make up the windows with mortise-and-tenon joints (FIG. 5-4D). Leave the sides too long until after assembly, to reduce the risk of end grain breaking out. Make the windows so they fit easily in their openings. Put stop strips around the inner edges of the framing (FIG. 5-4E). Hinge the windows at the top and arrange fasteners and struts inside at the bottom. You might want to lift the windows horizontally occasionally, but you can do that with a temporary strut or a cord from higher on the wall. When you are satisfied with the fit and action of a window, you can putty in the glass, although it might be better to putty after you have painted the wood. The building will look attractive if you paint the window frames and bargeboards a different color than the main parts, so you could paint the window frames and glaze them in advance of final assembly.

The roof is supported by the 2-inch-×-6-inch ridge, 2-inch-×-4-inch eaves laid flat, and 2-inch-square purlins halfway down each side of the roof. Nail the eaves strips and purlins to the sloping top frames of the ends and bevel the ridge to match (FIG. 5-6A). Let the ends project about 3 inches at each end of the building. Cut the shiplap-covering boards around them, and trim their top edges to match the roof (FIG. 5-6B).

On a 12-foot length, having rafters only at the center should be sufficient to prevent sagging of the roof. If you make the building longer or have doubts about the stiffness of the assembly, use two sets of rafters, spacing them equally. Cut a

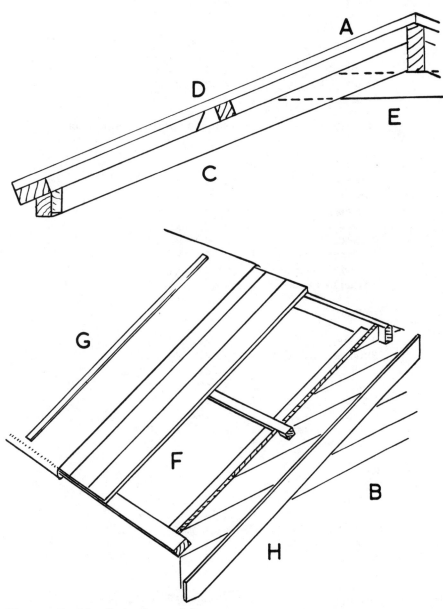

Fig. 5-6. *Roof details for the workshop.*

Materials List for Basic Workshop

Ends

5 uprights	2	×	3	×	80
2 uprights	2	×	3	×	100
3 uprights	2	×	3	×	90
4 rails	2	×	3	×	98
4 tops	2	×	3	×	54

Sides

10 uprights	2	×	3	×	80
8 rails	2	×	3	×	138
4 corners	1	×	2	×	80

Cladding   1- × -6 shiplap boards or ¾ plywood

Door

2 frames	1	×	4	×	80
1 frame	1	×	4	×	40
3 ledgers	1	×	6	×	38
1 brace	1	×	6	×	45
7 boards	1	×	6	×	80
2 window sides	1	×	2	×	16
4 window frames	1	×	2½	×	16
8 window fillets	1	×	1	×	16

Windows

6 frames	1	×	4½	×	20
3 frames	1	×	4½	×	36
1 sill	1	×	5½	×	36
1 sill	1	×	5½	×	74
6 stops	1	×	1½	×	20
6 stops	1	×	1½	×	36
6 window sides	1½	×	1½	×	20
6 window rails	1½	×	1½	×	36

Roof

1 ridge	2	×	6	×	160
2 eaves	2	×	4	×	160
2 purlins	2	×	2	×	160
16 battens	½	×	1	×	54
2 rafters	2	×	3	×	54
1 tie	2	×	3	×	40
4 bargeboards	1	×	5	×	60
Covering	1- × -6 boards or ¾ plywood				

pair of rafters to fit between the top pieces of the side frames and the ridge (FIG. 5-6C). Check straightness of the sides while cutting. If you get the length of a rafter wrong, it could make the side bulge or bend in slightly. You can have a nailing block at one or both ends of each rafter. A block below the purlin will locate and support it (FIG. 5-6D). Put a strip across the rafters below the ridge (FIG. 5-6E). No other lower tie is needed.

You can cover the roof with exterior-grade plywood, but FIG. 5-6F shows it boarded. Finish level at the eaves. Put covering material over the structure in single lengths from one eaves to the other, if possible, turning the ends under and nailing them. Any overlaps should be wide, and you should arrange them so water cannot run under. Nail on battens (FIG. 5-6G) at about 18-inch intervals to prevent the covering material from lifting.

Simple, narrow bargeboards are suggested in FIG. 5-6H, nailed to the roof ends after covering. You could make more elaborate ones, as shown on some earlier projects or use your own ideas. Make sure there is clearance for the door to swing open, at least to 90 degrees.

Large-door Workshop

Some activities involve the movement of large items in and out of the shop. You might wish to work on a large piece of machinery or a car conversion. You might want to build a boat. Even on something like a luggage trailer, prefabricated parts of another building, or parts of a deck, you need access doors larger than the ones you would use for more modestly sized projects.

The shop needs large doors, but if the project will be inside for a long period, you might not want to use the large doors for normal access, so you need a smaller door elsewhere. If the project and all that goes with it will occupy a lot of space, you will find it advantageous to have your bench and most machines at the back of the shop. The second door allows you to get in and out away from the clutter in the main area of the building.

It is possible to arrange the layout of a ridged or lean-to building to suit this sort of work, but the design shown in FIG. 5-7 has a flat, moderately-sloped roof and a porch. This design allows the double doors to be big enough, yet you can keep them shut to protect you against bad weather. The porch lets you get in and out away from the bench and machines. It might shelter you from rain and wind, and you could hang clothes on it.

Size will depend on your needs and the available space, but those shown in FIG. 5-8A are suggestions that you can modify considerably. The high end will have to be big enough to allow the doors to admit whatever you are making or working on. At the other end, you must have adequate head room. Couple these requirements with the slope of the roof. You need a moderate slope, even if your rainfall is slight and infrequent. Steeper slopes are advisable for heavy rain areas. Snow will not slide off this type of roof; you must make it strong enough to take the weight. Whatever your climatic situation, it is unwise to have a horizontal roof.

Fig. 5-7. *This workshop has large doors, a sloping roof, and a porch entrance at the back.*

The design shows a shop area about 7 feet × 10 feet, with a porch 3 feet square (FIG. 5-8A). It is assumed that the building will be clad with ³/₄-inch exterior plywood, although you could use shiplap boarding or other covering. The framing is mostly 2 inches × 3 inches, arranged with the 3-inch side in the front to back direction of the building. The sides have the 3-inch side towards the skin, and the front and back assemblies have the 2-inch side towards the skin. The bottom rails of all parts, however, have the 3-inch side towards the foundation. The main doors are about 66 inches wide and 7 feet high. The door under the porch is 27 inches wide. Two windows are at each side, and two or three are at the back. You can arrange windows to suit your needs by adjusting framing when making the walls.

You can prefabricate the sides and back and front, then assemble them on-site and add the porch and roof. The pair of sides are the key assemblies that govern the shapes of other parts, and you should make them first.

Make the side that will have the door under the porch (FIG. 5-9). Use any of the usual joints between the frame parts. Cut the sloping top to fit against the horizontal rail at the low end and nail it in place. Cover with plywood to the edges on the uprights, but at the top, the plywood should reach as high as the 3-inch rafters you will lay on. Allow extra plywood for this area so you can trim the edge level during assembly.

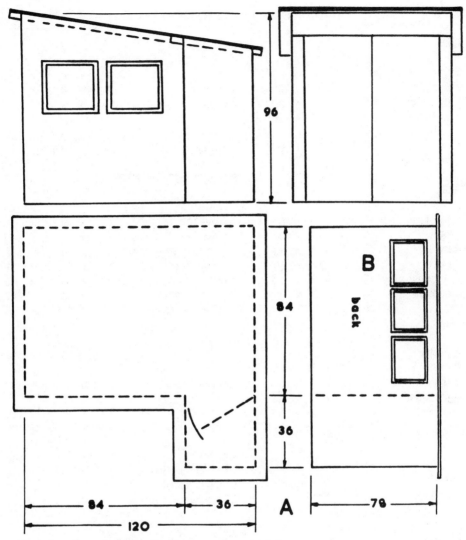

Fig. 5-8. Suggested sizes for the large-door workshop.

Make the opposite side to match as a pair, except you do not need the doorway. Carry the lower window rail across what was the door opening to provide support for the plywood covering. You can move the upright to take the place of the window upright, or you could increase the widths of the windows on that side. At the rear edge, take the covering plywood over the frame 2 inches to allow an overlap on the back.

Place the back over the two sides and extend it to form the rear of the porch (FIG. 5-10A). Arrange one upright between two windows or you could have two uprights equally spaced between three windows (FIG. 5-8B).

Sides

2 uprights	2	× 3	×	96
2 uprights	2	× 3	×	80
2 uprights	2	× 3	×	86
2 uprights	2	× 3	×	90
5 rails	2	× 3	×	120
1 rail	2	× 3	×	86
2 window posts	2	× 3	×	32

Back

4 uprights	2	× 3	×	80
2 rails	2	× 3	× 122
3 rails	2	× 3	×	86
2 rails	2	× 3	×	40
2 window posts	2	× 3	×	32
2 corners	1	× 2	×	80

Front

2 posts	2	× 3	×	96
2 posts	2	× 3	×	88
3 rails	2	× 3	×	80
2 diagonals	2	× 3	×	42
2 corners	1	× 2	×	96

Side door

2 sides	1	× 2	×	72
4 rails	1	× 2	×	33
2 panels	72- ×-33-× -½ plywood			
2 edges	½	× 3	×	72
2 edges	½	× 3	×	33

Cladding

Shiplap boards 1- × -6 or ¾ plywood (approximately)

Front doors

4 sides	1	× 3	×	84
8 rails	1	× 3	×	36
4 panels	36- × -84- × -½ plywood			
4 edges	½	× 3	×	84
4 edges	½	× 3	×	36

Door and window edges

4 uprights	1	× 4	×	84
1 front top	1	× 4	×	68
1 side-door top	1	× 4	×	33
8 window sides	1	× 4½	×	28
2 window tops	1	× 4½	×	66
2 window sills	1	× 5½	×	66
Stops from seven	1	× 1	×	82
16 window frames	1½	× 1½	×	30

Roof

	2	× 3	×	136
5 rafters	2	× 3	×	48
2 rafters	1- × -6 boards or ¾ plywood			
Covers	1½	× 1½	×	136
3 edges	1½	× 1½	×	100
1 edge	1½	× 1½	×	48
2 edges	1	× 6	×	100
1 fascia board	1	× 6	×	48
1 fascia board	½	× 2	×	130
4 battens				

Porch

2 uprights	2	× 3	×	82
4 rails	2	× 3	×	48
2 front rails	2	× 3	×	40
1 front edge	1	× 3	×	80

Make the height of the back to match the adjoining parts of the sides, and bevel the top edge to match the slope of the roof (FIG. 5-10B). When you nail on plywood, cut it level with the sides. At the top, leave enough plywood to trim later, since it must reach the roof and you must notch it around rafters (FIG. 5-10C). When you assemble the building, cover the plywood corners with strips (FIG. 5-10D).

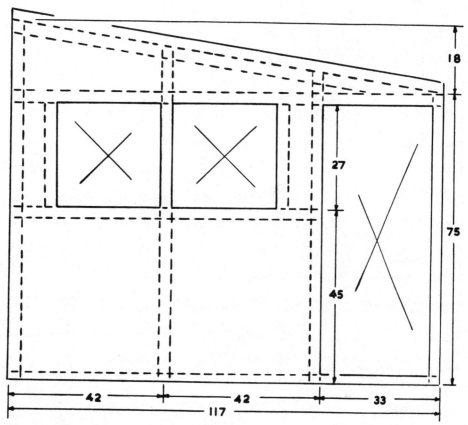

Fig. 5-9. The side of the large-door workshop.

Although the back will fit over the sides, the front is made to fit between them. With the large area cut out for the doors, it needs all the support it can get. Overlapping the sides gives some stiffening. Diagonal bracing above the doorway provides additional stiffening.

Make the front as shown in FIG. 5-11A. Although it is shown 78 inches across the frame, check this measurement with the back as a guide, allowing for the actual thicknesses of side framing and plywood. The overall width at the front will be the same as that over the sides where they meet the back. Similarly, check the height against the sides, allowing for the beveled top to match the slope of the roof (FIG. 5-11B). Make sure the frame parts are straight, particularly those that come around the doorway. Arrange strong joints and have the assembly square when you fit the diagonal struts in the top space (FIG. 5-11C).

Cover the framework with plywood. If necessary, pull the side framing of the doorway straight as you fit the plywood. At the sides, let the plywood extend 1 inch to overlap the building side, and allow a filler strip to go in during assembly (FIG. 5- 11D). At the top, the plywood will have to reach the roof, and you will have to notch it around roof rafters as you did on the back (FIG. 5-11E).

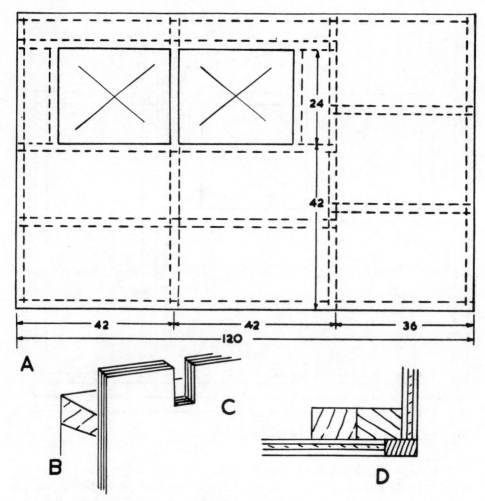

Fig. 5-10. Back of the large-door workshop.

Make the side of the porch the same size as the main side that includes the door, so it has the same height and top slope. Extend it so it gives good protection to the door. Frame it the same way as you framed a side, with enough plywood left at the top for trimming after you add the rafters (FIG. 5-12A). It will fit against the back in the same way as the main sides.

Make a front to the porch, framed and covered with plywood, to go across above the door level (FIG. 5-12B). You could put a bar across at ground level, but if you bolt the porch side down, that should be unnecessary. Cover the front edge of the porch side with a strip (FIG. 5-12C), and round its outer edges.

Make the porch door with two pieces of plywood with framing between them (FIG. 5-12D) and thin strips covering the edges (FIG. 5-12E). Fit the framing to one piece of plywood with waterproof glue and fine nails, then add the other

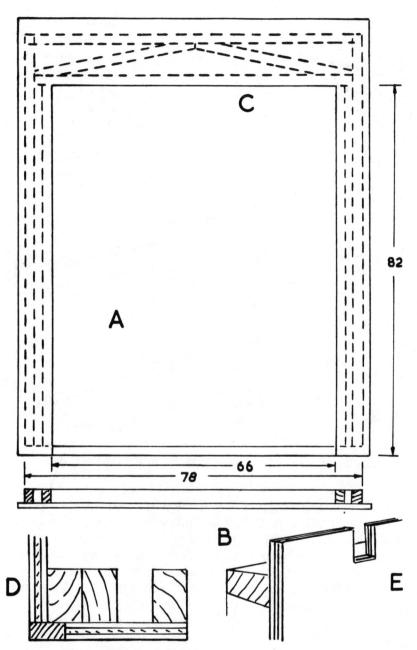

Fig. 5-11. Front details of the large-door workshop.

plywood. Widen the internal framing, if necessary, where hinges and a lock or latch will come. Put strips around the doorway edges, and stop strips on them (FIG. 5-12F).

Make and fit the pair of front doors in a very similar way as the other doors,

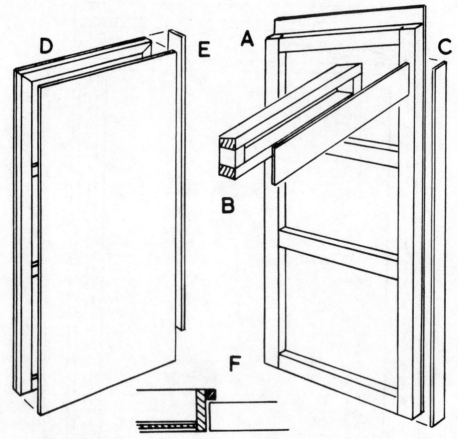

Fig. 5-12. *Details of the porch and its door for the large-door workshop.*

but allow for stouter hinges. One door should have bolts up and down and the other door should lock to it. If draftproofing is important, put an overlapping strip on the inside of the door which shuts first.

The roof should overhang about 6 inches all around, including the porch. Support it with rafters laid from front to back. Put one rafter directly above each side, and space three others evenly across the roof (FIG. 5-13A). Put matching short rafters over the porch, with a board across its front (FIG. 5-13B). Notch the plywood walls around the rafters where necessary, and level the top edges.

Lay plywood or boards across the rafters (FIG. 5-13C). Thicken all around the edges with strips underneath. Put roofing material over the boards, turn it under, and nail it securely underneath. Lay battens from front to back at about the same spacing as the rafters to prevent the covering from lifting.

At the front, make a fascia board to cover the roof and rafter ends (FIG. 5-13D). You should not need one at the back, but if you do, put one there, for the sake of appearance. Keep it low, so it will not interfere with the run-off of water.

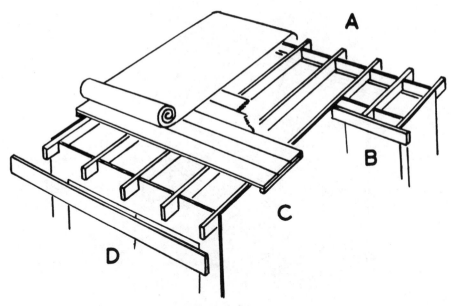

Fig. 5-13. The roof of the large-door workshop.

You can use either fixed or opening windows. Make them similar to the ones made in the last project. Start by lining the window openings with strips at the sides and top (FIG. 5-4A), and use wider sills at the bottom (FIG. 5-4B). For windows that open, arrange stops and make the window frames as described for that project (FIG. 5-4C,D,E). You can make fixed windows in the same way, attaching the windows to the stops. An alternative would be to putty the glass directly against the stop strips. It would look better if you use rabbeted strips instead of the stop strips.

Studio

Anyone practicing an art form needs good, all-around light that doesn't glare. This fact applies to three-dimensional carving and sculpture as well as to painting. There should be plenty of windows that let in light where needed, as broadly as possible, so there is no glare and so harsh shadows are not cast.

Sloping windows will pass light without glare better than upright windows, and they will spread the natural illumination. An artist usually wants one wall without windows. The size of a studio will depend on the work to be done and how many people are to be accommodated. The studio shown in FIG. 5-14 is designed for a single worker on projects of only moderate size. You can use the same construction for a studio of a different size. The suggested sizes are for an 8-foot-square floor space and the same size maximum height (FIG. 5-15). Lined walls and roof are advisable. The smooth interior, painted a light color, will help to disperse lighting evenly. Although you might use a concrete base, a wooden floor over it would be comfortable and kinder to dropped tools. Cladding is

Fig. 5-14. This studio gets good light from sloping windows.

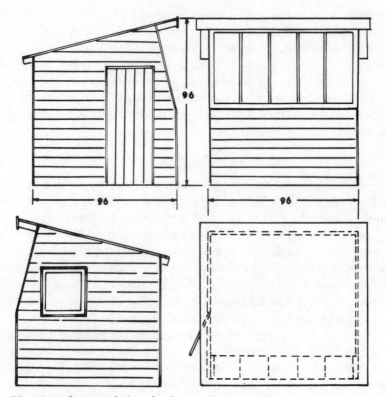

Fig. 5-15. Suggested sizes for the studio.

Materials List for Studio

Ends

6 uprights	2	× 2	×	80
2 uprights	2	× 2	×	90
2 uprights	2	× 2	×	50
2 uprights	2	× 2	×	56
6 rails	2	× 2	×	98
2 tops	2	× 2	×	98

Back

5 uprights	2	× 2	×	80
3 rails	2	× 2	×	92
2 corners	1	× 1	×	80

Lower front

5 uprights	2	× 2	×	50
2 rails	2	× 2	×	92
2 corners	1	× 1	×	50

Upper front

6 uprights	2	× 2	×	56
2 rails	2	× 2	×	92
1 sill	1	× 4½	×	92
2 cover pieces	1	× 5	×	56

End window

3 frames	1	× 3½	×	34
1 sill	1	× 4½	×	34
4 frames	2	× 2	×	34

Door

3 ledgers	1	× 6	×	32
2 braces	1	× 6	×	40
6 boards	1	× 6	×	78

Roof

5 rafters	2	× 3	×	116
1 fascia	1	× 6	×	116
4 edges	1½	× 1½	×	116

Covering: boards — 1- x -6 or ¾ plywood

Cladding

Shiplap boards — 1- x -6 or ¾ plywood (approximately)

assumed to be shiplap boarding, but you could use plywood. The 8-foot-square size makes for economical use of standard plywood sheets.

Start with one side that has a door (FIG. 5-16A). You can use any of the usual framing joints at most places. Where the sloping and vertical fronts join, use a halving joint, with screws both ways (FIG. 5-16B). Cover with boards cut level at the back and front edges, but with enough left at the top to trim to the same height as the rafters (FIG. 5-16C).

Make the opposite side identical, but instead of a doorway, you could allow space for an opening window, the same width as the door (FIG. 5-16D). Cover with boards in the same way as the first side.

The back is a simple, rectangular frame (FIG. 5-17A). Divide the width into four and put a central rail across. Check the height against the matching parts of the sides, and bevel the top frame member to match the slope of the roof. At the top, let the covering boards project about 3 inches. When you assemble the studio on-site, notch the covering boards for the rafters and trim level with their top surfaces. At the sides, allow the covering to extend by the width of the end uprights. Then when you assemble, the board ends will overlap and you can put a square strip in the corner (FIG. 5-16E).

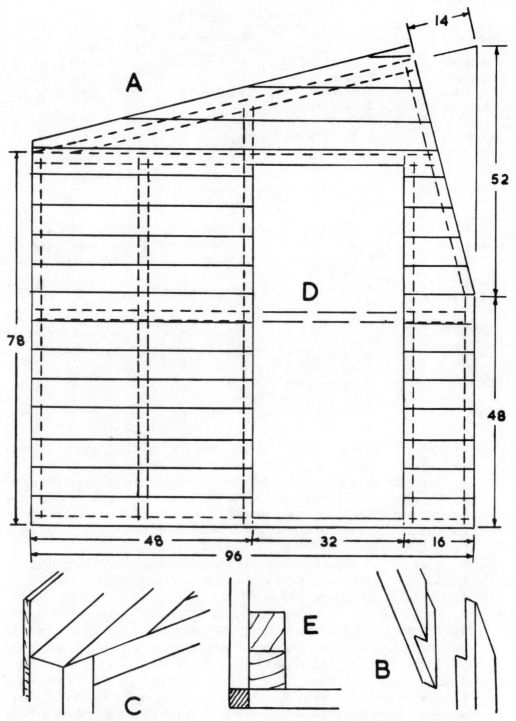

Fig. 5-16. The studio end.

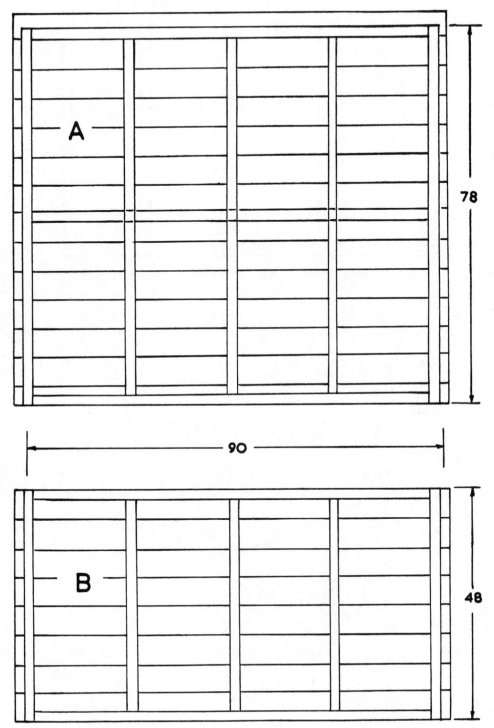

Fig. 5-17. Back and front of the studio.

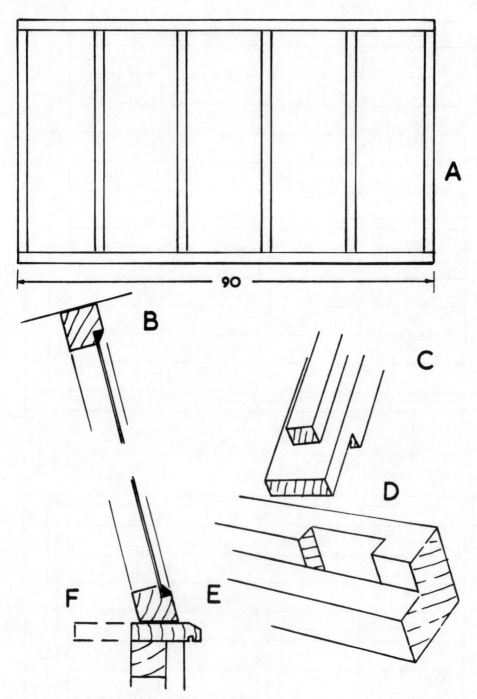

Fig. 5-18. Glazing arrangements for the studio.

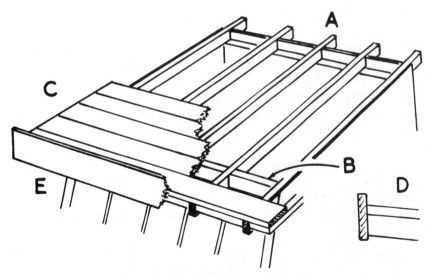

Fig. 5-19. *Roof details for the studio.*

Make the lower front to match the back width (FIG. 5-17B). The covering boards are level at top and bottom edges, but they extend at the sides in the same way as on the back.

Fully glaze the upper front. Divide it into five glass panels (FIG. 5-18A). The overall length should be the same as the lower front, and the height must match the sloping parts of the sides. All of the parts are rabbeted—⁵/₈ inch deep and ⁵/₈ inch wide should be enough. The outside parts have rabbets on one edge (FIG. 5-18B). The intermediate pieces have rabbets on two edges (FIG. 5-18C). It is possible to dowel parts together, but the best joints are mortise-and-tenon joints (FIG. 5-18D). Treat the corners similar to the intermediate joint shown, but reduce the width of the tenon at the outside. Do not fit the glass until after you have erected the building.

Arrange a sill on the lower front for the upper front to fit over (FIG. 5-18E). You can extend the sill inwards to make a shelf (FIG. 5-18F). It would be difficult to waterproof the joint between the upper frame and the sill with glue. It is better to embed it in jointing compound. Cover the ends of the upper front with strips over the edges of the studio ends, when you assemble it.

Make the opening window in the end the same way as described earlier (FIG. 5-4). Make the door with vertical boards and ledgers and braces (FIG. 5-5). If you do not include a window, put a second brace across. Braces should slope up from the hinged side. Line the doorway and arrange stop strips in the way described earlier for the door you are using.

Make the roof with rafters laid from back to front (FIG. 5-19A). Let the rafters project about 6 inches at back and 12 inches at front. Notch the plywood at the back. At the front, fill the gaps between the rafters with 2-inch-×-3-inch pieces, level with the front of the glazed part (FIG. 5-19B).

Cover the rafters with boards across (FIG. 5-19C) to give a 6-inch overhang at the sides. Thicken all edges with strips underneath. Bevel the front so it is vertical (FIG. 5-19D). Turn the covering material under and nail underneath to the strips. Put battens on top from front to back.

At the front, put a fascia board across (FIG. 5-19E). Do not make it too deep or it will restrict light in the windows. You could give it a decorative shape if you wish.

When you have completed assembly, you can line the walls and under the rafters with plywood or particleboard. If you mounted the building on a concrete base, there could be a wooden floor. Place the boards over the bottom framing parts and lay stiffeners across underneath at about 18-inch intervals. Fit the floor before lining the walls.

Substantial Workshop

If you need a small building to use as a shop for year-round work, or if you want to install several machines or other heavy equipment, the construction ought to be more substantial than many shops with sectional construction. If climatic extremes affect its contents, the building should be adequately insulated, which will also improve your personal comfort. It is probable that you will need to use plenty of electricity, which would include the accompanying switch gear and fuses or cutouts. It is much safer to install electricity in a building that is constructed more like a house than a temporary shed.

Such a substantial shop obviously will be more costly than one of lighter construction. Building it will involve more work, mostly on-site, but if you want a long-lasting shop of the best construction, this shop is it.

The walls should be lined and insulated. You might want to line the roof as well. The best foundation is a wooden floor covering a concrete base. You can install either a single door or double doors, or you might fit double doors at one end and a single door at the other end. Even if your normal activities do not require wide doors, make sure your door is wide enough for you to pass your largest machine through it. You can place windows in one side only, with more natural light coming from the opposite roof, or you can arrange windows to suit your needs during the initial planning stage. You probably will have a bench at the window side for hand work, assembly, and the use of portable machines. Check the sizes of fixed machines. Locate them so you can move around them safely and so there is clearance to work with sheet and long material. Think of storage. You might arrange racks inside, although a lower lean-to shelter could cover racks along one side. This design might be valuable for natural seasoning of wood.

Available space and access to it might control sizes. For example, it is assumed that the building is 10 feet wide, 14 feet long, and that there is a lean-to

Materials List for Substantial Workshop

Floor

10 joists	2 × 3 × 125
20 boards	1 × 6 × 86
	or equivalent area

Sides

12 uprights	2 × 3 × 98
7 rails	2 × 3 × 170
1 rail	2 × 3 × 120
4 sway bracings	2 × 3 × 36
4 sway bracings	2 × 3 × 56
6 fillets	2 × 2 × 34
4 fillets	2 × 2 × 48

Ends

4 uprights	2 × 3 × 98
4 uprights	2 × 3 × 118
5 rails	2 × 3 × 116
2 rails	2 × 3 × 38
4 sway bracings	2 × 3 × 48
4 top rails	2 × 3 × 66

Trusses

4 rafters	2 × 3 × 66
2 ties	2 × 3 × 100

Cladding

Cladding	1- × -6 shiplap boards or equivalent plywood
Lining	½ plywood or particleboards

Roof

6 purlins	2 × 3 × 180
60 boards	1 × 6 × 72 or equivalent area
4 bargeboards	1 × 8 × 76
2 finials	3 × 3 × 20
4 roof-light linings	1 × 5 × 25
3 roof-light frames	1½ × 3 × 30
1 roof-light frame	1 × 3 × 30
18 battens	½ × 1½ × 70
2 cappings	1 × 3 × 180

Door

2 linings	1 × 6 × 86
1 lining	1 × 6 × 44
5 boards	1 × 9 × 86 or equivalent area
3 ledgers	1 × 6 × 40
2 braces	1 × 6 × 42
1 top	1 × 2 × 42
2 stops	1 × 3 × 84

Windows

6 linings	1 × 6 × 38
3 top linings	1 × 7 × 38
3 top-hinge rails	1 × 5 × 38
3 sills	1½ × 7½ × 38
12 window moldings	2 × 2 × 38

store 4 feet wide (FIG. 5-20). The height is 8 feet to the eaves. One wall and one end are solid. The solid wall gives firm and adequate attachments for those machines you need to mount on the wall, and plenty of space for shelves and cabinets. Windows and doors take away a surprising amount of wall space, and you will have to weigh the value of cutting through these walls against their use when left solid.

The building will be fairly heavy. The equipment and stock you add will represent more weight. If you add machines with plenty of cast iron in them, the total weight on the base might be more than you first visualized. If an inadequate

Fig. 5-20. This workshop has an extra-strong construction to withstand the activities of many occupations and crafts.

base allows part of the building to sag, rectification at a later date will be difficult, if not impossible. Fortunately, you can prepare a concrete base of sufficient strength almost as easily as a thinner, poorly supported base. Dig deep enough to fill under the base with compacted stone, then lay more than 4 inches of concrete on top of it, taking it about 6 inches outside the building area and keeping the top surface above the surrounding ground.

Although it is possible to put the wooden floor directly on the concrete base, it is better to raise it. Several ways are possible. You could cement bricks or concrete blocks in place, or you could use railroad ties. If you use new wood, it should be pressure-impregnated with preservative. This type wood would be advisable for the floor framing as well. Use 2-inch- × -4-inch wood or larger. You can arrange the supports all around, but it would be better to have them only under the floor joists so there is ventilation (FIG. 5-21A). Spike or bolt the wood to the concrete. Alternate bearers might be full-length. You could place short pieces intermediately, depending on the stiffness of the floor. Put polyethylene or other plastic sheeting between the wood and concrete to reduce the amount of moisture meeting the wood.

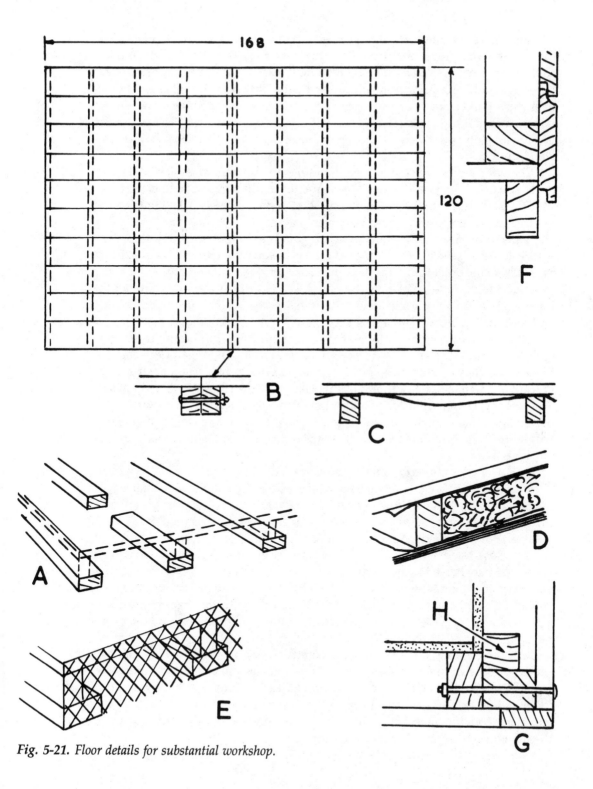

Fig. 5-21. Floor details for substantial workshop.

You could put the floor joists in position and nail full-length floorboards to them, but if you prefer to put the floor together away from its final position, it could be in two parts you would bolt together (FIG. 5-21B). Boards might be plain, but tongue-and-groove boards will prevent gaps, if there is shrinkage. Alternatively, use particleboard or thick plywood. Polyethylene sheeting between the floorboards and the joists (FIG. 5-21C) will act as a vapor barrier. For maximum floor insulation, sandwich insulating foam between the floorboards and plywood from below (FIG. 5-21D).

The floor settles the shape of the building, so take care to get it and its supports square. Compare diagonal measurements. Before proceeding with the walls, it is advisable to fix fine, metal mesh at open ends (FIG. 5-21E) to keep out leaves and vermin, without restricting ventilation.

You can do much of the assembly of sides and ends flat on the floor. The square corners of the base will serve as guides in squaring wall assemblies. Make the walls so the outside of a frame comes level with the outside of the floor, and take the siding a little way below the floor level (FIG. 5-21F). As you mark out the frames, allow for the corner joints. Bolt the 2-inch-×-3-inch uprights together and cover the siding with an upright corner strip (FIG. 5-21G). Include a fillet (FIG. 5- 21H) to support the lining. Joints between frame parts can be the same as in earlier buildings, preferably with open mortise-and-tenon joints at the corners. Shallow notches or halving joints are suitable elsewhere. Diagonal-strut-sway bracing is advisable in a building of this size, particularly if it will be exposed. This bracing resists wind loads and relieves the skin material of racking loads under strain that it might otherwise get. Plywood sheets as covering might provide stiffness without the need for diagonal struts, but with shiplap siding, they are advisable.

The two sides are rectangular frames the same length as the floor. They are shown 8 feet high, but if you will be covering with standard plywood sheets, you might reduce the height a little to allow for the sheets to project over the edges of the floor. For shiplap-board covering, you might keep the height to 8 feet, which will then suit the standard sheets you use for lining.

The closed side (FIG. 5-22A) has uprights at 24-inch intervals, and two equally spaced rails are halved to them. At the end, fit the fillets (FIGS. 5-21H and 5-22C), if you are going to line the walls after assembly. The four sway-bracing diagonals should fit closely and you should securely nail them to the framing. You can arrange this bracing easily by putting blocks in the corners and cutting the diagonal ends to fit against them (FIG. 5-22D).

Cut the cladding boards level at the ends. Along the bottom edge, allow a projection to overhang the floor (FIG. 5-21F). You can finish the top board level with the top of the frame, or you might prefer to fit it after you have assembled the building, as you will have a gap to fill after you have boarded the roof, and you might continue upwards with a wide board. If you cut the boards flush with the frame, you can put filler pieces on top later.

The side with the windows has the same overall size (FIG. 5-22B). You can

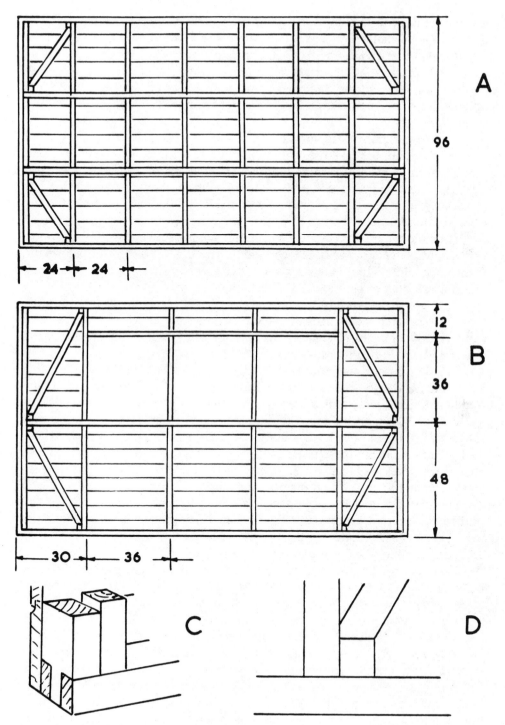

Fig. 5-22. Walls of the substantial workshop.

arrange the window opening to suit your needs, but the arrangement shown has three windows about 36 inches square, 48 inches above the floor. If you plan a different window layout, have sufficient uprights not more than 36 inches apart to support the cladding. Fit cleats and arrange sway bracing in the same way as on the other side. Put the cladding boards on in the same way. At the window openings, cut the boards level. You can cover their edges when you frame the windows.

The two end frames are almost the same (FIG. 5-23A). Make the closed end like the door end, but take the central rail right across (FIG. 5-23B). Although an overall width is given, it is important that the ends fit between the sides (FIG. 5-21G,H). Check on the floor that the ends will hold the sides the correct distance apart for you to take the cladding down outside the floor. Also check that the eaves height matches the sides.

Assemble the frames squarely. Halve the sloping tops to each other and to the uprights. The doorway is 42 inches wide, and the top is 84 inches above the floor. You could modify these sizes at this stage, if you wish. Include sway bracing similar to that on the sides.

Three 2-inch-×-3-inch purlins are on the edge at each side. In this building, there is no separate ridge. Instead, the top purlins are fairly close to the apex, to support the roof boards there. Arrange lower purlins close to the eaves and the others midway. Put supporting cleats on the frame (FIG. 5-23C).

Cladding has to overhang on all edges. At the bottom, allow the same amount to go over the floor as at the building sides. At the vertical edges, let the cladding project 1 inch, so it will overlap the side uprights, and leave a space for a filler (FIG. 5-21G). At the top, the cladding has to fit around the purlins and extend high enough to be level with their top edges under the roof boards (FIG. 5-23D). You might trim these boards to shape at this stage, or leave fitting those above eaves level until after you have erected the building. Cut the board edges level with the framing around the door opening.

You need two roof trusses, spaced at about 56-inch centers to support the purlins and prevent distortion of the roof or development of a sag. Make the trusses (FIG. 5-23E) with their 3-inch size vertical. Check that they match the ends and have matching cleats for the purlins.

Bolt or nail the ties to the surfaces of the truss rafters. During assembly of the building, check that the rafters are vertical and in line with the ends. Nail the rafter ends between supporting blocks on the tops of the side frames (FIG. 5-23F).

Nail the purlins to the end frames and trusses via the cleats. Let them extend about 6 inches at each end. Cover the roof with boards about 6 inches wide, preferably with tongue-and-groove edges. Cut the boards to fit closely at the ridge (FIG. 5- 24A), and let them overhang about 5 inches at the eaves. Cover completely and tightly, except if you want to fit a roof light (directions to follow). Use roofing felt or other covering material (FIG. 5-24B), preferably taken from one eaves over the ridge to the other eaves in one piece. If you must make a joint in the felt or covering material, allow a good overlap arranged in the direction that will allow

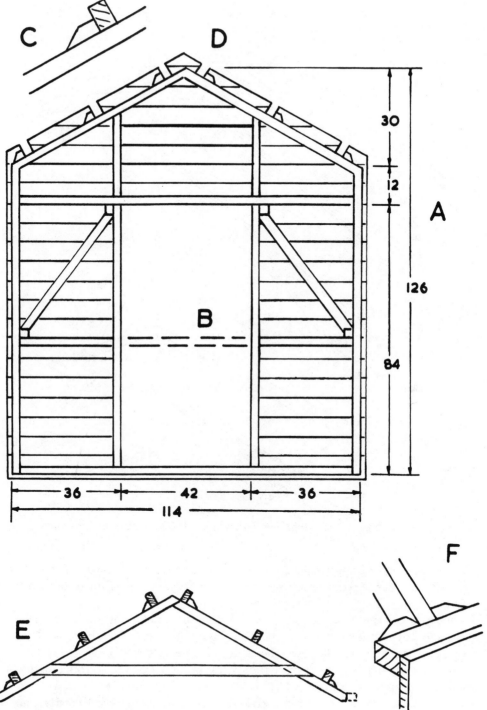

Fig. 5-23. *End and roof truss of the substantial workshop.*

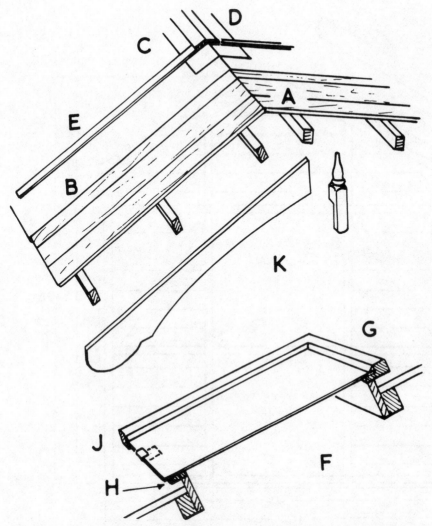

Fig. 5-24. Roof, bargeboard, and roof light details for the substantial workshop.

water to flow away from the joint. Turn under and nail at the eaves. If there is any tendency for the board ends to warp or go out of line, nail strips underneath before turning the covering material under.

You can nail another wide strip of the same material along the ridge (FIG. 5-24C) and put wooden capping strips over them (FIG. 5-24D). Nail battens down the slope of the roof (FIG. 5-24E) at about 18-inch intervals.

If you want to make one or more roof lights, arrange them most conveniently between the upper two purlins (FIG. 5-24F). Cut the opening in the boards. A width of 24 inches is the maximum advisable. Line the opening with strips that stand 1 inch above the roof level. It is important that the joints around the opening are waterproof. Use waterproof glue in the wooden joints, then cover the roof with felt. Turn the felt up the projecting frame, and embed it in jointing compound and nail it closely.

Make a frame into which you can putty glass. Allow ample depth for the glass, which might be a reinforced type about 1/4 inch thick. The inside edges of the frame might come level with, or inside, the lining of the opening. Make the top and both sides of the frame with rabbets to take the glass and putty (FIG. 5-24G). So you will not trap rainwater, let the lower part of the frame only come under the glass, which might project there slightly (FIG. 5-24H).

Mount the frame in position by gluing and screwing it to the lining pieces. Complete painting this woodwork before embedding the glass in putty. If you have doubts about the putty being able to prevent the glass from slipping, nail two sheet-metal pieces to the lower part of the frame and bend their ends around the glass (FIG. 5-24J). Fit bargeboards to both ends of the roof. They could be straight or you can decorate them in the ways described for some earlier buildings. A different decorated pattern is suggested in FIG. 5-24K. With this pattern goes a turned finial on a square part notched over the apex of the meeting bargeboards.

Line the door opening (FIG. 5-25A) with strips at sides and top. Round the projecting edges, and at the floor continue the lining pieces over the floorboards.

Ledge and brace the door in the usual way, except there is a covering piece at the top, with the brace immediately below it. At the bottom, the door overlaps the floor, as weatherproofing. Put stop strips in the sides of the doorway (FIG. 5-25B), but leave space at the top to clear the covering piece.

Use tongue-and-groove boards for the door. At the top, glue and screw the covering piece on (FIG. 5-25C). Make the ledgers short enough to clear the stop strips. Fit the braces sloping up from the hinge side. Arrange hinges and fasteners over the ledgers.

If you are going to line the building, you can do it before you fit the windows, so their framing can cover the lining boards, which might be plywood or particleboard. Include polyethylene sheet as a vapor barrier, if you wish. You can include insulating material in the space.

At the roof, close any spaces around the edges with cladding carried up to the roof boards or with pieces on top of the side frames. Nail lining material to the undersides of the purlins.

At the sides of the window openings, fit lining similar to that at the sides of the doorway. You can line the top in a similar way, but it would be more weatherproof if a piece extends and there is another strip below it for the window hinges, if you wish to make them open (FIG. 5-25D). At the bottom, make a wider sill to shed water (FIG. 5-25E).

Make the windows with rabbeted strips, with mortise-and-tenon joints at the corners (FIG. 5-25F). Fit hinges at the top and a stay and fastener at the bottom, if the window is to open. Screw other windows into their openings, preferably embedding them in jointing compound.

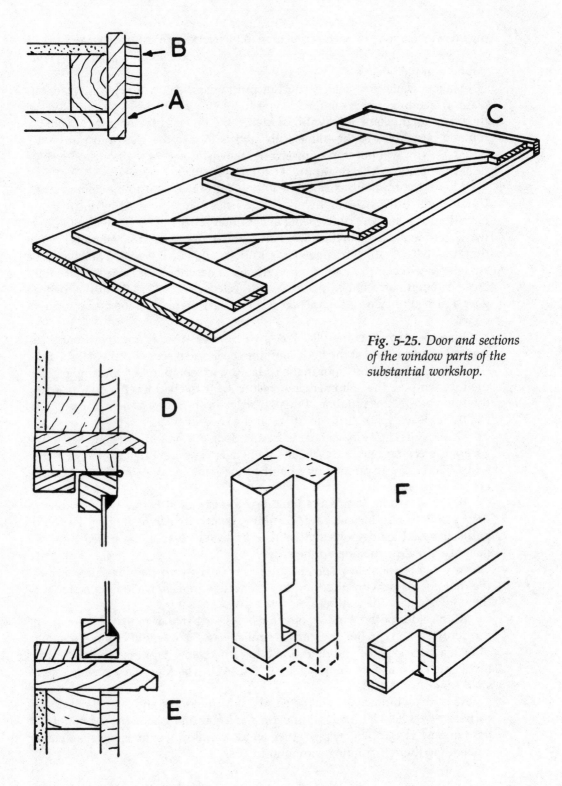

Fig. 5-25. Door and sections of the window parts of the substantial workshop.

Because the shop floor is above the surrounding concrete base, you might make a wooden or concrete step at the doorway. If there is to be a storage lean-to along one side, you can make it with a roof similar in construction to the main roof, with open-frame supports and racks underneath.

Greenhouse

A greenhouse is a gardener's workshop. Besides a place for growing some things completely and for starting others before putting them in the ground, it is a shelter to work in when conditions outside are uncomfortable, and it is a place to plan new horticultural projects. It extends the gardener's season for his occupation or hobby. For an enthusiastic gardener, a greenhouse is almost essential. A second stage in preparing plants to be put outside is to place them in a *cold frame* to harden them off. Quite often, that structure is a crude improvisation. In this building, a cold frame is included as part of the same unit, so you can efficiently tackle that stage of gardening (FIG. 5-26).

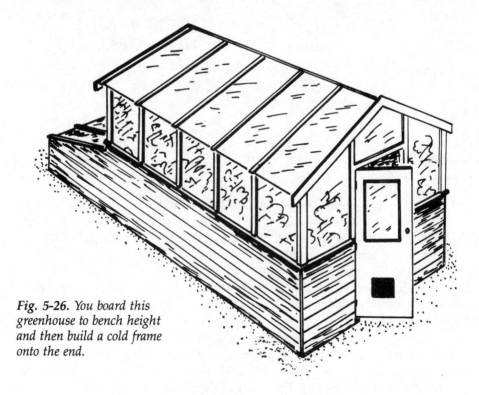

Fig. 5-26. You board this greenhouse to bench height and then build a cold frame onto the end.

Construction of a greenhouse can be very similar to that of any other building of the same shape, except you cover large areas of the walls and roof with glass instead of wood. You can prefabricate this building to a large extent, with ends and walls ready to bolt together. You make the roof on-site and glaze after

Materials List for Greenhouse

Ends

4 uprights	2	×	2	×	78
4 uprights	2	×	2	×	90
3 rails	2	×	2	×	96
7 rails	2	×	2	×	34
4 rafters	2	×	2	×	60
2 sills	1	×	4	×	34
1 sills	1	×	4	×	100

Sides

12 uprights	2	×	2	×	78
2 rails	2	×	2	×	124
2 rails	2	×	2	×	172
2 rails	2	×	4	×	124
4 uprights	2	×	2	×	20
2 strips	2	×	2	×	24
2 strips	2	×	2	×	56
2 sills	1	×	4	×	128

Cold frame

3 rails	2	×	2	×	96
2 rails	2	×	3	×	96
2 covers	1	×	4	×	56
1 cover	1	×	4	×	96
5 glazing bars	2	×	2	×	56

Roof

1 ridge	2	×	6	×	124
12 glazing bars	2	×	2	×	66
4 bargeboards	1	×	6	×	70

Door

2 sides	1	×	2	×	80
6 rails	1	×	2	×	30
2 window posts	1	×	2	×	40
2 edges	½	×	2	×	80
2 edges	½	×	2	×	32
2 window edges	1	×	2	×	40
2 window edges	1	×	2	×	26
2 panels	30	×	78	×	¼ plywood

Cladding

1- × -6 shiplap boards

Rabbets and fillets   ¾ × 1

erection, although a careful worker might prefer to fit some glass while the walls are flat on the floor. One problem is flexing, which could loosen putty or even break glass. In most cases, it is better to leave glass until you are satisfied that you have finally, and rigidly, assembled the greenhouse.

The sizes suggested are for a building of modest size (FIG. 5-27A,B), but you can use the same method for other sizes. Most of the structure is made from 2-inch-square wood, with some wider pieces where you need extra strength. Use shiplap boarding outside to near bench level. Above that, use glass. The door is at one end. A shuttered hole provides control of ventilation. Locate this hole low in the door and another one high in the opposite end. Make the cold frame by extending the sides so you can finish it with access via a lifting top. It does not have any connection through to the inside of the greenhouse. As a result, it is not affected by any heating in the greenhouse, and if you put soil into it, it is kept away from the floor of the main building.

The greenhouse could have a wooden floor, but because of water often running about, it would be better to lay a concrete base. The concrete base could go

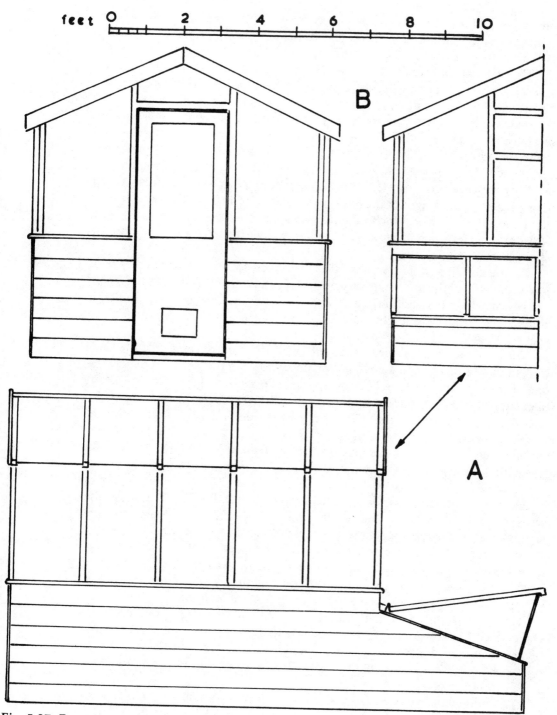

feet 0 2 4 6 8 10

B

A

Fig. 5-27. Four views of the greenhouse, showing sizes and proportion.

under the cold frame, or that might be preferable with a soil base. You can cut drainage channels in the concrete and lead them under the greenhouse walls to take away surplus water.

The two ends fit between the sides. For an overall width of about 96 inches, you can arrange the uprights to be 30 inches between centers. This spacing gives a suitable width for the door, and you simplify glass cutting by making all panes the same width (FIG. 5-28A). Joints in the upper parts of the frames will be without the additional strength of boarding. It is advisable to use open mortise-and-tenon (or bridle) joints, with waterproof glue, and drive either nails or dowels across each. The lower joints can be the same or the simpler, halving joints.

Start with the door end (FIG. 5-28B). The bottom rail goes right across. Other short rails mark the height of the doorway and the cladding. At the apex, leave a gap to take the 2-inch-×-6-inch ridge standing 2 inches above the framing (FIG. 5-28C), and put a short rail below the opening to brace the rafters and support the ridge (FIG. 5-28D).

Let the cladding project on each side to go halfway over the side posts (FIG. 5-28E). You will fill the space with a strip when you assemble the building. There will be a sill above the cladding (FIG. 5-28F). Since the sill looks best if you miter it around the corner, you might want to install it after you have assembled the walls.

The opposite end has a matching outline, but the rail at the top of the cladding should be taken right across and another short rail put 12 inches below the one in the door top position. The space between the railings is the ventilation opening (FIG. 5-28G). Clad that end across, up to the same level as the opposite end. Let the board ends extend to fully cover the side uprights. Make rabbets in all the openings for the glass with strips nailed in. Use 3/4-inch-×-1-inch pieces, making them level with the inside edges of the framing (FIG. 5-28H). At cladding level, allow for the sill to be fitted. The sill will have its own strip.

Arrange the uprights on the pair of sides so they are 24-inch centers and, as a result, you can cut all glass the same width (FIG. 5-29A). Put cladding up to the same height as at the ends. Include the cold-frame extensions, boarded to the top (FIG. 5-29B). The top member is a 2-inch-×-4-inch section, and rafters have to rest on it. Instead of cutting its top to suit the roof slope, leave it square, except for notches at the roof angle where the rafters will come directly over the uprights (FIG. 5-29C,D). After you assemble the building, you can put filler pieces on the squared tops to close the gaps between the wall and the roof glass.

Cut off the ends of the cladding boards level with the end uprights. At the end of the cold frame, make a piece the same width as the greenhouse ends so it fits between the sides (FIG. 5-29E), with cladding to the top. Cut the cladding at the same angle as the sides. Let the ends extend to cover the side uprights in the same way as the door end (FIG. 5-28E).

Assemble all the parts made so far, using 3/8-inch bolts at about 15-inch intervals through the posts. Put filler pieces in the corners of the cladding. Check squareness and fasten the bottom frame members down to the base.

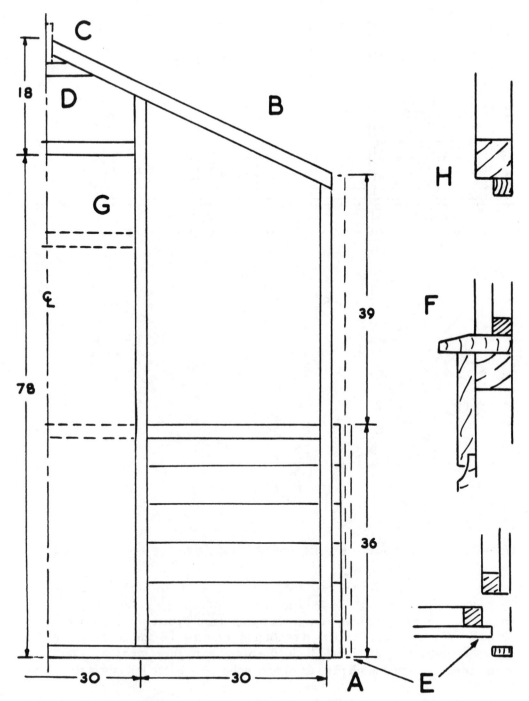

Fig. 5-28. The door end of the greenhouse and sections through windows and corners.

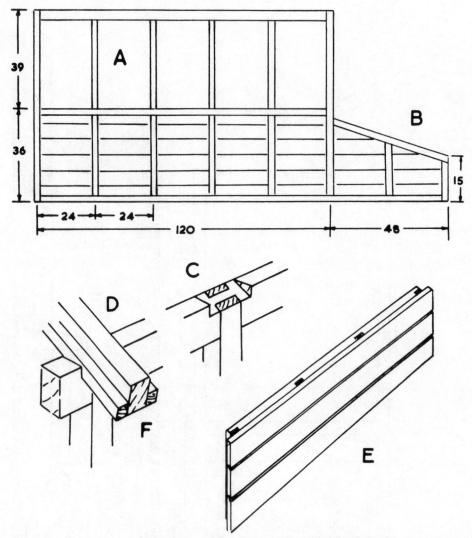

Fig. 5-29. A greenhouse side (A,B), rafter details (C,D) and the end of the cold frame (E).

Fit a sill all around. Level the sill inside and taper it outside from just outside the edges of the uprights (FIG. 5-28F). You can extend it a few inches inwards if you want to make it into a shelf. You could make the sill in sections, but you can obtain the neatest finish by making it continuous on the sides and ends. For the strongest construction, notch the sill into the uprights about 1/4 inch (FIG. 5-30A). At the corners, extend the sill parts to miter together (FIG. 5-30B). Put rabbet strips in place.

Make the 2-inch-×-6-inch ridge to fit in the slots in the ends and be level outside. Mark on it the positions of the rafters to match the positions of the slots on

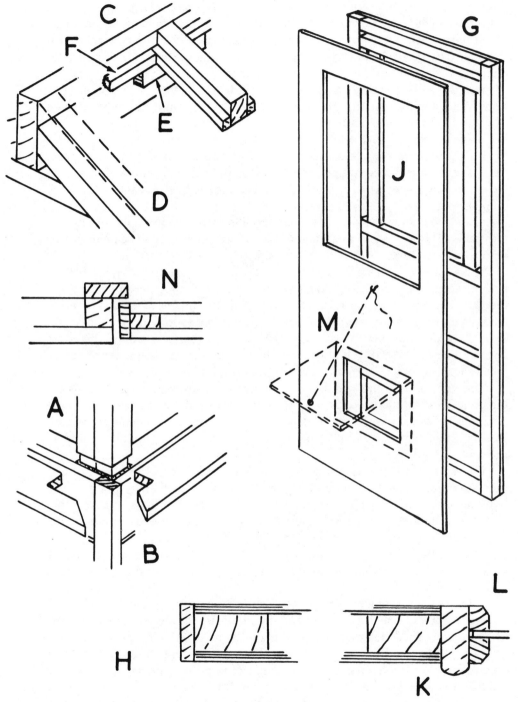

Fig. 5-30. Constructional details of the greenhouse and the way you assemble its door.

the tops of the building sides. Prepare the rafters with rabbet strips on each side of the intermediate ones (FIG. 5-29F) and on the inside edges only of the end ones. Using the angle of a building as a guide, cut the tops of the rafters to fit against the ridge (FIG. 5-30C). Make the length of a rafter enough to overhang the walls by 6 inches. Prepare all twelve rafters so they match.

Nail the end rafters on top of the frame ends (FIG. 5-30D). At the other positions, put a supporting strip underneath (FIG. 5-30E) as you position each rafter. Nail the lower end into its recess. Make rabbet strips with sloping tops to go between the rafters (FIG. 5-30F).

This procedure completes the assembly of all parts that you must glaze. Putty and the alternative compounds do not bond well with untreated wood, so either paint all the woodwork or just the rabbets, so they will dry while you work on other parts.

Glaze the door to the same level as the walls. A ventilation hole is in its bottom panel. The suggested construction has 1/4-inch plywood panels on each side with a frame of 1-inch-×-2-inch strips inside (FIG. 5-30G).

Make the door an easy fit in the doorway, with its bottom above the bottom framing strip. The plywood could go to the edges without further protection, but it will be better to cover with 1/2-inch strips (FIG. 5-30H). Allow for this covering when marking out the plywood panels. Make one plywood door panel first and check its sizes. Glue and fix with thin nails the framing strips around the edges and openings (FIG. 5-30J). When you are satisfied with this panel, make the other panel slightly oversize so that when you have fixed it, you can have true edges.

Line the window and ventilation openings with strips that are level inside, but project with rounded edges at the front (FIG. 5-30K). Because movement of the door, particularly if it is slammed, might loosen putty, it will be better if the door glazing is held between two fillets (FIG. 5-30L). Use jointing compound to embed the glass tightly.

Cover the ventilation opening with fine-mesh wire gauze, to keep out vermin. To control ventilation, hinge a flap on the inside of the door, with a cord to a hook above to regulate the amount of air allowed to pass (FIG. 5-30M). At the other end of the building, arrange a similar flap inside the high opening there, with a cord up to a ring or pulley and down to a cleat within reach.

Strips inside the doorway framing (FIG. 5-30N) will act as stops. Hang the door to swing outwards on three 3-inch hinges, and fit a handle and catch or lock.

Although pieces of glass could be as large as the openings each panel has to fit, you might prefer to use shorter pieces, with the upper pieces overlapping the lower ones, to shed water. This design might be more economical and the first fitting might be handled easily. It also might be easier and cheaper if you ever have to replace a broken pane. Embed the glass in putty, with fine nails (*sprigs*) holding the glass, then neatly putty over them (FIG. 5-31A).

At the cold frame, cover the top edges with strips (FIG. 5-31B). At the end of the greenhouse, fit a piece of 2-inch-×-3-inch wood over the cover strips and

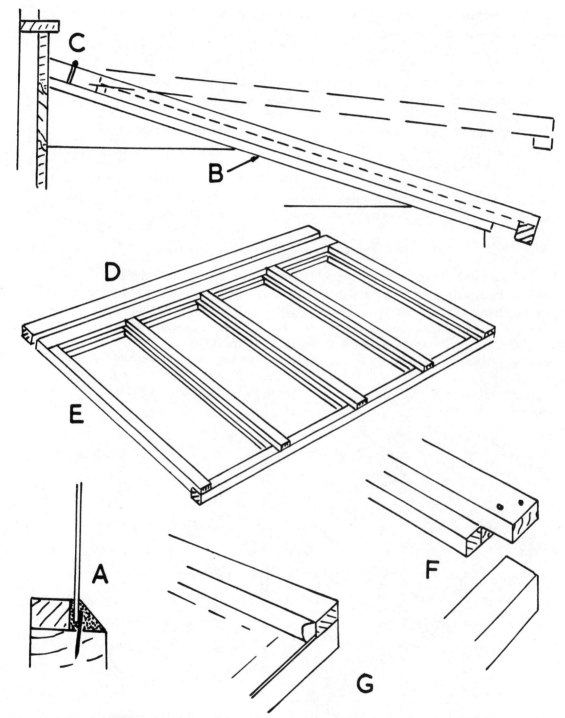

Fig. 5-31. The cold-frame cover and its construction and mounting.

bevel it to fit close to the cladding on the greenhouse (FIG. 5-31C,D). Make the lifting cover to fit against this strip of wood with a 6-inch overhang at the bottom. This cover is built up with a 3-inch-wide piece at the top and all other parts are 2 inches square, with $3/4$-inch-$\times$-1-inch rabbet strips (FIG. 5-31E).

Mortise-and-tenon joints are best for the joints to the top rail, but the 2-inch-square bottom piece has to be kept down below the glass level, so water will run off. Halve the ends of the sloping pieces, and glue and screw the crosspiece to them (FIG. 5-31F). When you glaze the frame, carry the glass to the edge of the bottom piece (FIG. 5-31G).

The frame with glass will be fairly heavy. Use four strong 4-inch hinges at the top. Arrange a strut to hold the top open.

Finish the ends of the greenhouse with bargeboards. They need not be elaborate, but they will improve appearances by covering the ends of the roof structure (FIG. 5-27B).

Canoe Shed

Canoes and kayaks might not suffer much if left outside, but open storage lacks security, particularly for paddles and other loose equipment. A building will protect these craft from the weather, as well as allow camping gear, paddles, and other associated equipment to be kept secure. The building could have a bench, so could make repairs and alterations on the spot and in comfort.

Adjust sizes and details of the building to suit canoes, kayaks, sailboards, and similar craft which you wish to store. The canoe shed shown in FIG. 5-32 is intended to provide storage on racks for four canoes or kayaks about 16 feet long.

Fig. 5-32. This canoe shed has racks for canoes and their equipment. The roof admits the only light, so the walls are secure.

Materials List for Canoe Shed

Ends

2 uprights	2	×	3	×	86
2 uprights	2	×	3	×	110
2 uprights	2	×	3	×	96
2 uprights	2	×	3	×	105
5 rails	2	×	3	×	86
2 rafters	2	×	3	×	100

Back

7 uprights	2	×	3	×	86
3 rails	2	×	3	×	212

Front

7 uprights	2	×	3	×	110
4 rails	2	×	3	×	212
4 fillers	1	×	2	×	110

Roof

8 rafters	2	×	3	×	100
2 fillers	2	×	3	×	26

Roof light

2 frames	1	×	6	×	26
2 frames	1	×	6	×	32
2 sides	2	×	2	×	36
1 top	2	×	2	×	30
1 bottom	1½	×	2	×	30

Door

6 boards	1	×	6	×	78
3 ledgers	1	×	6	×	30
2 braces	1	×	6	×	40
2 sides	1	×	5	×	80
1 top	1	×	5	×	32

Racks

3 rails	2	×	3	×	212
15 rails	2	×	3	×	40

Cladding 1-×-6 shiplap boards

Roof 1-×-6 plain or tongued-and grooved boards

Racks are about 36 inches wide, and there is clearance vertically of about 18 inches. At one end of the building, there can be a bench, either built-in or loose. The opposite side can have racks for paddles and other items. If you have sailing gear, you can hoist it into the roof. It is possible to have the canoe racks on the high side and get one more canoe in. Then, however, you have the problem of lifting the canoe above your head height, and the slope of the roof does not allow for easy access. The sizes and layouts are for four canoes on racks and floor at the lower side (FIG. 5-33A).

Most of the framing is 2-inch-×-3-inch wood, and the cladding suggested is shiplap boards, but you can use plywood or vertical tongue-and-groove boards. The sides do not have any windows, but there is one in the roof. If you plan to use a bench often, you might wish to put a window in the end. Having no windows in the walls helps security, as breaking in becomes more difficult. Board the roof and cover it with tarred felt.

Start by making the ends. All of the framing has its 2-inch side towards the cladding, except the rafter, which is better with its 2-inch side at the top. The ends are a pair, except one has the doorway (FIG. 5-34A). Make the other end the same, but put a rail across at half the door height and board that end all over. Cut cladding level at the edges.

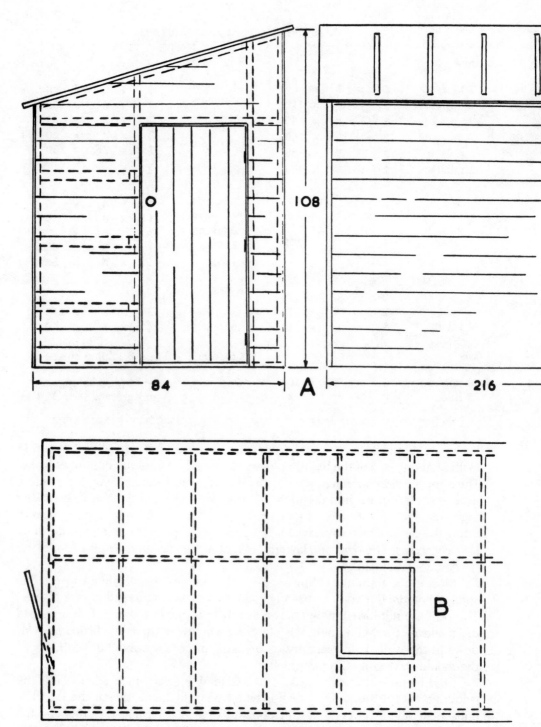

Fig. 5-33. Suggested sizes for the canoe shed, to hold four canoes up to 16 feet long.

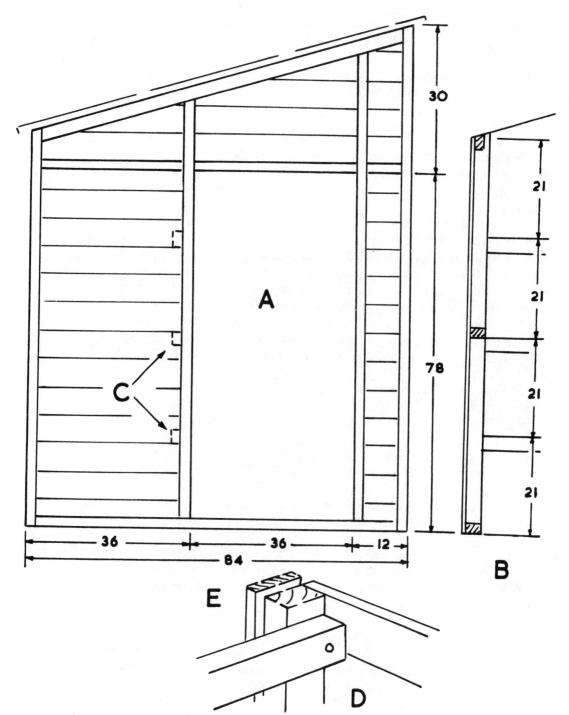

Fig. 5-34. The door end of the canoe shed, and spacing of racks.

Make the back (FIG. 5-35A) with all its framing with 2 inches towards the cladding, except the top, which is the other way. Bevel the top edge to match the slope of the roof (FIG. 5-35B). At the corners of the building, the back and front cladding extends halfway over the end posts (FIG. 5-35C), and a filler piece is fitted in. Cover the back completely, with the cladding extended at both ends.

The front (FIG. 5-35D) is made similar to the back. Bevel the top to fit the roof slopes the other way and equally space two intermediate rails.

Vertical spacing of the rack is suggested at 21 inches (FIG. 5-34B), but you might want to adjust this if you have one deeper canoe. One rack will take surfboards or a kayak, if made quite shallow. Allow plenty of vertical clearance or you might have difficulty in stowing craft. Width is not as important; boats can overhang a rack.

Each rack has a front piece the full length of the shed (FIG. 5-36A). Pieces come from the back framing (FIG. 5-36B) to tenon into it. There could be one piece at every back upright, or you could fit them to alternate ones, but if you will use the racks at different times for craft of different lengths, crosspieces at every upright are advisable. If you have comparatively fragile and flexible racing craft, close support is advisable. For greater support you might lay plywood on a rack.

Do some preparation for the racks before assembly. To allow for slight variations, the actual fitting is best done after you join the walls and attach the building to its base. Join the building corners with 3/8-inch bolts at about 18-inch intervals.

It might be sufficient to merely bolt racks to the back uprights, but plywood brackets are shown in FIG. 5-36C,D. Use screws in the plywood, but bolt the racks through the uprights. At the outer ends, tenon into the long support (FIG. 5-36E). At the ends of the building, bolt the long piece to the end uprights (FIG. 5-34C,D). Cover the edges of the doorway with strips (FIG. 5-34E). Put stop strips inside this doorway, and fit a ledged and braced door, made in the way described for several other buildings.

There is plenty of space for shelves and racks on the high wall. Battens across the framing will make paddle racks. A shelf will keep paddles off the floor (FIG. 5-36F).

Make the roof with rafters on the same level as the tops of the ends, spaced about 24 inches apart (FIG. 5-37A). Notch the rafters into the back and front (FIG. 5-37B), securing them with nails or screws. At the roof light position—halfway along, unless you need it elsewhere (FIG. 5-33B)—put pieces across (FIG. 5-37C).

Lay boards lengthwise to cover the roof (FIG. 5-37D). Allow a 3-inch overhang all around. If you need joints lengthwise, make them over rafters. Trim the boards level around the roof light opening. Put a framing of boards around the opening (FIG. 5- 37E) to hold the glazed part a few inches above the roof level.

Cover the roof with tarred felt or other flexible roofing material (FIG. 5-37F). Take this over all edges and nail underneath. At the roof light, trim the covering so you can turn it up the framing boards (FIG. 5-37G). Nail it there. If there have to be any joints in this vicinity, embed them in a jointing compound.

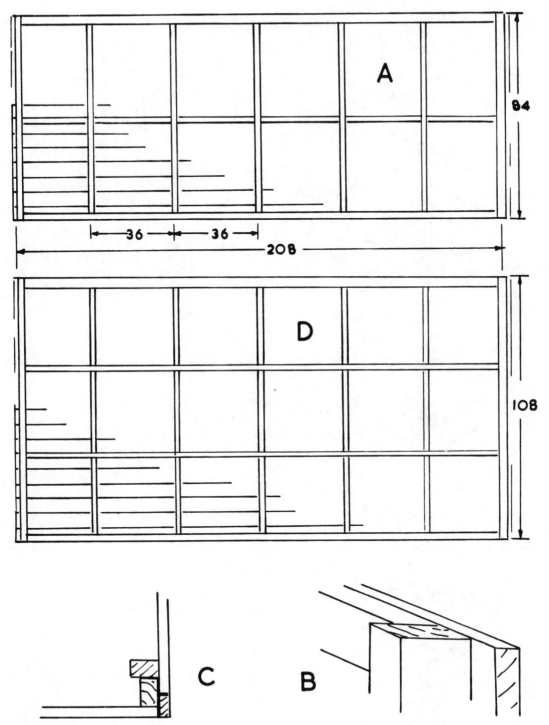

Fig. 5-35. Back (A) and front (D) with corner arrangements (B,C).

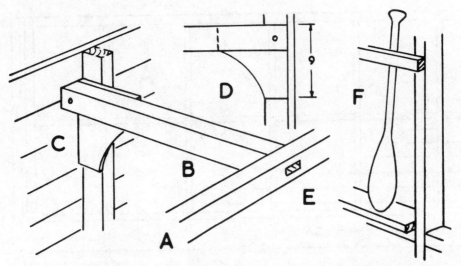

Fig. 5-36. Details of canoe rack construction and a method of paddle storage.

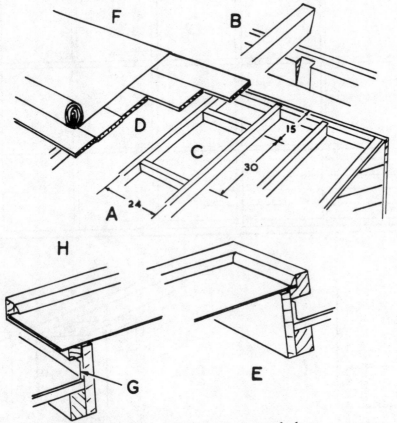

Fig. 5-37. Roof and roof-light details for the canoe shed.

For the roof light, make a rabbeted frame for the two sides and the top, but at the lower end make a piece to go under the glass only, so water can run off. Have the size of the frame so it will fit over the framing boards and so you can screw to them from inside (FIG. 5-37H). Although you could glaze the window when it is on the ground, it is easier to get the frame closely fitted and the glass accurately puttied in, if you delay the glazing until the roof light is in position.

No bargeboards are shown, but if you want to give the roof a more solid appearance, couple bargeboards to a fascia board along the front edge. If you put a board at the back, make sure it does not interfere with water running off. Lay battens down the roof at about 18-inch intervals, to hold down the covering.

Asymmetrical Workshop

Standard small buildings are arranged with their roofs made symmetrical, so a ridge roof has similar slopes on each side. For most purposes this is satisfactory, but if you are making your own small building you can arrange details, including the roof, to suit your needs.

This can apply to a workshop. You need the greatest head room over the front edge of the bench, which might not be the center of the building. In this small hobby workshop (FIG. 5-38), it is assumed you will have a bench along one side under the window and the roof ridge is arranged to come above the edge of the bench instead of at the center of the building.

This should suit many activities, such as light woodworking or metalworking, maybe with a lathe or other machine. You could also do fabric work, pottery

Materials List for Asymmetrical Workshop

4 end posts	2	×	2	×	86
2 end posts	2	×	2	×	108
6 end rails	2	×	2	×	72
8 side posts	2	×	2	×	86
8 side rails	2	×	2	×	108
4 side posts	2	×	2	×	48
5 rafters	2	×	2	×	56
5 rafters	2	×	2	×	40
4 window frames	1	×	1	×	32
4 window frames	1	×	1	×	44
4 window frames	1	×	2 1/2	×	32
4 window frames	1	×	2 1/2	×	44
2 door frames	1	×	3	×	80
1 door frame	1	×	3	×	32
1 ridge piece	2	×	6	×	110
roof	1/2 or 3/4 plywood				
5 roof battens	3/8	×	1	×	54
5 roof battens	3/8	×	1	×	38
cladding	3/4 or 1 × 6 shiplap boards				

Fig. 5-38. *A small workshop can be made with an asymmetrical roof so the greatest height comes where it is most needed.*

or sculpture in the shop. Access is via a door in one end. You should get sufficient natural light from the windows in one side, but you could arrange another door or extra windows if you wish. The building is described as unlined, but you could line the walls and roof with plywood for insulation and year-round use. A wood floor would be better insulation than a concrete one and less likely to damage dropped tools.

Framing should be 2-inch softwood, mostly square, but with some wider sections. The project is described with cladding of shiplap boards, but you could use other boards or exterior-grade plywood.

The suggested sizes (FIG. 5-39) give you a floor area of 6 feet by 9 feet and ample head room through the doorway and inside. You could modify the sizes within reason, but if you want a much bigger workshop, you should consider projects described late in the chapter. Decide on which end you need the door.

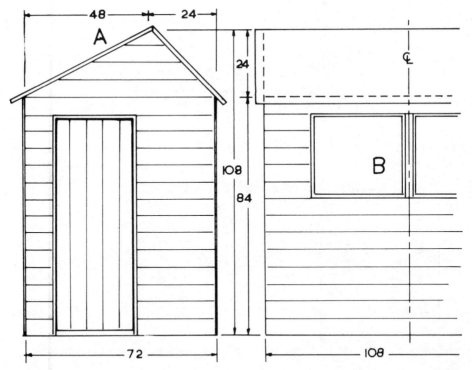

Fig. 5-39. Overall sizes of the asymmetrical workshop.

Make the end with the doorway first (FIG. 5-40). Corner joints will be as used in earlier buildings, with the side cladding extending over the end assemblies. Allow for the overlapping cladding (FIG. 5-40A) when setting out the framing. The apex is off-center (FIG. 5-39A). The frame parts may be notched into each other about 1/4 inch, but cut a halving joint where the door head crosses the main upright (FIG. 5-40B). A halving joint would be best at the rather steep front corner (FIG. 5- 40C) .

At the top, the 2-inch-×-6-inch ridge piece has to fit between the framing rafters (FIGS. 5-40D and 5-42A). It is supported by a short crossbar notched in (FIGS. 5-40E and 5-42B). Check the actual section of the wood to be used for the ridge piece so you allow the correct space.

Cover the frame with shiplap boarding, cut level at all outer edges and around the doorway.

Make the opposite end as a pair to the first one, except you do not have to allow for a door. Instead of the shorter doorpost, you can put in another post with the rail taken right across (FIG. 5-40F).

The front wall is shown with two large windows (FIG. 5-39B) that will be about 15 inches above the usual bench. You could arrange smaller windows by extending the boarded parts or by altering the rail heights. Make the height of the front

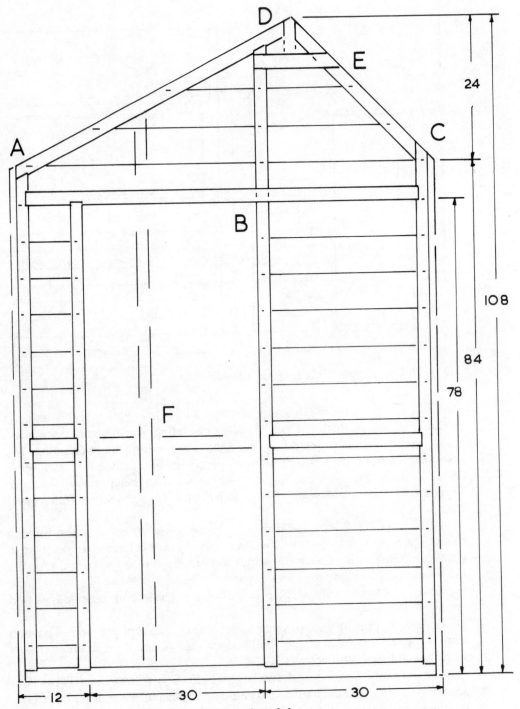

Fig. 5-40. Details of ends of the asymmetrical workshop.

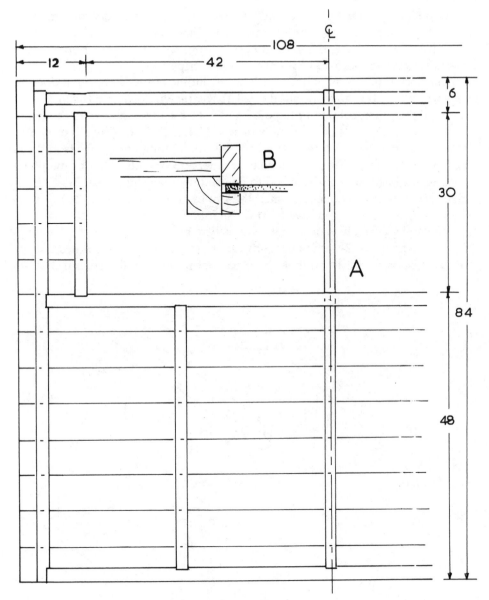

Fig. 5-41. Side details of the asymmetrical workshop.

wall to match the edges of the end assemblies. Allow for the cladding to extend over the end cladding and posts.

Make the framework with joints notched and nailed, except the center post should be halved where it crosses rails (FIG. 5-41A). Cover the framing with ship-lap boards, extending enough at the corners to overlap the end assemblies. Cut the wood level with the edges of the window openings. Put a board to make up the thickness between the window openings. The window glass will be held by strips (FIG. 5-41B). Fitting the glass is best left until after the workshop has been assembled on-site, but you could fit the inner strips now.

The back wall assembly has to match the outline of the front, but it does not have windows. You can leave out the rail above the windows and the outer window uprights, then continue the posts shown below the windows to the top.

Assemble the walls on a concrete or wood base. Drill for $3/8$-inch or $1/2$-inch bolts at about 18-inch intervals through the overlapping corner posts and drill the bottom rails for holding-down bolts or other attachments. Check squareness.

Check straightness of the wood to be used for the ridge piece. Bevel its top edge each side of the center to match the slopes of the roof (FIG. 5-42C). Cut the wood to fit between the end walls, and nail it in position.

The roof will be plywood, but it is unlikely to be stiff enough without internal support, which can be arranged with rafters (FIG. 5-42D). For stiffness, it will probably be sufficient to arrange three pairs of rafters equally spaced, but you

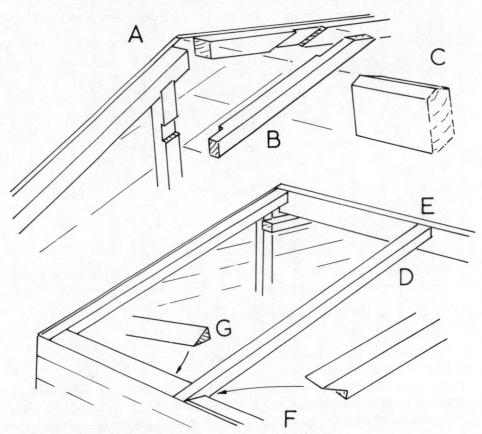

Fig. 5-42. Roof arrangements for the asymmetrical workshop.

will have to arrange joints in the plywood over rafters, and you could position them to allow for economical cutting of sheets.

A rafter could be notched into the ridge piece, but it should be sufficient to nail it in place (FIG. 5-42E). At the eaves, the line of a rafter should extend to the other edge of the wall, so notch it over the frame (FIG. 5-42F). For the most waterproof joint along the eaves, fill the spaces between rafters with strips that match the slope (FIG. 5-42G).

Arrange the roofing sheets to have at least 3 inches overhang all around. Stiffen the edges. Nail the plywood in place and cover with tarred felt turned under at the edges. Put battens over the covering at about 18-inch intervals.

You could leave the roof ends untreated, or cover one or both ends with bargeboards and a finial (FIG. 5-38). Glaze the windows.

The door can be of the type with three ledgers and braces, as described for earlier projects. Line the doorway with strips level with the boarding. The bottom rail could be extended as a step. Allow for the door being an easy fit. Three 4-inch butt or T hinges will hang it. Put a stop strip at the opposite side and arrange a handle or knob and fastener.

If you want to insulate the workshop, nail thin plywood inside the walls and under the rafters. Finish the wood with preservative or paint. When you equip the shop, anything built in that touches two or more walls provides mutual support. A bench attached to walls stiffens the structure and makes the bench more rigid to work on. This applies to built-in shelves and cupboards as well.

Wide-door Large Workshop

If your activities include making light furniture, carving or making toys, turning or modelmaking, then you can take all you need in and out of a small doorway. If you restore old cars, build boats, or even make more buildings, you will have to provide doorways that will not impede the passage of materials in or of what you make, out. It would be frustrating to have to remove a wall to get a boat out!

Besides making the building large enough for you to move around what you are working on, you should also provide space for a bench and probably some machine tools. The doorway has to be wide enough, but you do not always want to swing back a large door, particularly in cold and wet weather. You could arrange another door for normal access or, as in this case (FIG. 5-43), make part of the large double or treble doors to swing independently. This arrangement allows you to open doors 2 feet, 3 feet, 5 feet, or 8 feet.

The building is drawn (FIG. 5-44) to cover a floor area 10 feet by 12 feet, with a height to the eaves of 8 feet and a doorway 8 feet wide. Windows are shown in the sides only, but you could put more in the back, and there might be a small door at one side or in the back. You could make the building without insulation, or include some insulation during construction. You could add a lining afterwards. Shiplap board cladding is suggested. That could be nailed on over tarpaper or plastic sheeting. You could then line the walls with plywood and include

Materials List for Wide-door Workshop

Front and back

10 uprights	2	×	4	×	115
5 rails	2	×	4	×	144
2 uprights	2	×	4	×	44
4 rafters	2	×	4	×	84
1 rail	2	×	4	×	100
6 wind bracings	2	×	4	×	48

Sides

8 uprights	2	×	4	×	100
16 rails	2	×	4	×	60
8 window frames	2	×	4	×	50
2 uprights	2	×	4	×	54

Roof truss

2 rafters	2	×	4	×	84
1 post	2	×	4	×	24
2 ties	1	×	4	×	140
2 joint covers	1	×	8	×	14

Other parts

8 window frames	1	×	3	×	50
8 window frames	1	×	3	×	40
8 window frames	1	×	2	×	50
8 window frames	1	×	2	×	40
2 door liners	1	×	5	×	78
1 door head	2	×	2	×	110
4 roof ends	2	×	4	×	84
4 bargeboards	1	×	7	×	100
6 purlins	2	×	4	×	130

Doors

6 ledgers	1	×	6	×	40
3 ledgers	1	×	6	×	30
6 braces	1	×	6	×	40
stops from	1	×	1	×	84

Covering

Walls   shiplap boards 1 × 6
Doors   tongue-and-groove boards 1 × 6
Roof   corrugated iron

Fig. 5-43. If you work on large things you need doors that will open wide enough, yet can also be used at lesser widths.

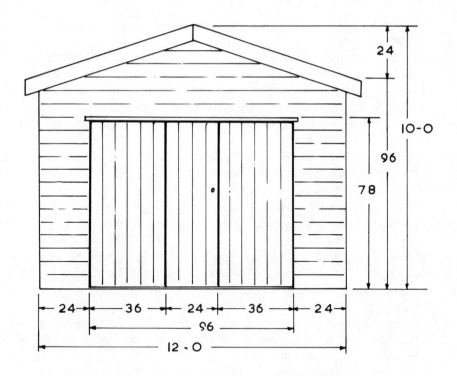

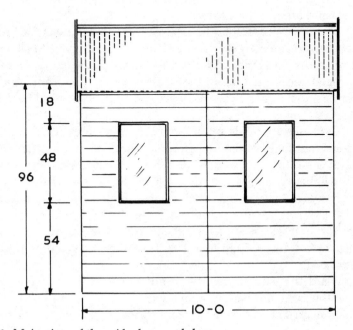

Fig. 5-44. Main sizes of the wide-door workshop.

foam or other insulation in the cavities. Plywood nailed under the purlins would insulate the roof.

The walls are made in sections. The front and back go right across. The sides are in two pairs of assemblies that bolt together, and a roof truss is supported by the double uprights where they meet. Purlins notch into back and front walls and rest on the truss to support the corrugated galvanized iron or plastic sheeting. The key part, which controls the sizes of some other parts, is the front, which should be made first.

Framing of the front (FIG. 5-45) is all 2-inch-×-4-inch pieces arranged with the 2-inch faces toward the cladding, except the rafters (FIG. 5-45A) are on edge and there is a stiffening piece that way up over the doorway (FIG. 5-45B).

Lay out the front framework squarely. Squareness of the door opening is particularly important. Nailing will secure most joints, but parts can be positively located if ends fit into shallow notches (FIG. 5-45C). Cut halving joints where the rail at the doorhead crosses the uprights (FIG. 5-46A). Cut the edgewise piece above the doorway to fit closely between the uprights. Nail or screw it securely to the horizontal piece below it (FIG. 5-45D). It is there to provide rigidity and resistance to sagging above the door opening.

Where upright parts join the edgewise pieces, notch and nail them behind (FIG. 5-45E) so surfaces towards the cladding are level. Notch the rafters to half their depth to take the ends of the purlins (FIG. 5-45F). Top purlins should be close to the apex. The bottom purlins are 5 inches from the corner and the others midway. At the apex, put a joint cover (FIG. 5-46B) between the purlin notches.

Cover the framing outside with shiplap or other boards, finishing level on all edges and around the doorway.

Use the front assembly as a pattern for the outline of the back (FIG. 5-46). This is boarded completely, so the framework does not have to allow for the doorway. Arrange uprights and rails crossing with halving joints and with all uprights notched over the rafters, in the same way as at the front. Add wind bracing in four positions, as shown (FIG. 5-46C and D). Cover with boarding cut level at all edges.

The sides are made up of two pairs of sections (FIG. 5-47). The boarding on the side sections overlap the front and back assemblies (FIG. 5-47A), so enough cladding has to be allowed beyond the corner uprights (FIG. 5-47B). The roof truss has to fit between the side frames (FIG. 5-47C), so the frame corners are made with notches (FIG. 5-47D), which are formed with pieces inside the main uprights (FIG. 5-48A). Allow for sufficient clearance for the roof-truss rafters to fit in easily. At that corner it will be stronger to halve the parts together, but other joints can be notched and nailed. You might want to alter the window opening sizes to suit your needs.

Board the side sections with enough extending at the corner uprights to cover the front and back section edges. Cut the opposite edge with boards level with the upright and extending to the same position over the notch for the truss.

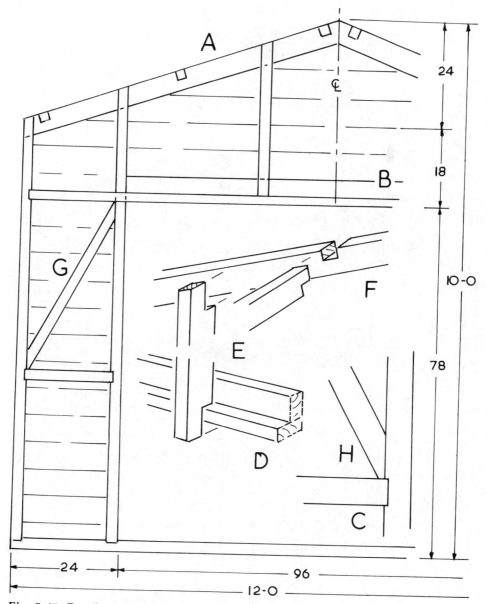

Fig. 5-45. Details of the front wall of the wide-door workshop.

Use the front or back assembly as a guide when marking out the roof truss (FIG. 5-48B). The truss slopes match those of the back or front, but the rafter edges come under the purlins. The rafters are notched at the eaves to fit over the frame uprights. Check the actual depth of wood being used for purlins, and arrange the amount of notching (FIG. 5-48C) so the line of roof will fit over the side clad-

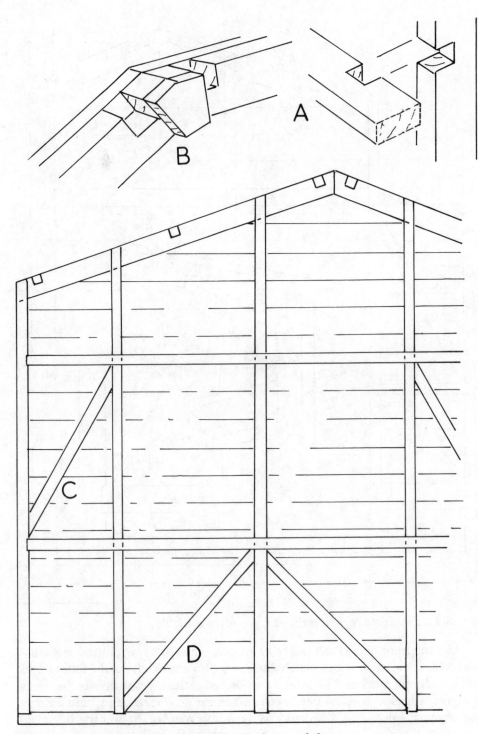

Fig. 5-46. Details of the rear wall of the wide-door workshop.

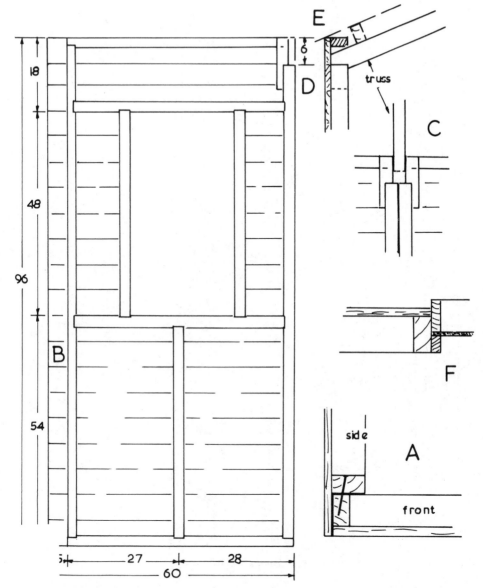

Fig. 5-47. *Sizes and details of side wall sections for the wide-door workshop.*

ding (FIG. 5-47E). Prepare joint covers for each side of the apex of the truss (FIG. 5-48D). Make a pair of ties (FIG. 5-48E) to go across the truss and a strut to fit centrally under the apex (FIG. 5-48F). The ends of the ties are best bolted through the rafters (three $1/2$-inch bolts at each end would be suitable), but you can use nails between the joint covers and the ties to the strut (FIG. 5-48G). Put cleats at the purlin positions (FIG. 5-48H and J) securely nailed to the rafters. Check that these line up with the slots in the back and front rafters.

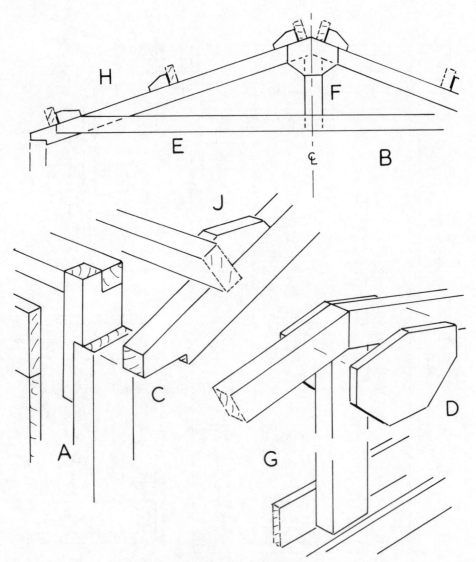

Fig. 5-48. *Roof truss details for the side-door workshop.*

Mark out the concrete base squarely. Join the pairs of side sections. Join the four walls by nailing or bolting the corners and fasten them down to the base. Put the roof truss in position, and nail its ends.

Notch the ends of the purlins to fit at the front and back. Nail them there and to the cleats on the truss. As you do this, check squareness at the top of the assembly, and see that there is no twist in the walls.

You might not wish to glaze the windows until after construction is completed, but you can prepare the wood now. The glass will be held between strips (FIG. 5-47F). Fit those around the front of the opening permanently and projecting forward of the cladding. You should fit the inner strips with screws so they can be removed easily if you ever have to replace the glass.

The suggested door arrangement has two doors about 36 inches wide hinged at the sides of the doorway, with provision for bolting them inside. Then there is a door about 24 inches wide hinged to one of them and lockable. You then can use the small door for getting yourself in and out, but it can open to greater widths when necessary.

To prepare the doorway, put lining strips at each side (FIG. 5-49A). You could put a similar strip across the top, but a stouter piece in front (FIG. 5-49B) will give better protection from rain. A groove underneath it stops water running back below. At the bottom, you could cut away the frame crossbar once the sides have been fixed down, but if you leave it, it could be widened to form a step (FIG. 5-49C).

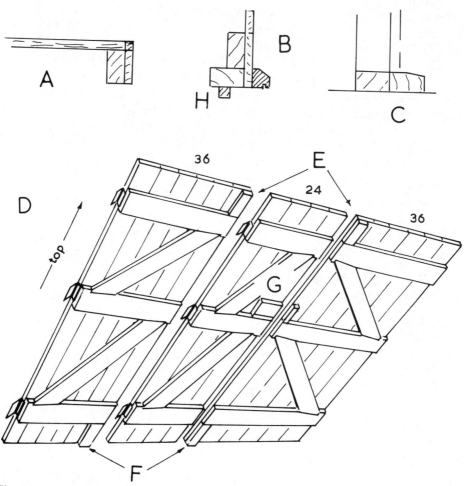

Fig. 5-49. *Door and window surrounds. Three door sections.*

Measure the doorway and allow for clearance between the doors and at top and bottom, then prepare the doors to suit (FIG. 5-49D). Tongue-and-groove boards about 1 inch × 6 inches would be suitable for the upright parts, and plain boards of similar section are good for the ledgers and braces.

The two outer doors, about 36 inches wide, can be made as a pair, with their braces sloping up from the hinged sides. Notch into the ledgers for the strongest construction. Try these doors in position, and make the narrow door to fit into the remaining space. All hinges have their knuckles to the front, so all doors swing outward. You could use 4-inch or larger butt hinges let into the door edges or put T hinges on the surface.

Put blocks to take bolts up and down for securing the outer doors (FIG. 5-49E and F). Put a block for a lock on the narrow door (FIG. 5-49G) with a keyhole through. Alternatively, put a hasp and staple for a padlock outside.

Put the doors in position. Drill the framing for the securing bolts. Put stop strips across the top of the doorway (FIG. 5-49H) for the doors to close against. Avoid letting the surfaces of the doors project in front of the framing, to reduce risk of rainwater getting into the end grain.

The roof can be covered with 7-foot corrugated sheets, which will overhang about 6 inches at the eaves (FIG. 5-50A). Arrange them to meet on the ridge, and add a ridge piece nailed through to the top purlins (FIG. 5-50B). You could use shorter sheets with an overlapping joint on the intermediate purlins.

In heavy rain, this is a sufficient roof area to shed a lot of water and you may wish to provide gutters and downpipes to collect the water or disperse it to a drain. Gutter brackets can be screwed over framing uprights (FIG. 5-50C).

If appearance is not very important, you could let the roof sheets project a

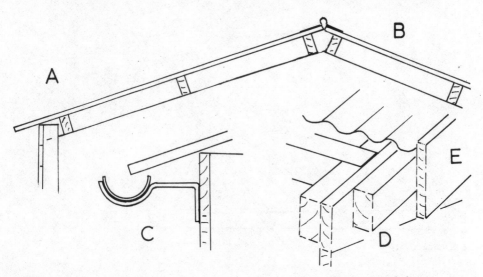

Fig. 5-50. *Roof covering and gutter arrangements for the wide-door workshop.*

few inches over back and front of the building without further covering. This would be functional, but the edge would be better protected and have a more pleasing appearance with bargeboards.

Put 2-inch-×-4-inch pieces along the rafter lines of each end (FIG. 5-50D). Fit the corrugated sheets to the edge of this strip. Arrange bargeboards to project above and below (FIG. 5-50E). Leave them plain, or decorate the ends and add a finial at the apex.

If you are insulating the building, it will be best to protect the wood inside with preservative before fixing a plywood lining. Paint outside to match surroundings.

Site Shop

If you need to set up a small workshop in one place for a short time, then move it to another site, it has to be strong and easy to disassemble or re-erect. If you might have to leave it on-site unattended, possibly for days, it should be secure. Determined thieves will break into almost anything, but your small shop should resist casual pilferers or vandals.

There are practical limits of size if you are to transport the workshop parts on a truck of moderate size. This site shop (FIG. 5-51) is designed to use two uncut 4-foot-×-8-foot sheets of plywood as roof. This gives a floor area of 78 inches by 84 inches. There is standing head room, and a sectional wooden floor braces the

Materials List for Site Shop

9 end uprights	2	×	2	×		96
4 end rails	2	×	2	×		78
1 end upright	2	×	2	×		24
4 end rafters	2	×	2	×		48
5 side uprights	2	×	2	×		80
3 side uprights	2	×	2	×		42
4 floor framing	2	×	2	×		80
10 floor framing	2	×	2	×		44
2 roof frames	2	×	3	×		84
2 roof frames	2	×	2	×		84
10 roof frames	2	×	2	×		48
2 roof edges	3/4	×	1 1/2	×		98
4 roof edges	3/4	×	1 1/2	×		50
2 shutter frames	1	×	2	×		30
3 shutter frames	1	×	2	×		26
2 window frames	1	×	3	×		32
2 window frames	1	×	3	×		28
2 door linings	1	×	3	×		80
1 door lining	1	×	3	×		32
2 door frames	2	×	2	×		76
4 door frames	2	×	2	×		30

All covering 3/4 exterior plywood

Fig. 5-51. If you need a shop on-site then want to move it, it can be a basic one, but it must also be easy to take down and re-erect.

assembly. One window is shown without glass but with a hinged shutter for security.

Construction is with ¾-inch exterior plywood, which is stronger and more resistant to anyone trying to break in, than any form of boarding. The framing behind it is mainly 2-inch-square strips. Parts are nailed, but it will be an advantage to use waterproof glue between the plywood and framing.

Make the four walls, and temporarily assemble them so the floor parts and roof can be fitted to match. Make the door end first and use this as a guide to sizes of some other parts. Suggested building sizes (FIG. 5-52) can be modified, but remember that they suit single sheets on the roof. Anything larger will complicate joints there and possibly create bigger wall sections to transport.

Mark out the door end (FIG. 5-53) on two sheets of plywood meeting vertically at the center of the end. Allow for the end wall coming inside the side wall plywood when assembled (FIG. 5-53A). You could cut joints between the framing parts, but there is considerable strength in the plywood, and it should be sufficient to merely butt framing parts to each other and secure them with glue and

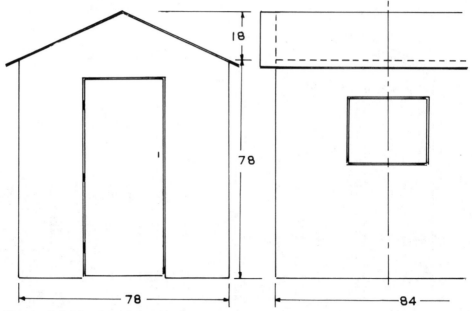

Fig. 5-52. Main sizes of the site shop.

nails. Cut the door opening, and glue and nail the sheets closely on the vertical strip above the doorway.

Make the opposite end to the same outline. Because there is no door, you can continue the framing both ways across (FIG. 5-53B). Drill the corner uprights of both ends for ³/₈-inch bolts at about 18-inch intervals. When you make the first assembly, use these holes as drill guides to make matching holes in the adjoining uprights.

When you make the front (FIG. 5-54A), allow for the plywood extending enough to cover the edges of the front and back assemblies (FIG. 5-53C). Arrange for the sheets to meet with a vertical joint over the central upright. Cut out and frame the window opening with uprights (FIG. 5-54B).

Make the height to match the end assemblies, but bevel the top rail to suit the roof angle (FIG. 5-54C).

Make the back in a similar way, but leave out the window uprights and continue the central upright/joint cover all the way (FIG. 5-54D).

Assemble the four walls temporarily on a level surface, and check squareness. Cut plywood floor panels to meet centrally across the shop (FIG. 5-54E). Arrange them to rest on the bottom rails of the walls. Notch them to fit at corners. Don't aim for a precise fit, or you could have difficulty when assembling on some sites. Clearances should be between ¹/₄ inch and ¹/₂ inch.

Put sufficient framing below the floor sections to resist bending under expected loads. Frame to fit easily inside the wall rails (FIG. 5-54F) and at the meeting edges, then put others across (FIG. 5-54G).

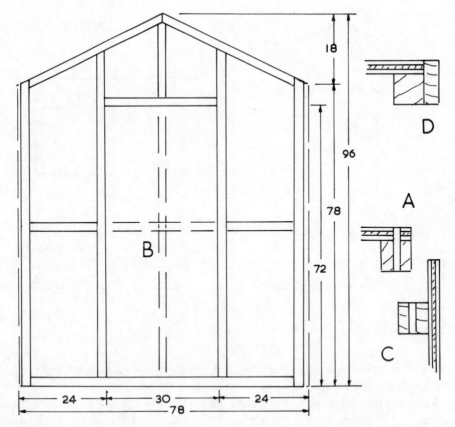

Fig. 5-53. Details of ends of the site shop.

With the floor holding the building in shape, try roof panels in turn. Allow for the plywood meeting closely along the ridge and with even overhangs at the edges (FIG. 5-55A). Frame the outer edges with strips to provide stiffness and fastening places for turned-in roof covering (FIG. 5-55B). Make other framing to provide stiffness and to locate the roof panel by fitting loosely inside the walls. The strips (FIG. 5-55C) need not meet closely at corners. For stiffness along the otherwise unsupported ridge, use 2-inch-×-3-inch wood, beveled to suit (FIG. 5-55D).

When the two roof sections are put in position, they should rest against each other along the ridge, and the locating strips inside should hold them in place, with not more than 1/2-inch tolerance. You could paint the roof sections, but it would be better to cover them individually with tarred felt or other material. Turn it in and nail it all around. When you assemble on site, drive screws at about 12-inch intervals downwards into the walls, using washers under the screw heads for waterproofness and easy withdrawal. Seal the ridge with a 6-inch-wide strip of covering material tacked on. That will have to be scrapped when you disassemble.

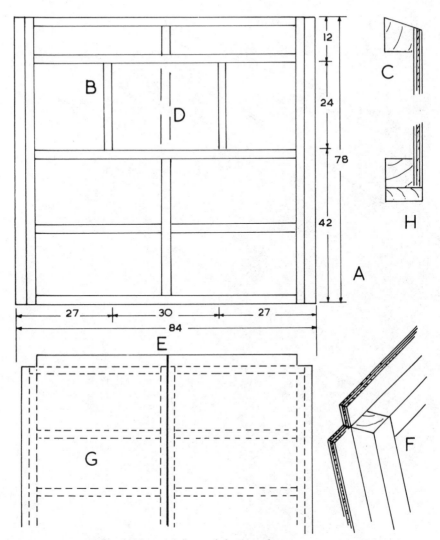

Fig. 5-54. Details of sides and floor of the site shop.

Line the edges of the window opening (FIG. 5-54H) all around. Make the shutter to fit easily in the opening (FIG. 5-56A) with plywood edged with 1-inch-×-2-inch strips. Hinge the shutter at the lower edge (FIG. 5-56B). Put stop strips on the sides of the opening, and arrange a catch at the top center inside.

Line the door opening (FIG. 5-53D) at sides and top. Make the door (FIG. 5-56C) of plywood framed with strips. Use three 4-inch butt hinges at one side and a lock at the other side. For compactness in packing for transport, you might omit a handle and rely only on a key for pulling the door open. Put a stop strip inside the frame.

Paint the walls, but it would be better to use preservative on the floor.

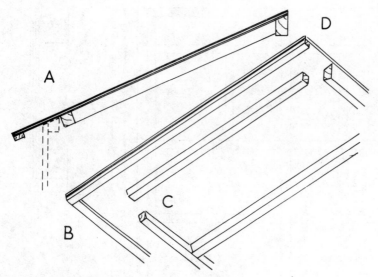

Fig. 5-55. Details of the roof on the site shop.

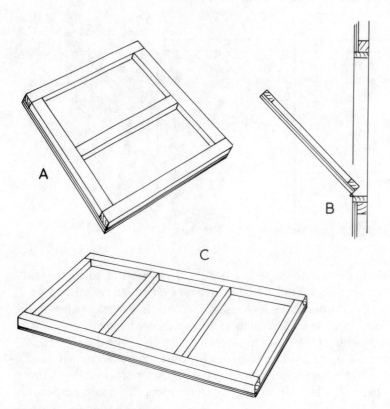

Fig. 5-56. Shutter and door for the site shop.

Shop with Inside Storage

If you do much woodworking or large-scale metalworking, you will accumulate materials that have to be stored. It is always worthwhile to obtain wood in advance of its use so it will season and stabilize before you start work on it. There is also an advantage in buying lumber in bulk: Besides allowing you to select wood from your stock for particular purposes, it should be cheaper. Quite often wood has to be stored outside the workshop or in some other place. If you build your own shop, you can arrange for wood or metal to be stored inside the building without interfering with work space.

This workshop (FIG. 5-57) covers a floor area of 12 feet × 15 feet. This is arranged with 10 feet × 12 feet as work space and 5 feet × 12 feet as storage. If you do not need that much storage you can extend your work into part of the storage area, as there is no division between the parts. In effect, this is a building 10 feet wide, with a further 5 feet arranged by extending the roof. There is ample head room in the main part, and the storage part has standing head room except quite close to the rear wall.

The design is capable of many adaptions to suit needs, but the building is shown with fixed windows in both ends and an opening window and the main door in the front (FIG. 5-58). At both ends of the storage part there are doors for passing through long lengths of wood, metal, or other material. You could make one end without windows or doors. The main door could be moved to one end.

Fig. 5-57. This large workshop has storage space as well as ample working area.

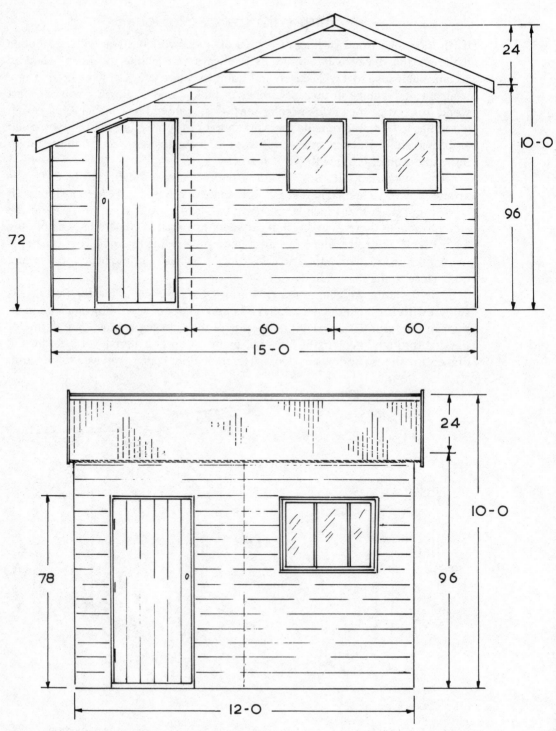

Fig. 5-58. Main sizes for a shop with inside storage.

Ends

8 uprights	2	× 4	×	120
8 uprights	2	× 4	×	96
2 rails	2	× 4	×	182
4 rails	2	× 4	×	120
14 strips	2	× 4	×	42
2 rafters	2	× 4	×	72
2 rafters	2	× 4	×	136

Front

4 uprights	2	× 4	×	98
8 rails	2	× 4	×	70
8 strips	2	× 4	×	48

Back

8 uprights	2	× 4	×	74
8 rails	2	× 4	×	70

Truss

1 rafter	2	× 4	×	72
1 rafter	2	× 4	×	136
1 strut	2	× 4	×	24
2 ties	1	× 4	×	120

Doors

6 ledgers	1	× 6	×	39
4 braces	1	× 6	×	48
12 boards	1	× 6	×	80

Roof

8 purlins	2	× 4	×	150
2 wind bracings	1	× 4	×	150
2 wind bracings	1	× 4	×	90

Trim

4 door edges	1	× 6	×	80
2 door edges	1	× 6	×	40
2 door stops	1	× 1	×	80
16 fixed window fillets	1	× 3	×	32
16 fixed window fillets	1	× 3	×	26
1 window hinge rail	1	× 5	×	44
2 window stops	1	× 1 1/2	×	44
2 window stops	1	× 1 1/2	×	32
4 window frames	1 1/2	× 1 1/2	×	32
1 window frame	1 1/2	× 1 1/2	×	44
1 window frame	1 1/2	× 3	×	44
6 window edges	1	× 6	×	34
4 window edges	1	× 6	×	28
2 window edges	1	× 6	×	46
Cladding	1	× 6 shiplap boards or similar		
Floor framing	2	× 2 3/4 plywood		
Floor covering		or particleboard		

There could be more or fewer windows. Overall sizes can be altered, but as drawn, the slopes of both sides of the roof are at the same angle. For the sake of a balanced appearance, the tops of all windows and doors are shown at the same level.

Construction is mostly with 2-inch-×-4-inch wood covered with shiplap boards. The roof is covered with galvanized corrugated iron sheeting. Instructions are for an unlined building, but you could line the walls and roof with plywood and fill cavities with insulation material.

Most of the work will have to be done on-site. The two ends are too large to be prefabricated elsewhere and transported easily. Front and back sections and the roof truss could be made elsewhere (at least partially), but you will need to refer to the ends for some sizes and angles. Prepare a concrete base larger than the building, and lay out the main lines on that.

Make the pair of ends first (FIG. 5-59A). It is assumed they will be a pair, but you might want to alter framing and cladding layout on one or both to suit a closed end or repositioned door. Framing is 2-inch-×-4-inch wood, all with the 2-inch face towards the cladding, except the rafters and the strengthened post

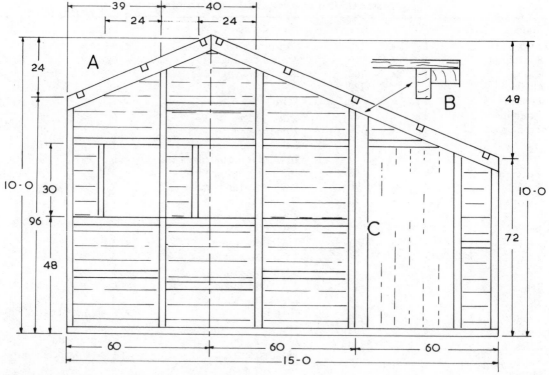

Fig. 5-59. An end wall for the shop with inside storage.

beside the storage door (FIG. 5-59B). When laying out an end, note that the 10-foot width from the front edge is the same as if it was a symmetrical building to eaves level, but the rear slope continues down to form the store.

It would probably be strong enough to nail framing parts together, but you will get a positive location and a resistance to movement if you fit parts into shallow notches (FIG. 5-60A and B). You might prefer to halve the parts at corners (FIG. 5- 60C), and you will have to cut halving joints where parts cross (FIG. 5-60D).

Cut away uprights where they have to fit against rafters (FIG. 5-60E) so surfaces against the cladding are flush. Purlins will also fit into rafters with halving joints (FIG. 5-60F).

Make the door opening to suit your needs, but it is shown with the hinged side against the strengthened post and about 12 inches of wall beside it. You could swing the door the other way if that would better suit the situation. A small part of the door will have to be cut away to fit under the rafter.

Arrange for purlins to be fairly close at the apex, so a metal ridge covering piece over the sheets can be nailed to them. Have purlins close to where the top edges of the front and back sections will fit. The spacing of other purlins might have to be arranged to suit the lengths of available corrugated iron or plastic sheets. The front slope can be covered with single 6-foot sheets. With a central

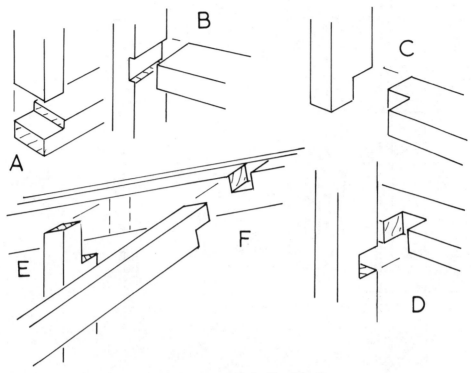

Fig. 5-60. Some joints used in the shop with inside storage.

purlin on the long rear slope, you can overlap two 6-foot sheets there. Position other purlins to give intermediate support. Cut notches in the rafters ready for the purlin ends.

Cover the end framing with shiplap or other boarding with all edges cut level, including around the window and door openings. Check that the outlines of the two ends match as a pair.

The front wall is made in two parts bolted together at the center. The bolted uprights provide extra strength under the central roof truss. The outlines of these wall sections form a pair (FIGS. 5-61 and 5-62). Where the walls meet the end assemblies at the corners, allow for the board covering extending over the joints (FIG. 5-62A) so the uprights there are set in. Where the wall sections meet, there has to be a recess at the top to take the end of the roof truss (FIG. 5-62B and C). The space left at the top between the bolted sections should suit the thickness of the truss rafter. As drawn, the door opening is 36 inches wide and the window width is 42 inches. This is the stage where you can modify these sizes, if you wish.

Check that the height of the wall sections matches the adjoining parts of the end walls. Join the framing parts in the ways suggested for the end walls (FIG. 5-60). Cover the framing with similar boarding to that on the end walls. Let the boarding extend enough to cover the corner joint. Where the two sections will

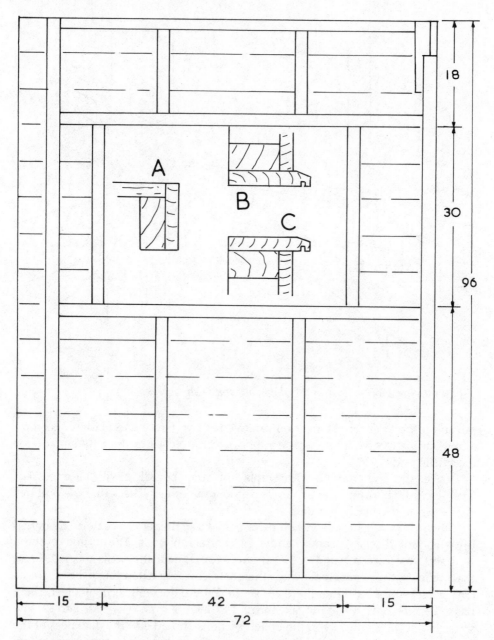

Fig. 5-61. A front wall section for the shop with inside storage.

meet, cut the boards level with the upright and continue this line to cover the truss recess. Trim level around door and window openings.

Make the back wall in two matching sections (FIG. 5-63A) in a similar way to the front wall. Check height against the end walls. Allow for a similar overlap of

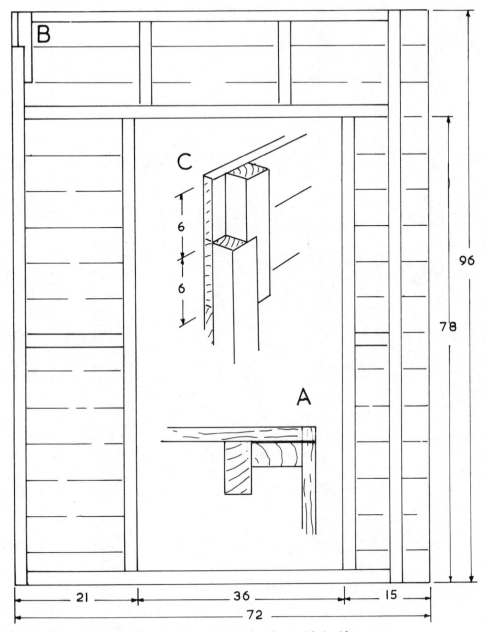

Fig. 5-62. A wall section with doorway for the shop with inside storage.

cladding at the corners and make a recess for the truss rafter at the top of the meeting uprights.

You could put windows in the rear wall if that would suit your needs, but, as a material store, it might be better to have full boarding.

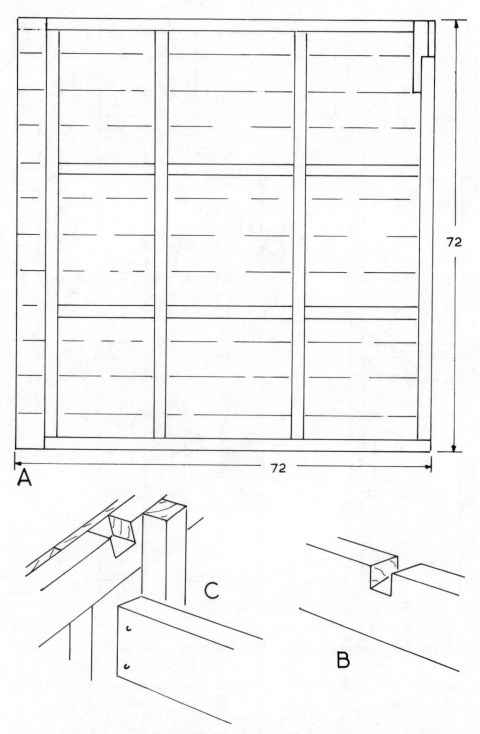

Fig. 5-63. *Wall section and inside constructional details for the shop with inside storage.*

Although the building will be assembled as a permanent structure and nails could be used in many joints, it is advisable to use bolts between the pairs of front and back sections of walls. Drill the meeting uprights for 3/8-inch or 1/2-inch bolts at about 18-inch intervals.

The roof on its purlins will be supported centrally by a roof truss. It is important that this matches the slopes of the ends and is at the same height. Use one of the ends as a pattern for laying out the truss (FIG. 5-64A). The rafters come below the purlins.

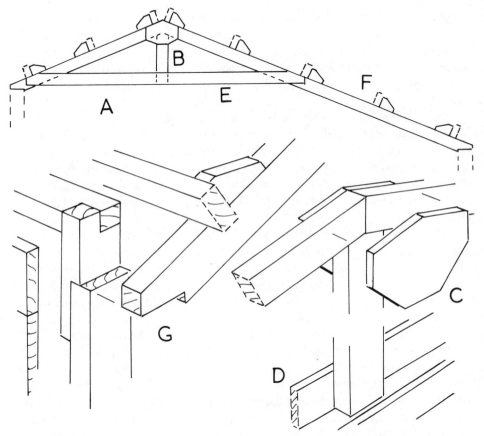

Fig. 5-64. Roof truss shape and details for the shop with inside storage.

Arrange a strut (FIG. 5-64B) under the apex and cover the meeting with joint covers both sides (FIG. 5-64C). Put ties across (FIG. 5-64D and E). There could be considerable strain on the joints between the ties and the rafters, and bolts through would be preferable, even if you use nails elsewhere on the truss. Position cleats on the tops of the rafters (FIG. 5-64F) to match the purlin positions on the end walls.

It will be advisable to delay cutting the notches at the ends of the rafters until the building is being assembled. The truss rafter has to fit between the bolted wall sections (FIG. 5-62C), and the roof line must just clear the top edge of the wall. Cut the notch during assembly to get this result (FIG. 5-64G).

With all wall sections and the truss made, you are now ready to assemble the main parts of the building. Prepare lower edges of the walls for fastening down to the concrete base. Have square lines marked out. Bolt front and back wall sections together. Nail, screw, or bolt corner uprights together. Fasten down to the concrete. Fit the truss. This should pull all parts into place. Check overall squareness at eaves level. Notch the purlins into the end rafters and nail them to the truss cleats.

In most situations, there will be enough rigidity in the building to resist winds, but if it will stand in an exposed place, you might want to add wind bracing in the roof. This could be strips of 1-inch-$\times$-4-inch-section wood nailed diagonally under the purlins (FIG. 5-65A). If you line the roof with plywood, that should provide ample resistance to distortion under wind pressure, without the addition of bracing.

It is possible the long slope of the roof might develop a sag after some time. Much depends on the stiffness of the truss rafter. If you have any doubts about stiffness, fit a supporting beam during construction. It goes between the strengthened posts in the ends (FIG. 5-59C) and is notched to take the truss rafter at its center. Use wood 2-inch-$\times$-6-inch section cut to fit between the end posts. Notch it to fit under the truss (FIG. 5-63B). Bolt to the extending part of the post (FIG. 5- 63C).

Roof covering with corrugated sheets can be arranged in a similar way to that of the wide-door workshop. Bring the sheets close at the ridge so a cover piece can be nailed through to the purlins (FIG. 5-50B). For neat ends, put strips down the slopes outside the boarding (FIG. 5-50D) and continue the sheeting over them. Cover the ends with bargeboards (FIG. 5-50E). It will be advisable to provide guttering at back and front, with supports over the framing (FIG. 5-50C).

You will probably want a wooden floor. This could be solid boards or sheets of particleboard or plywood, at least 3/4 inch thick. Arrange a pattern of 2-inch-square strips of wood over the concrete, preferably using wood treated with preservative. Spacing depends on the use of the shop, but for heavy use, spaces should not be much more than 12 inches across (FIG. 5-65B). Arrange the covering to overlap the insides of the wall framing, and notch around corners (FIG. 5-65C). At doors there should be solid-wood protection (FIG. 5-65D). An entry step could also protect the edge of particleboard or plywood (FIG. 5-65E). If you intend to line or insulate the building, do that at this stage.

Edge door openings with solid wood (FIG. 5-61A) at sides and top. Arrange this to cover any lining material. Front edges could be level with the cladding or project about 1/4 inch, but do not let this extend very far, as it would limit the swing of a door.

Window openings are better edged so the wood projects (FIG. 5-61B and C). Treat top and bottom in this way, but the side linings could be level with the cladding or only project slightly. Grooves plowed in the undersides of the top and

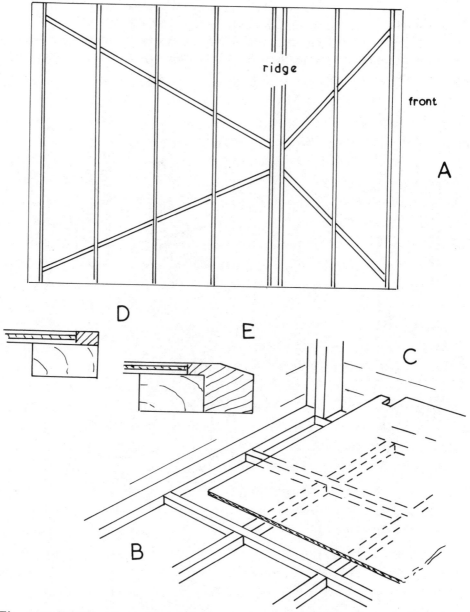

Fig. 5-65. *Purlin and wind bracing arrangements. Flooring details for the shop with inside storage.*

bottom pieces prevent rainwater creeping back underneath. Sloping the top surfaces encourages water to run off.

You could make fixed windows or arrange some to open. In this design, it is suggested that the windows in the ends are fixed and the front window is hinged along its top edge. It can be opened a short way for ventilation or swung out of the way if you need to pass work through.

For a fixed window, you can arrange the glass between fillets (FIG. 5-66A). Alternatively, you could frame the glass in the same way as for an opening window, but screw it in place.

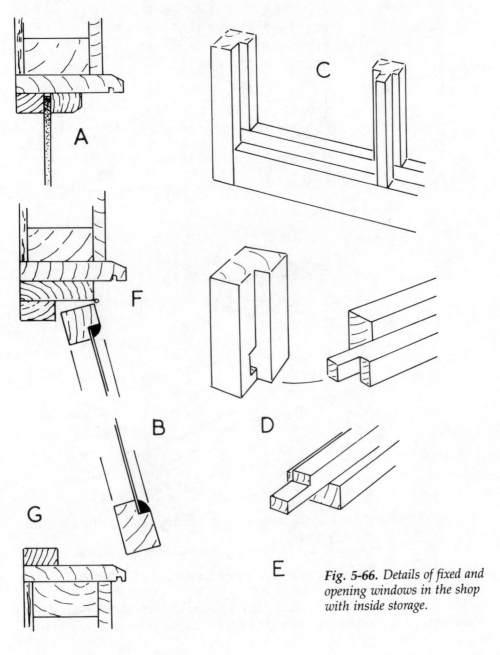

Fig. 5-66. *Details of fixed and opening windows in the shop with inside storage.*

For an opening window the glass has to fit into a rabbeted frame. You might be able to buy window molding that includes decorated edges, but for a workshop you can plow rabbets in plain wood. The frame could be the same size all around, or you could use a wider piece across the bottom (FIG. 5-66B). Although it would be possible to glaze the window with a single sheet of glass, it would be better to divide the window vertically into two or three panes, with strips rabbeted both sides (FIG. 5- 66C). Use mortise-and-tenon joints in the window frame (FIG. 5-66D and E). You might arrange dowels, but tenons would be stronger. Fit the glass with a few pins and putty.

Arrange a strip across to take the hinges (FIG. 5-66F), and put strips all around inside as stops and draft excluders (FIG. 5-66G). A bought metal strut will allow you to adjust the amount of opening.

The doors could be covered with vertical tongue-and-groove or plain boards, ledged and braced inside. The amount you cut off the corner of the storage door is not much, but check the opening and arrange the top ledger below it (FIG. 5-67A). Use butt hinges on both doors. Cut back the ledgers on the opening side to clear a stop strip (FIG. 5-67B). A 4-inch hinge at each ledger position should be satisfactory. Locks with keyholes outside will be best at the other edges. Put stop strips inside the frames and add handles to the doors. If there are steps to the doorways, cut the doors with enough clearance, but otherwise let the doors close against the bottom crossbar.

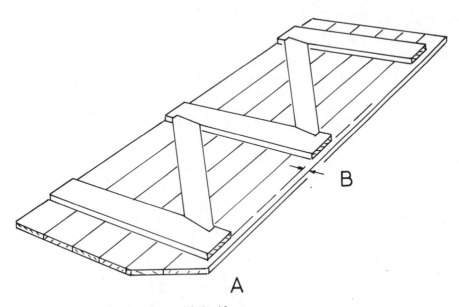

Fig. 5-67. Door for the shop with inside storage.

6

Decorative Structures

Some small buildings might have practical uses but are mainly intended to be decorative features in a yard, garden, or park. In some cases, it is the foliage growing on or around them that forms the main decoration. The building might be as much a support for climbing trees, creepers, vines, and other foliage as it is a practical building for storage or just sitting in. Sometimes what you build is enveloped by natural growth, for which its only function is to provide support. Of course, many functional buildings are decorative in themselves and, even when they are plain, the foliage covering them and around them can provide charm to the general scene. Plants and flowers in pots and boxes can add decoration to what is otherwise a rather austere building.

A decorative building might be a complete structure with walls, door, and roof, particularly if you intend to use it as a storage place. You can build other decorative buildings without a door and/or even without some or all of the walls and roof. In that case, the woodwork might be there mainly to support trees or bushes chosen for their ability to form a close covering of tightly packed branches, twigs, leaves, and flowers. What you build is a skeleton on which the growing things fill in to just be decorative or to make a natural wall and roof.

Many names are used for these structures—pergola, gazebo, arbor, summerhouse, or sun shelter. It is important to remember that if the structure is mainly there to support foliage, it might become engulfed with branches and foliage in years to come, so it has to be durable. Replacement or repairs might be impossible without wrecking the years of growth that it has to support. Use a wood with a good resistance to rot, or a wood that is thoroughly impregnated with preservative, which will not have an adverse effect on anything growing near it.

Pergola

One of the simplest structures to erect is a framework for roses or other plants to climb and cover. Such a framework on posts is called a *pergola* if the assembly is more than a single-line screen. Parallel posts might be alongside a path, and you could include an arch. The framework on top allows the climbers to spread and make a roof of foliage, providing an attractive arrangement, shelter from the sun, and an impenetrable shelter from rain. Besides making a floral cover over a path, a pergola can act as a shelter for seats and would make a good division in a garden, possibly between the vegetable plot and a flower and grass arrangement.

As shown in FIG. 6-1, the pergola is arranged with parallel posts, with a bay on each side of a raised part that can form an arch over a walkway. In the other direction, there could be a narrow path, or the area could be taken up by the plants that produce the foliage. This design is offered as a specimen of a pergola, but you could modify the layout to suit your available space or to suit a particular garden or yard layout. It might take a few years for the foliage on a pergola to

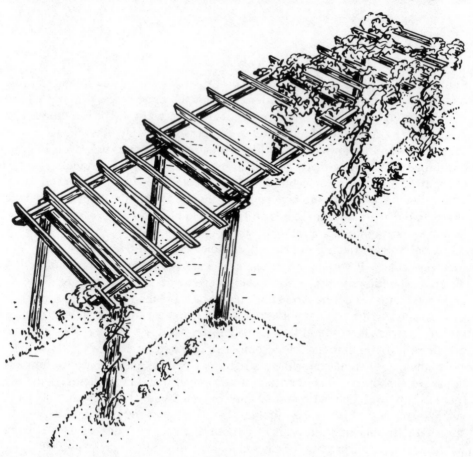

Fig. 6-1. A pergola supports foliage, so that it grows to form a roof.

reach perfection, and you need to visualize how it will look in relation to other features. It is quite large and will form a background to a large floral display, or it might form a screen for a less attractive part of the view. It might also serve as a windbreak when the foliage is in leaf and bloom. In the winter, however, it will be more of a skeleton through which wind might blow with little hindrance, although its appearance still can be regarded as attractive.

Because of its size and the effects of wind, as well as the dead weight of what is growing on it, you should build a strong pergola. Parts cross squarely. It would be unusual to include wind bracing. Secure mounting of the posts, and use strong joints to provide adequate stiffness. As with other buildings, squareness is important. The ground probably will not be level. It would be a mistake to use the ground as a datum, as parts that are not vertical or horizontal will be very obvious to an observer, especially if you can see parts at different angles. Check levels and plumbs throughout the assembly. See that posts are upright from every viewpoint. Check the levels of horizontal parts, not only with a level, but also by sighting across. When you have one piece known to be level, sight across the other parts and see that they are parallel.

Materials List for Pergola

8 posts	4 × 4 ×	78
4 bearers	4 × 4 ×	86
2 beams	4 × 4 ×	94
4 beams	4 × 4 ×	114
4 packings	4 × 4 ×	18
15 tops	2 × 3 ×	98

If the ground is not level in different areas under the pergola, it might be advisable to bring it nearer level before starting to build. A difference of 6 inches or so between one end and the other might not matter, but if you are faced with more of an incline, a large difference in height of the pergola between one end and the other will not look right if you attempt to keep the top level. In that situation, it might be possible to get an attractive effect by taking the top up in steps.

The most vital parts of the pergola are the posts. You can mount a durable wood or other wood impregnated with preservative in the ground, but rot still might occur eventually. It would be better to keep the wood above the ground by bolting it to concrete spurs you have buried a suitable amount.

It might be possible to buy suitable concrete spurs, but they are not difficult to make. The section of spurs should be about the same as the posts. Length will depend on the soil. Sandy soil will need longer posts than clay. Allow for about 18 inches above the ground. The example shown in FIG. 6-2A has 15 inches below ground. In most ground, it should be sufficient to compact dirt around the spur, but in very soft ground, you might have to put more concrete under and around the spurs before covering them with dirt.

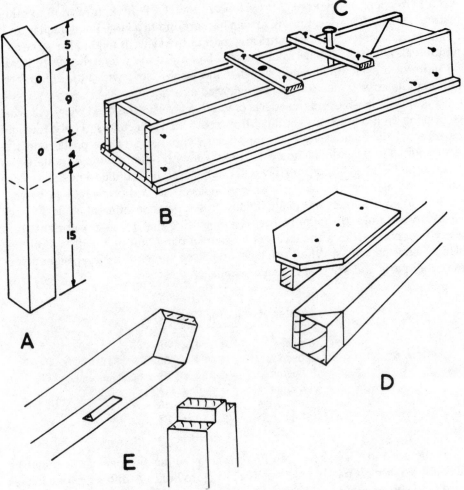

Fig. 6-2. *Casting a concrete post spur (A,B,C) and woodwork details (D,E).*

A suitable mold for making a spur is a three-sided box with nails only partly driven. A block at one end makes the tapered top (FIG. 6-2B). Allow for two bolts to hold the wood. To make the holes in the concrete, place ¹/₂-inch bolts wrapped with Scotch tape into the wet cement (FIG. 6-2C), then you can knock them out after the concrete has set. Coat the inside of the box with oil or liquid detergent to prevent the wood from sticking to the concrete.

Use a sand and cement mix. If you include stones, they should be very small. After half-filling the box, lay in two ¹/₄-inch or ³/₈-inch steel rods as reinforcements. Fill the box and tamp down the concrete to remove air bubbles, then trowel the top surface level. Leave to set, then remove the nails and loosen the wood so the spur can be put aside to harden. Put the box back together to make the next spur.

When you bolt the posts to the spurs, make sure the bottom of the wood is a short distance above the ground. In subsequent gardening, be careful to avoid building up soil around the posts. Something should be between the wood and the concrete to insulate the wood from moisture. This insulation could be a liberal coating of a waterproof mastic or some sheet plastic, such as polyethylene. Use coach bolts with their heads at the wood side. Grease them before driving them. Do not fully tighten until after erection, in case you must make slight adjustments if the spurs do not finish quite plumb.

Bevel the ends of all the top members. It does not matter what the exact angle is, although 45 degrees looks right. All angles, however, ought to be the same size. Do not cut to a feather edge, but finish with a small amount left square. A simple template will help in marking ends the same (FIG. 6-2D).

The pergola is based on pairs of posts that you join to a cross member. Start from an end, or the center if that is more convenient, and truly mount one of these assemblies. Measure further assemblies from this datum, which you will use to check if they are square and true. Posts and cross members should be 4 inches square.

Ensure correct location of the parts meeting by using stub tenons (FIG. 6-2E). Obviously, spacing at the top must be the same as at ground level. Nail a temporary batten across, near the ground level to maintain the correct distance there. To check that the cross member will be level, put a temporary strip and a level across the shoulders, below the tenons. If necessary, recut shoulders or adjust the amount of spur let into the ground. Sizes of the example are shown in FIG. 6-3A. The stub tenons are there for location and provisional assembly. You will strengthen the joints with rods later.

Erect the next assembly in the same way. Check that the tops are not only level across, but level with each other when you test them with a temporary, lengthwise piece and a level. Make two long pieces. It will be helpful in assembly if you give these pieces shallow notches to hook over the cross members (FIG. 6-3B).

Drill at the center of each joint so you can drive a steel rod to be used as a dowel down into the post (FIG. 6-3C). This hole could be $1/2$ inch in diameter, but if you have the equipment to make larger holes, $5/8$-inch or $3/4$-inch holes would be better. Taper the end of the rod so it drives smoothly. The rod should not fit tightly or the wood might split. A dry joint should be satisfactory, but you could put epoxy glue in the hole, especially if the rod does not fit tightly.

Make the other side in the same way. If you want the assembly to be straight, check alignment with a string stretched along the foundation line. You could follow a moderately curving path, if you wish, by making one side shorter than the other, but in the example, it is assumed the assembly will be straight.

For the central arch, make packing pieces (FIG. 6-3D), then put lengthwise pieces above them, and join the parts with more rod joints.

What you do at the top depends on what you want to grow over the framing. You might need fairly close cross pieces for some foliage. It even might be advis-

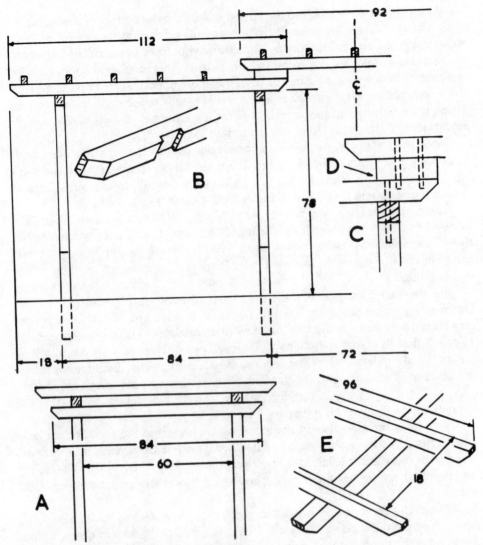

Fig. 6-3. Suggested sizes for pergola parts.

able to use wire netting on a light frame. The best-looking pergola has an arrangement of cross pieces, evenly spaced and projecting to the sides with matching ends. This arrangement is suitable for most roses, vines, and similar climbing plants.

In the example, 2-inch- × -3-inch-section strips are laid across (FIG. 6-3E) and held with long nails. Place one of these pieces near each end and space the others fairly evenly between them.

If you wish to treat the entire wood with preservative or paint, choose material that does not affect plant life. It is advisable to only treat in this way well in advance of the time you expect anything to climb up and over the pergola, so any solvents dry out. As plants start climbing, you might have to tie them on or provide strips of projecting wood for them to grip, then remove them after the plants have grown higher.

Summerhouse

You can use a building with a sheltered porch for sunbathing or sitting out in chairs even when the weather is not perfect, since the structure provides shelter from wind and rain. It can provide a peaceful retreat for anyone who wants to get away from activities inside the house. It might be a place for studying. It could be a play center for children, although it is not primarily a playhouse. The enclosed part of the building will provide full shelter when you need it, and it makes a place to store chairs, tables, games, equipment, or gardening tools.

The summerhouse shown in FIG. 6-4 has a base that is 9 feet square, divided in half by a partition with a door and windows (FIG. 6-5). The upper part is open, with sheltering lower sides and a rail front. The door is arranged to lift off so you can put it inside, instead of it swinging and interfering with seating on the porch.

Fig. 6-4. This summerhouse has a sheltered porch and ample inside accommodations.

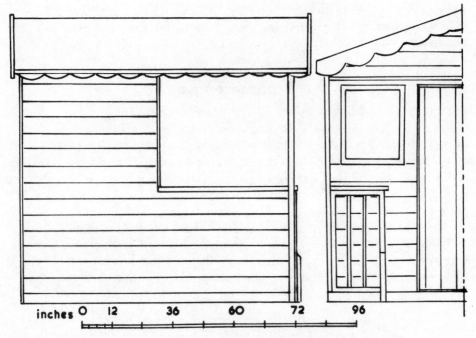

inches 0   12   36   60   72   96

Fig. 6-5. Two views of the summerhouse of the suggested size.

The exterior probably will look best with shiplap siding, and you could use that on the partition. You could, however, cover all the building or just the partition and door with plywood. The summerhouse is built on a floor, which forms part of the assembly.

Most of the framing can be 2-inch-square wood, although you could increase that to 2-inch- × -3-inch wood for greater strength. The roof is boarded, without separate purlins, and is covered in the usual way. Much of the decorative appearance comes from the bargeboards and matching eaves strips. The fence at the front has square uprights, but if you have the use of a lathe, they would look attractive if you made them as turned spindles with square ends.

Start with the floor, which should be 9 feet square. Use 1-inch boards and 2-inch- × -3-inch joists at about 18-inch centers (FIG. 6-6A). Close the joists' ends with strips across (FIG. 6-6B).

Make the building to fit the floor. Let the cladding overlap the floor—either just the top boards or to the bottoms of the joists. Use the floor as a guide to sizes when making the other parts.

Make the partition (FIG. 6-6C) and use it as a height guide when making other parts. It probably will be best to make the bottom part of the frame right across at first (FIG. 6-6D), then cut out the part for the doorway when you nail or screw the partition to the floor. Halve the frame parts or use open mortise-and-tenon joints. Make the frame width to fit inside the sides when they stand on the floor (FIG. 6-6E). The side cladding should go over the edge of the floor. At the apex,

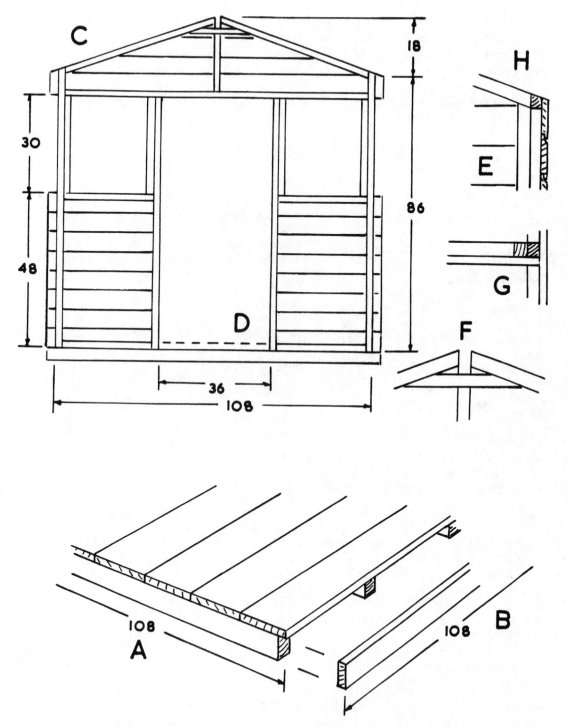

Fig. 6-6. The summerhouse floor (A,B), its front (C,D) and constructional details (E,F,G,H).

allow for a 2-inch-×-4-inch ridge to be slotted in (FIG. 6-6F), with a supporting rail underneath. Vary door and window sizes, if you wish.

When you have erected the building, the partition will fit between uprights on the side, with its covering overlapping, whether it is boards or plywood (FIG. 6-6G). Consequently, when you cover the partition, let the covering extend enough at the sides. At top and bottom, the covering should be level with the framing.

Materials List for Summerhouse

Floor

7 joists	2	× 3	×	110
14 boards	1	× 6	×	110
	or	equivalent		
2 ends	1	× 3	×	110

Partition and back

6 uprights	2	× 2	×	88
2 uprights	2	× 2	×	24
4 window uprights	2	× 2	×	32
5 rails	2	× 2	×	110
4 rails	2	× 2	×	36
4 tops	2	× 2	×	60

Sides

8 uprights	2	× 2	×	88
2 uprights	2	× 2	×	40
4 rails	2	× 2	×	110
2 top tails	2	× 2 or 3	×	120

Front

1 rail	2	× 2	×	110
2 rails	2	× 2	×	60
3 uprights	2	× 2	×	24
4 uprights	2	× 2	×	42
4 rails	2	× 2	×	28
4 posts	1¼	× 1¼	×	42
2 post supports	2	× 2	×	24
2 rail tops	1¼	× 3	×	28

Edge covers

2 side-edge tops	1¼	× 4	×	54
2 side uprights	1	× 4	×	70
2 window sides	1	× 7	×	30
2 window sides	1	× 5	×	30
2 corner fillers	1	× 1	×	88

Windows

8 surrounds	1	× 4	×	28
8 stops	1	× 1	×	28
8 frames	2	× 2	×	28

Door

6 boards	1	× 6	×	80
	or equivalent			
3 ledgers	1	× 6	×	36
2 braces	1	× 6	×	36
2 pegs	1½	× 1½	×	12

Roof

32 boards		× 6	×	60
	or equivalent			
2 battens	1	× 3	×	108
2 edges	2	× 1¼	×	120
4 ends	1¼	× 1¼	×	60
2 edge decorations	1	× 3	×	120
4 bargeboards	1	× 6	×	66
8 battens	¼	× 1	×	60

Cladding

1-×-6 shiplap boards or equivalent

Make the back of the building the same as the partition, except leave out the door and windows and extend cladding over the floor edge. This procedure means the framing could be the same as the partition, with the center and bottom rails right across. Cover in the same way as you did the partition, since there is a similar overlap at the corners, which you will cover with a filler strip between the meeting boards.

The pair of sides could have windows, but they are shown closed (FIG. 6-7A). Cladding is taken to the front edge, but you could arrange open rails similar to the front, if you wish. Cladding should be level with the frame all around, except you should allow for going over the floor edge and for going over the ends of the covering at the front of the partition. Cover pieces will be over this joint and along the top edge of the porch. Bevel the top edges of the sides to match the slope of the roof (FIG. 6-6H). The top part of the frame extends 6 inches at the front and 3 inches at the back to support the roof. This top part can also be 3

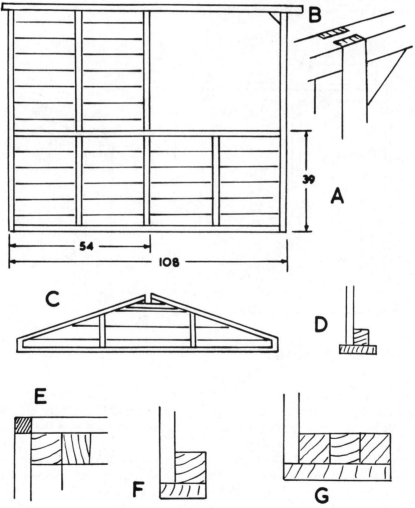

Fig. 6-7. *A side of the summerhouse (A,B), a roof truss (C), and assembly details (D,E,F,G).*

inches deep for extra stiffness, and you could build small angle brackets into the front, open corners (FIG. 6-7B).

Use the top part of the partition as a guide when making the front, which fits between the side uprights (FIG. 6-7C) where you will nail and screw it. Extend its cladding over the side uprights. Slot the apex to take the ridge piece. Make its bottom edge 5 inches below the eaves. Fit a covering piece over this edge (FIG. 6-7D) and around its edges.

The rails or fence at the front are shown extending 24 inches from the sides, but you can make them any other width. This width gives a good space for moving chairs and other things in and out, as well as for allowing several people to pass. Make two identical frames with strong corner joints. Use planed wood and take the sharpness off the exposed edges. Two uprights about $1^1/_2$ inches square should be enough intermediately (FIG. 6-8A).

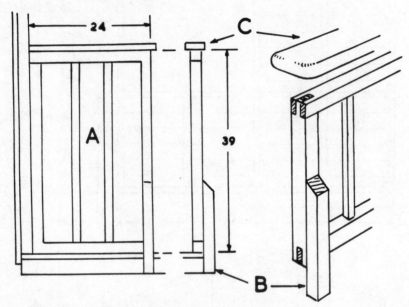

Fig. 6-8. Sizes and details of the fence at the front of the summerhouse.

You will mount this assembly on the edge of the floor and you should securely screw or bolt it to the floor and the side uprights. Arrange an overlapping piece to extend to the bottom of the floor (FIG. 6-8B) to stiffen the post at the open end of each piece.

Start erection of the building by bolting the two sides to the back and the partition—$3/_8$-inch coach bolts at about 24-inch intervals should be sufficient. Square this assembly on the floor, and nail the bottom edges down. Cut out the bottom piece across the doorway. Put square filler pieces in the rear corners (FIG. 6-7E). Cover exposed cladding edges at the partition and front (FIG. 6-7F). Put strips on each side of the window frames so they are the same thickness as the cladding (FIGS. 6-7G and 6-9A).

Fix the front rails and make an overlapping covering piece (FIG. 6-8C) with well rounded edges. It will look best if you fix it with counterbored screws and cover them with plugs.

The two windows are shown fixed, but you could arrange for them to open, either with hinges at the top or on the outer edges. They are protected from the

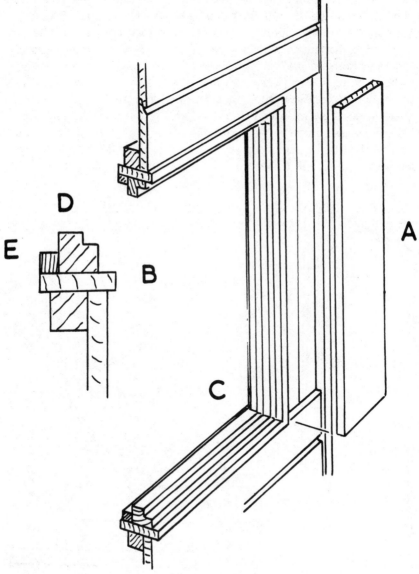

Fig. 6-9. Window construction for the summerhouse.

weather by the porch, so there is no need for a sill. Put strips all around the window openings (FIG. 6-9B), extending out a little, and rounding all exposed edges. Make the window frames to fit closely (FIG. 6-9C), using rabbeted strips (FIG. 6-9D). You could screw the strips directly in place, but it will probably be easier to make a good, weathertight fit with stop strips inside (FIG. 6-9E). Fit the glass with putty after you paint the woodwork.

Line the sides and top of the doorway in the same way as the window openings. Put stop pieces near the inner edges (FIG. 6-10A). Make the door (FIG. 6-10B) an easy fit in the opening. Have the edge of the bottom ledger about 2 inches from the bottom of the door. If the top ledger has only a small clearance below the top stop strip in the opening, you can fit a lock with a keyhole there or arrange a catch that turns with a knob. Place the other ledger centrally and arrange braces both ways.

At the bottom, fit two pegs to go into holes in the floor (FIG. 6-10C). Notch over the bottom ledger and taper the extending ends slightly (FIG. 6-10D). Glue and screw these a few inches in from the sides of the door. Mark holes in the floor where you can drop the pegs in while you angle the door forward so they hold it fairly close to the stop strips. When the top of the door is held with a lock or catch, the building will be secured.

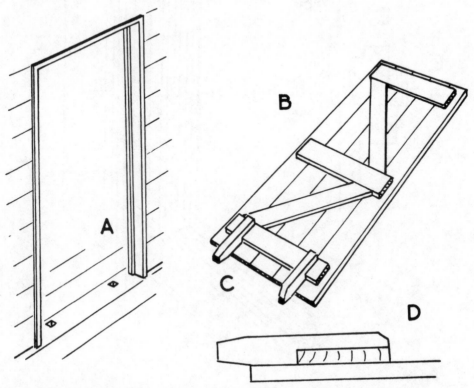

Fig. 6-10. The doorway and lift-out door for the summerhouse.

Fit the ridge to extend 6 inches at the front and 3 inches at the back. If necessary, trim the ends of the eaves strips to the same length (FIG. 6-11A,B). You can board the roof direct, using 1-inch-×-6-inch boards, preferably tongue-and-groove. If you use boards with plain edges, there can be a central batten (FIG. 6-11C) to prevent the boards from warping out of line. You do not need to fix the batten to the back or partition.

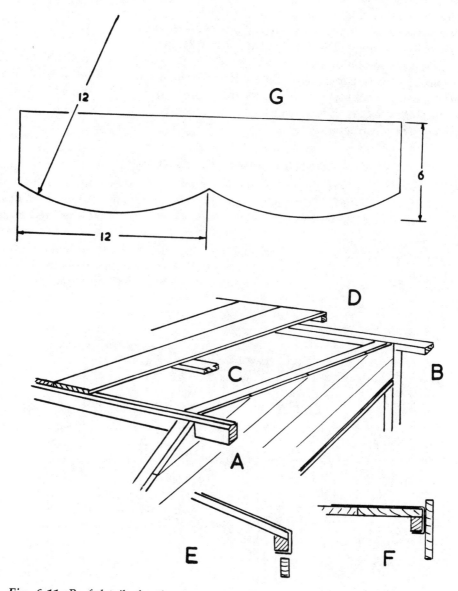

Fig. 6-11. *Roof details for the summerhouse (A,B,C,D,E,F) and a template for marking edge decorations.*

Nail the boards to the ridge and to the eaves, where they should extend about 4 inches (FIG. 6-11D). At the eaves, put a strip underneath, with its edge and the ends of the boards cut vertically, if you are adding the side decoration (FIG. 6-11E). Put similar square-edge strips down the end boards (FIG. 6-11F) to support the bargeboards.

Carry roof covering over from eaves to eaves and turn under for nailing. Turn under at the ends. Allow ample overlap where there are any joints, and make joints in the direction that will let water run away from them. You could add capping strips, but they probably will not be necessary on this small roof. Nail battens down the slope at each side at about 18-inch intervals.

If the decoration on the lower edges of the bargeboards and eaves boards is to look right, the curves should be uniform. Make a template of at least two curves, using scrap plywood or hardboard (FIG. 6-11G). Use this template to mark all the shaped edges and to check them after shaping. Nail the boards to the roof to complete construction.

Folding-door Sun Lounge

When the weather is bright and warm, you might wish to take the sun directly, but in cooler conditions, you might enjoy it better through glass. Even on a dull day, it might be pleasant to sit behind an expanse of glass while sheltered from the wind.

This sun lounge is a complete building (FIG. 6-12), but it is arranged so you can open most of the high side to give you shelter while letting the sun in. If all or some of the doors are closed, you are sheltered more, although the glass lets the sun shine through.

Fig. 6-12. The sun lounge has a front made of doors that fold back.

Of course, you might have uses for such a building if it does not face south, but if the main purpose is to let in the sun, you need to face it south where the sun's rays are not shaded by trees or buildings. Allow for the lower arc of the sun in winter, if you want to get the most from the sun lounge in cooler weather.

The building is large enough for several other uses. You could enjoy a hobby there. Children might use it as a play room. At a sports field or recreational area, you could use it for storage and for viewing events, or as a judge's enclosure. Spectators could find shelter inside while participants brave inclement weather or a passing storm. For year-round use, line the walls and insulate them. Double glazing would help, but if you plan to use the building after dark, heavy drapes would more than serve the same purpose as secondary glass.

As shown in FIG. 6-13, the building is 6 feet × 12 feet, and the doors and back wall are 6 feet 6 inches high. The four front doors are each 30 inches wide, so

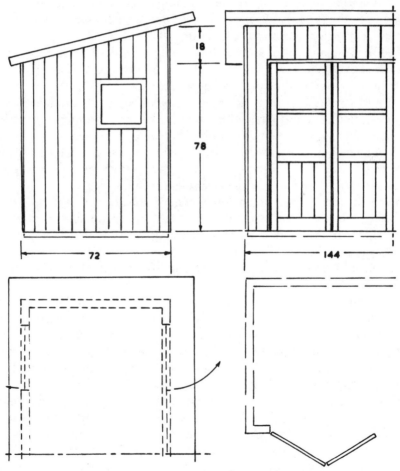

Fig. 6-13. Sizes and layout of the folding-door sun lounge.

they open to 10 feet. A single door is in the back, and there can be windows in the ends. It might be possible to buy suitable standard doors. If so, you might have to modify some dimensions to suit them. The making of the doors is included in the following instructions.

The drawings show a covering of vertical, tongue-and-groove boards, but you could use horizontal shiplap boards or sheets of plywood or other covering material. The framing suits upright boarding. If you use horizontal boarding, you might need more uprights for its support.

The roof is given a solid, square-edged appearance, and there are no barge-boards or fascias. Several roof coverings are possible. Treated felt or similar material could be laid over boards. It would be possible to use wood or composite shingles on boards or plywood. There is a solid-wood edging all around.

You could lay a wooden floor on joists over a concrete slab, arranging the structure so the walls stand on the floor and the sheathing continues over the floor. An alternative is to mount the building directly on concrete, stones or bricks, and fit the floor inside after erection. If you wish to make the floor first, follow the instructions used in earlier examples.

The following instructions are for fitting a floor inside the building. This type of floor is slightly shallower, which might be an advantage if you do not want much of a step up from the surrounding surface.

You might make the main structure of softwood, but a durable hardwood would be better for the doors, which have to be strong enough to withstand rough use. There would be a risk of broken glass if they were weak enough to flex when moved violently, possibly by the wind. If it is possible to get tongue-and-groove boards in the same wood, you would obtain an attractive effect by giving it a natural look with an oil or varnish finish.

You could erect the building before you make the doors, but as their sizes are important to the rest of the assembly, you might prefer to make them first, then you can allow for any slight differences in the doorway with less trouble than if you had to alter the sizes of the doors. The rear door, if fitted, can be almost identical to the others, or you can panel it fully with wood, instead of having the glass panels.

Prepare the parts for all the doors together, and cut and fit joints at the same time, so they finish identical. Use planed wood, which will be about $1/4$ inch under the nominal size, so 2-inch-$\times$-3-inch for the top and sides will actually be $1^3/4$-inch-$\times$-$2^3/4$-inch. Make the door with the lower part filled with tongue-and-groove boards (FIG. 6-14A). The glass panels have their bar slightly above halfway, which looks better than dividing the space equally (FIG. 6-14B).

Rabbets will have to be put in the upper parts for the glass and grooves in the lower part for the boarding. If the rabbets are made 1 inch wide (FIG. 6-14C), the tenons may be $1/2$ inch wide. You can continue this design into the lower part, where the grooves are $1/2$ inch wide (FIG. 6-14D), and the mortises and tenons will fit into them. Prepare the top of the door with a rabbet right through (FIG. 6-14E). Make the central-glazing bar with similar rabbets on both sides (FIG. 6-14F). The

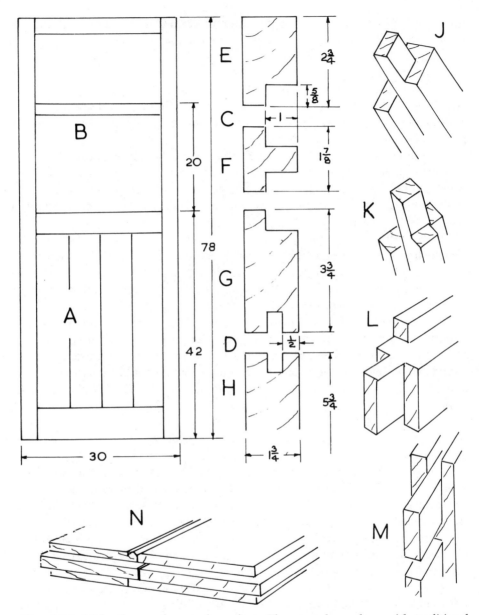

Fig. 6-14. *Make the sun-lounge doors first. They are shown here with traditional joints.*

bar between the glass and wood panels needs a rabbet on the top and a groove underneath (FIG. 6-14G). For the bottom of the door, cut a groove right across (FIG. 6-14H). Prepare the door sides in pairs with rabbets down to the dividing bar and grooves below that.

Have the door sides too long until after you have cut mortises and glued in the tenons. This procedure prevents the end grain from breaking out and protects the doors while they are handled, if the extensions are not cut off until you are about to fit the doors. Tenons need not go through the sides, but should be about 1^1/$_2$ inches deep.

Mark all the crosswise parts together, so they are the same length between shoulders. Cut back the tenon widths at the top so there is solid wood left in the sides, and set back the shoulders to suit the rabbets (FIG. 6-14J). Cut mortises in the sides to suit. Cut the glazing bar similarly (FIG. 6-14K).

At the center bar, cut the shoulders the same length and also the tenons between the bottoms of the rabbets and the bottoms of the grooves. Notch the back to fit over the rabbeted part of each side (FIG. 6-14L). At the bottom, cut back the tenon width in the same way as the top. Because of the depth, divide the tenon into two, with a ^{1}/$_2$-inch gap (FIG. 6-14M).

If you can get tongue-and-groove boards only ^{1}/$_2$ inch thick, they could go directly into the grooves, but the boards are more likely to be thicker than that. If so, cut down the edges to fit in the grooves (FIG. 6-14N). Do not force them too tightly in the width, as there should be a little allowance for expansion and contraction. Lengthwise, they should be a tight fit.

Be careful to check squareness as you assemble the doors. Check the shape of each door on those you previously assembled. See that they remain flat, as a twist in any door will affect the fit of the whole set. If you clamp tightly as you assemble and use a waterproof glue, the door joints should be strong, but you could drill through the centers of the tenons and glue ^{1}/$_2$-inch dowels though the joints.

Although you might not be painting or varnishing yet, you should apply putty over paint. It is worthwhile painting in the rabbets now, so it is dry when you start glazing.

The pair of sides are straightforward frames (FIG. 6-15A). Use 2-inch-×-3-inch wood with the 2-inch direction towards the skin. Corner joints might be any of the usual type, although open mortise-and-tenon joints (FIG. 6-15B) should make the strongest corners. If you will be covering with vertical boards, there is no need for intermediate uprights. If you will be using horizontal shiplap boards, continue the window upright nearer the center to the full depth. Check squareness and see that the opposite ends match.

Cover with upright tongue-and-groove boards, making them level with the edges all around. When you have erected the building, cover the meeting corners with a filler strip (FIG. 6-15C).

Trim the boards level with the frame around the window. At the top, fit a covering piece with a taper and groove to shed rainwater (FIG. 6-15D). At the bottom, arrange a similar piece (FIG. 6-15E). Notch both covering pieces and continue them a short distance over adjoining boards. Cover the vertical edges with narrower strips (FIG. 6-15F). Put stop pieces all around inside the frame (FIG. 6-15G).

Frame the back (FIG. 6-16A) with 2-inch-×-3-inch strips with their 2-inch face towards the skin, except for the top piece. Face the top piece the other way to

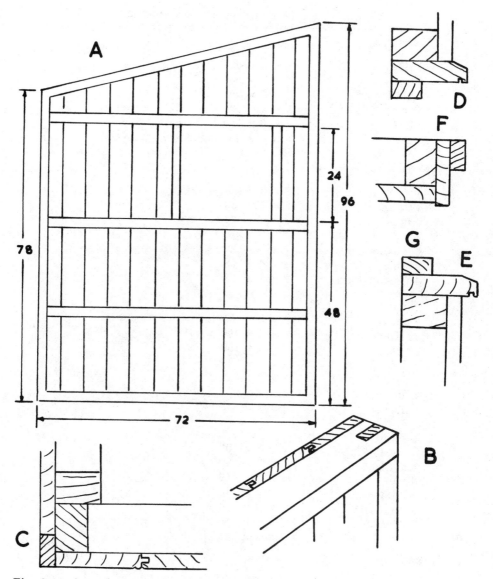

Fig. 6-15. A sun lounge end, with sections of edges and joints.

allow enough wood here and again at the front for the bevel to match the roof (FIG. 6-16B). Position the rear door, if you want one, in a position to suit your needs. It cannot be quite as high as the front doors.

When you cover the back, cut the boards level with the frame at top and bottom, but allow extra at the sides to overlap the ends (FIG. 6-15C). The overlap should be an amount that will allow you to fit a filler piece during erection. If you cover with horizontal-shiplap boards, include more uprights at 30-inch intervals or less. The length of back and front shown allows for fitting inside the ends to

Materials List for Folding-door Sun Lounge

Doors (five)

10 sides	2 × 3 × 80
5 tops	2 × 3 × 30
5 glazing bars	2 × 2 × 30
5 center rails	2 × 4 × 30
5 bottoms	2 × 6 × 30
20 panels	1 × 6 × 40 tongued-and-grooved

Ends

4 uprights	2 × 3 × 100
4 uprights	2 × 3 × 80
8 rails	2 × 3 × 74
2 tops	2 × 3 × 78
4 window sides	2 × 3 × 26
4 window linings	1 × 4 × 26
4 window frames	2 × 2 × 26

Back

5 uprights	2 × 3 × 80
2 rails	2 × 3 × 140
2 rails	2 × 3 × 100
2 door linings	1 × 4 × 78
1 door lining	1 × 4 × 32
2 door stops	1 × 2 × 78
1 door stop	1 × 2 × 32

Front

2 uprights	2 × 3 × 100
2 uprights	2 × 3 × 80
3 rails	2 × 3 × 140
1 upright	2 × 3 × 18
2 diagonals	2 × 3 × 74
2 door linings	1 × 4 × 80
1 door lining	1 × 4 × 122

Roof

10 rafters	2 × 4 × 96
2 rafter ends	2 × 4 × 168
6 spacers	2 × 4 × 12
2 edges	1 × 4 × 96
2 edges	1 × 4 × 168
16 boards	1 × 6 × 168 or plywood ½ to fit under

Floor

8 joists	2 × 2 × 72
12 boards	1 × 6 × 144 or equivalent
1 step	2 × 4 × 122

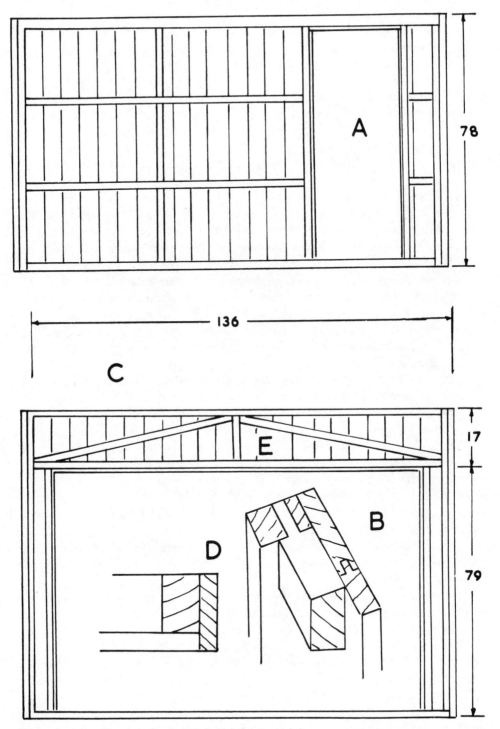

Fig. 6-16. Details of the back and front of the sun lounge.

give an overall length of 12 feet. You can increase this length, but do not shorten it if you are to include four front doors 30 inches wide. You must have some of the front boards on each side of the doorway to provide stiffness.

Make the front (FIG. 6-16C) in a similar way to the back, with a strip-on edge at the top, beveled to match the slope of the roof. Measure the doors together and allow for the cover pieces (FIG. 6-16D) at the sides and top when positioning the frame parts for the doorway. To keep the long, horizontal parts straight and to hold the frame in shape, join a short, central upright and two diagonal braces (FIG. 6-16E) to the other parts.

Cover the front in the same way as the back, with extending parts at the sides. Trim level with the doorway and cover the edges. Each side piece will have to take the weight of two doors on the hinges, so fasten the cover pieces with waterproof glue and screws. When you mount the doors, use screws in the hinges long enough to penetrate the wood behind the door frame. Fit stop pieces at top and sides that will hold the front surfaces of the doors level with the front surfaces of the wall.

Assemble the four walls together with 1/2-inch bolts at the corners about 18 inches apart. Check squareness by measuring and comparing diagonals. If necessary, put temporary diagonals across to hold the building square while you add the roof, which is based on 2-inch-×-4-inch rafters from front to back. The finished roof is intended to project 12 inches at the front, 6 inches at the back, and 9 inches at each side.

Fit the first two rafters over the ends of the building. Other rafters at about 24-inch intervals should be adequate (FIG. 6-17A). Join the ends of the rafters with pieces that project far enough to hold the rafters at the side overhang (FIG. 6-17B). Provide further support with short pieces between the end rafters (FIG. 6-17C).

You could cover the roof with thick plywood, but 6-inch boards are suggested (FIG. 6-17D). Shingles, plastic tiles, or any flexible covering materials could go over these boards. After covering, edge all around with strips (FIG. 6-17E). The strips at the front and sides could stand up slightly, but at the back, keep the top edge low, so it does not stop the runoff of water (FIG. 6-17F). You could mount a gutter there, leading to a downpipe.

Cover the undersides of the overhanging rafters. You could cover with boards, but it is probably easier to use 1/2-inch exterior plywood (FIG. 6-17G) fitted closely to the wall boarding.

The windows in the end might be fixed or opening, hinged at the top or side. You can putty glass for a fixed window directly into the stop strips, but it is better to make separate frames, as described for earlier buildings (FIG. 5-25).

If you wish to build in a wooden floor after you have erected the building and fastened it down to a concrete base, lay down joists the same height as the bottom parts of the wall frames (FIG. 6-18A) at about 18-inch intervals from front to back. You can attach them to the walls, but after you have laid the boards, they will hold in place. Lay these joists and the bottoms of the frames on plastic sheeting or be sure they are coated well with a waterproof mastic.

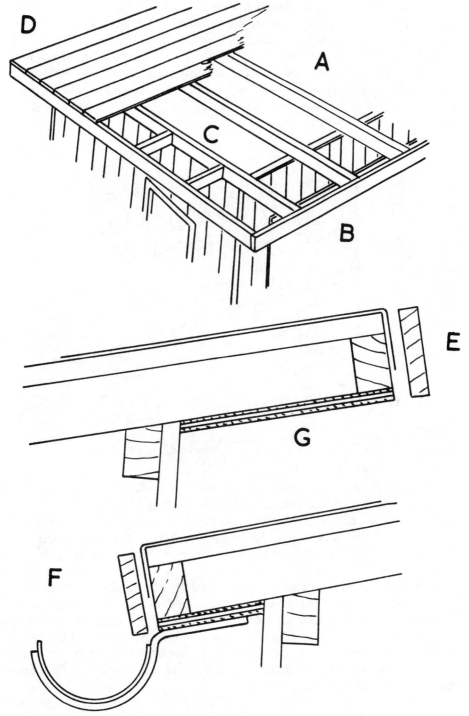

Fig. 6-17. Roof construction of the sun lounge.

Lay the floor boards lengthwise, going over the frame parts and cutting around uprights (FIG. 6-18B). You can make joints lengthwise over joists. At the front, the floor will act as a doorstop. Fit the floor boards there with their edge level with the stop pieces on the side (FIG. 6-18C). Fit a strip across in front of the bottom part of the frame, either level with the covering boards or projecting to form a step (FIG. 6-18D). Because this high-traffic area will have to take wear from feet, you might want to use hardwood. You also might want to put a hardwood lip on the front floorboard.

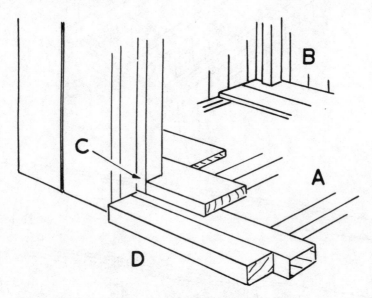

Fig. 6-18. *Details of the floor and front corner of the sun lounge.*

The doors close flat, but when opened, each center door swings in against its outer door. The two fold against each other and back against the wall (FIG. 6-19A). If they are to open this way, the knuckles of the outer door hinges must be clear of the surfaces (FIG. 6-19B), and the hinge knuckles of the inner doors must project inwards (FIG. 6-19C). Three 4-inch steel or brass hinges, placed in the sides of each door, should be suitable.

Each door should have a little top and side clearance and move freely above the strip at the bottom of the frame. To secure the doors, fit bolts at top and bottom of the edge of each door towards the center of the building, so they can go into holes in the surrounding wood. In this way, you can secure the front doors from the inside. After fastening them, you can leave by the back door. You do not need a fastener between the inner doors, and you do not need to fit handles since the doors are operated by pushing.

Fit the back door in a similar way, but provide it with a lock operable from either side and a knob or handle.

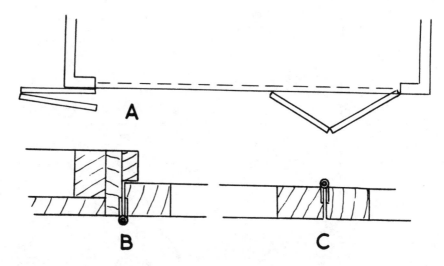

Fig. 6-19. How you fold and hinge the doors of the sun lounge.

Hexagonal Gazebo

Although most buildings have square corners, they can be other shapes. You might want to fit a building into an awkwardly shaped plot of ground. This requirement would need to be individually designed. Buildings might be made of special shapes for the sake of their appearance. A round building is difficult to make in wood, but a multi-sided one need not be much more difficult to construct than a square one. Making a building with an odd number of sides is an interesting geometric problem. An eight-sided building, not necessarily a regular octagon, involves angles of 45 degrees, but you will be dealing with twice as many sides as the more usual square-cornered building. If you have six sides, you will not need to make so many walls and roof sections. Some advantages exist in giving the building a regular hexagon as a floor plan. One advantage is the attractive appearance. Another is the ease with which you can set it out.

The sides of a regular hexagon are the same length as the radius of the circle on which you base it, so the lines from the corners to the center divide the area into equilateral triangles (FIG. 6-20A). As all the angles in an equilateral triangle are 60 degrees, this is convenient. You can set many saws and planers accurately to this angle.

To set out a large hexagon, make an improvised compass with a strip of wood, placing an awl through at half the distance you want the shape to be across the points (FIG. 6-20B). With a pencil against the end, draw a circle. Now move your "compass" so you can step off the radius around the circumference (FIG. 6-20C). Join the points you have marked to make your regular hexagon (FIG. 6-20D). You can make a hexagon using the size across the flats, but it is easier to work using the distance across the points.

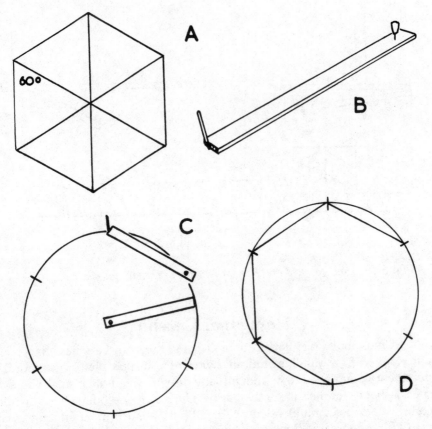

Fig. 6-20. The method of marking out a large hexagon.

The gazebo shown in FIGS. 6-21 and 6-22 is based on a hexagon that is 9 feet across the points. It is 7 feet from the floor to the eaves. One side has glazed double doors, the sides next to it have windows, and the other three sides are boarded solidly.

The covering is shown as tongue-and-groove boards laid diagonally. There could be horizontal shiplap boards or you could have tongue-and-groove boards vertically. A painted plywood skin might suit some locations. Shingles are suggested for the roof, but you can use other coverings.

To mark out the floor shape, put down sufficient floor boards with their undersides upwards. With an improvised compass, obtain the positions of the points and join them to get the hexagonal floor shape (FIG. 6-23A). It is convenient to have the floor boards parallel with two sides. On this floor shape, lay out the floor beams, which you might halve at the corners and other joints (FIG. 6-23B).

Assemble the beams together, then turn the floor over and nail down the floor boards. Trim the edges level. This design should make a strong, flat assembly on which you can base the building (FIG. 6-23C). If the building is to be

Fig. 6-21. *This hexagonal gazebo is 9 feet across and has two windows and double doors.*

mounted on concrete, you might want to raise it with blocks at the corners so there is ventilation below.

You can mount the walls on the floor in two ways. In the first method, keep the wall framing level with the edges of the floor, then continue the cladding down to cover the floor edges (FIG. 6-23D). This method requires careful control of sizes.

The second method is more tolerant of small errors, and it has a better appearance. Cover the edges of the floor all around with boards (FIG. 6-23E). When you fit the building walls, include a sill (FIG. 6-23F), which will direct rainwater away from the floor edges. If you do not get the wall sizes quite the same as the floor edges, small differences will not show.

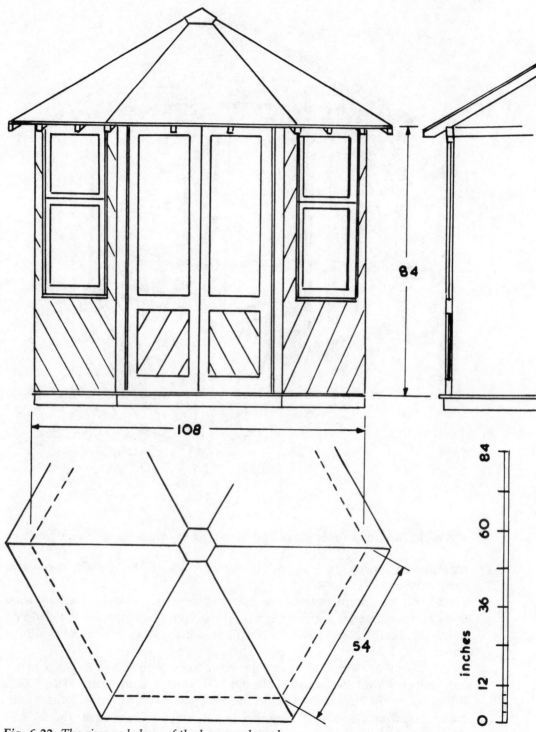

Fig. 6-22. *The sizes and shape of the hexagonal gazebo.*

inches

84

60

36

12

0

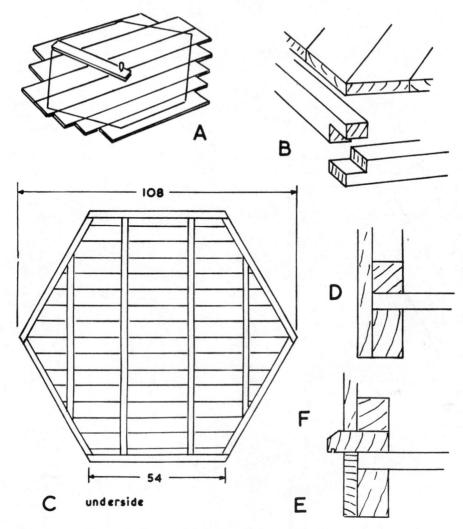

Fig. 6-23. *Making the floor of the gazebo.*

Although you should strive for perfection, it is difficult to get all six sides of the hexagon exactly the same. When you start making the walls, decide which edge, with floor boards parallel to it, will be the doorway. Then, as you make the wall panels, match them to the floor edges and mark where each will be.

Make the three closed walls, which are the same except for the need to match widths to the floor. Diagonal cladding is shown, but you could have vertical or horizontal boards.

If a wall is to stand on a sill, the outside of the cladding should be the same width as the length of the side of the floor (FIG. 6-24A). If you intend to take the cladding over the edge of the unbordered floor (FIG. 6-23D), it is the framing that should be the same width as the length of a floor side. Cut the upright edges of

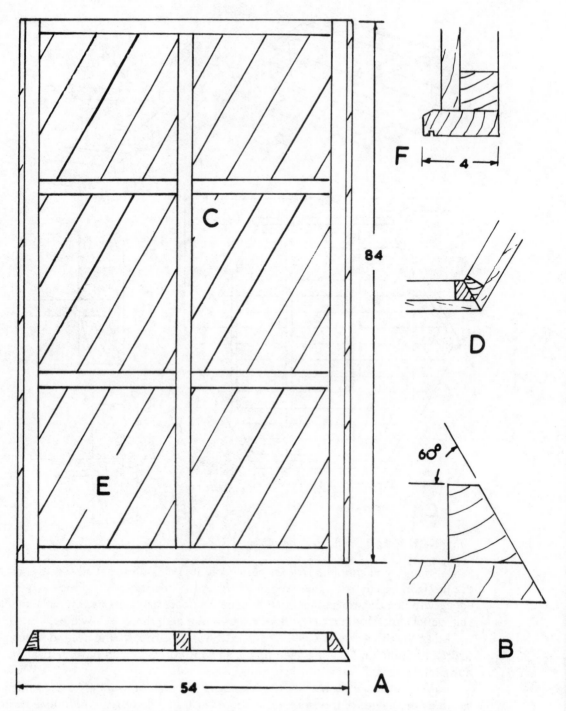

Fig. 6-24. One solid side of the gazebo, showing diagonal boards and sections at corners and bottom.

the frame and the cladding, when you fit it, to 60 degrees (FIG. 6-24B). Top and bottom edges are square. Other framing divides the panel into two across and three vertically (FIG. 6-24C). When these walls meet (FIG. 6-24D), it is impossible to put bolts through. It probably will be easier and more satisfactory to nail or screw the uprights together. You can use any of the usual frame joints for assembly of these walls.

The cladding is shown as tongue-and-groove boards laid at a 60-degree angle to the floor (FIG. 6-24E). You could use 45 degrees or any other angle, but the upward angle gives an illusion of height. You can clad all the walls in the same way, but you improve appearance if you arrange slopes alternate ways, preferably so the joints on one panel match those on their neighbor.

You could fit the sills to the panel now, or you could fit them after you mount the walls on the floor. Let a sill project about 1 inch. Slope the exposed top and plow a groove underneath to prevent water from running back (FIG. 6-24F). Miter the corners at 60 degrees to match the panel sides.

The two sides with windows and the one side with the doors should have the same overall sizes as the closed panels. Make their outer frames and any cladding or outside boards to match. The final assembly of six sides will be symmetrical on the floor.

The panels with windows (FIG. 6-25A) are identical. Include two uprights to leave a window opening 40 inches wide (FIG. 6-25B). Put a rail across at the bottom of the window. The cladding probably will be stiff enough to support itself below the window, but if you think it is necessary, put another rail across the center of this space.

Clad the sides to match the closed walls. Short pieces of cladding are shown above the window space (FIG. 6-25C), but as this part will not show very much under the roof, you might prefer to put a single board there. Put a sill at the bottom of the window opening (FIG. 6-25D) and line the sides and top with pieces that project a short distance outside the cladding (FIG. 6-25E).

Arrange the windows in each side with a lower fixed part and an opening top section. This design should provide enough light and ventilation, coupled with the glazed pair of doors.

Make the lower fixed windows from planed 2-inch-$\times$-3-inch strips, rabbeted to take the glass on the outside (FIG. 6-25F). Glue and screw these windows tightly to the frames.

For the opening windows, put stop strips around the opening (FIG. 6-25G). Make the window with a 2-inch-square top and sides, and a 3-inch-deep bottom (FIG. 6-25H). Hinge the window at the top, and fit a strut and catch to the lower edge.

When you make the frame for the pair of doors, make a temporary bottom rail to keep the frame in shape until you erect it. When you assemble the six sides on the sill and floor, take that rail out so the doors fit over the sill and swing inwards (FIG. 6-26A).

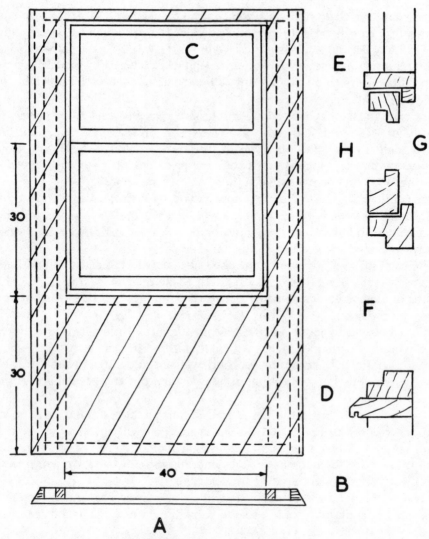

Fig. 6-25. A gazebo side with a window.

You will not have space to fit diagonal cladding on each side of the doorway, but you should fill in with vertical pieces (FIG. 6-26B) and fill the top to the same thickness. Line the sides and top (FIG. 6-26C). Make the two doors the same and in the same way as described for the previous building (FIG. 6-14). There is no intermediate glazing bar, and you should arrange the bottom panels with boards diagonally. Reduce the thickness of the boards to fit in the rabbets the same way as the earlier door.

Hinge the doors to swing inwards (FIG. 6-26D), and put strips outside at top and sides (FIG. 6-26E). Three 4-inch hinges should be satisfactory. One door might have bolts up and down and the other door might have a lock to it.

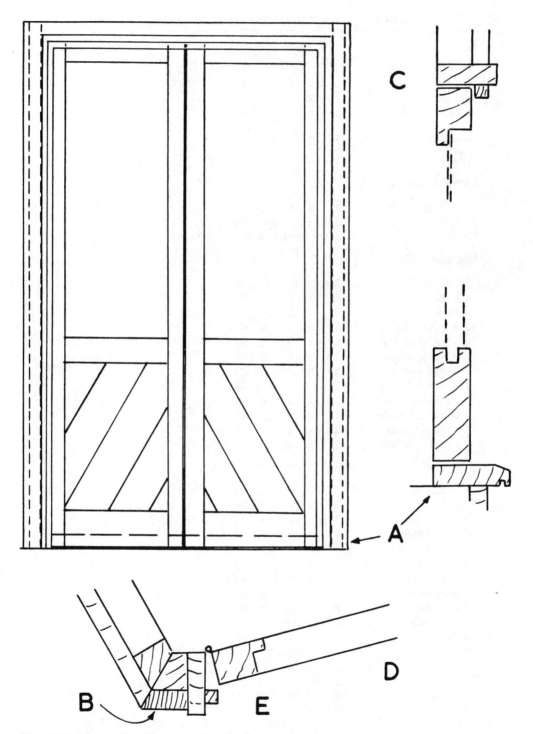

Fig. 6-26. *The gazebo side containing the doors.*

Materials List for Hexagonal Gazebo

Floor

6 joists	2	×	3	×	58
2 joists	2	×	3	×	112
2 joists	2	×	3	×	72
6 edges	1	×	4	×	58

Covering   1 × 6 or equivalent

Sills   1¼ × 4 × 60

Closed walls

9 uprights	2	×	2	×	86
12 rails	2	×	2	×	56
Covering	1- × -6 tongue-and-groove or equivalent

Window walls

8 uprights	2	×	2	×	86
4 rails	2	×	2	×	56
2 rails	2	×	2	×	46
2 window linings	1	×	3½	×	42
4 window linings	1	×	3½	×	54
2 window stops	1	×	1	×	42
4 window stops	1	×	1	×	26
4 window frames	2	×	2	×	42
2 window frames	2	×	2½	×	42
2 window frames	2	×	3	×	42
4 window sides	2	×	2	×	24
4 window sides	2	×	3	×	30

Door wall

2 uprights	2	×	2	×	86
2 rails	2	×	2	×	56
1 door frame	1	×	3½	×	52
2 door frames	1	×	3½	×	84
1 door stop	1	×	1	×	52
2 door stops	1	×	1	×	84
2 side pieces	1	×	3½	×	86
4 door sides	2	×	3	×	84
2 door tops	2	×	3	×	22
2 door rails	2	×	6	×	22
2 door rails	2	×	4	×	22
Panels	1- × -6 tongue-and-groove or equivalent

Roof

6 rafters	2	×	4	×	78
12 rafters	2	×	4	×	48
Covering	½ plywood, 1- × -2 battens and 16-inch shingles

Although it is possible to prefabricate the floor and the six sides almost completely before erection, it is advisable to work on the roof in position. Build the walls on the floor before starting on the roof. See that there is no twist. The floor will keep the bottom in shape, but check diagonals at the top. If there are any errors, put temporary struts between offending corners and leave them in place until the roof is far enough advanced to hold the walls in the correct shape.

At the top, fit 2-inch-×-3-inch strips laid flat to serve as wall plates when you build on the roof (FIG. 6-27A). To help tie the walls together, halve and screw the corner joints in this assembly.

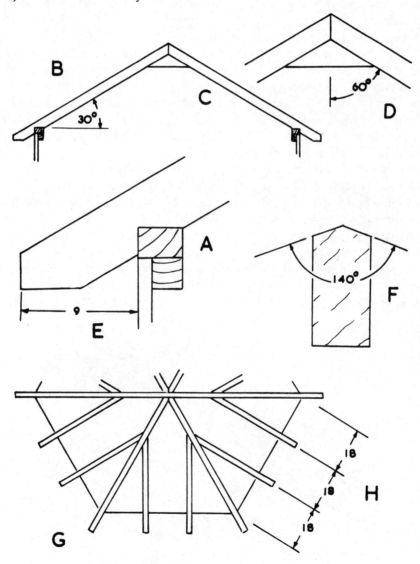

Fig. 6-27. Roof construction of the gazebo.

The roof slopes at 30 degrees from the corners of the building (FIG. 6-27B). As the distance is less across the sides, it is slightly steeper on the surfaces. Although you can do a certain amount of preparatory work, it is better to do much of the fitting of parts as you progress.

A pair of rafters across opposite corners are the key parts in making the roof (FIG. 6-27C). Cut their meeting ends at 60 degrees and link them with a piece underneath (FIG. 6-27D). Notch over the wall plates and trim the ends to shape (FIG. 6-27E). The roof covering has to rest on the rafters, so bevel their top edges to suit. The angle shown in FIG. 6-27F is approximate, and you should test this when you have temporarily assembled all the rafters by laying a straight piece of wood across. It does not matter if you do not achieve perfection, but it is easier to cover the roof neatly if parts cross reasonably flat.

Make the rafters to the other corners in the same way, but allow for the thickness of the main rafters at the top (FIG. 6-27G). When you are satisfied with the top angles and assembly so far, nail the rafters to the wall plates and to each other. For most roof coverings, it is advisable to add more rafters spacing them equally along each side (FIG. 6-27H). Their tops are flat. Cut their lower ends in line with those of the corner rafters. This step completes the skeleton of the roof. Check flatness of the surfaces in all directions.

Whatever the method of covering the roof, it will help to first cover the rafters with exterior plywood. This plywood gives a smooth base and acts as a lining for the roof. Use 1/2-inch plywood (FIG. 6-28A). Where plywood joints come on the six main rafters, cover with sheet plastic or other waterproof, flexible material with a good overlap, and glue it down or make sure it is held in place by covering it later. Cover any joints in the plywood in the same way.

Arrange battens to suit the shingles, if that is the type of covering you prefer (FIG. 6-28B). As shown in FIG. 6-28C, the shingles are 16 inches long with a 4-inch exposure (FIG. 6-28C) so the battens are 4-inch centers. Work from the eaves

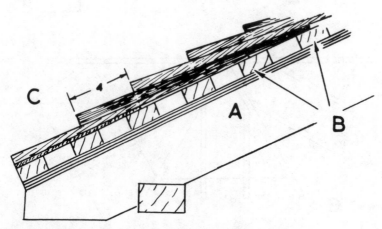

Fig. 6-28. A roof section showing shingles over plywood.

upwards. Where the shingles meet over the main rafters, miter them. You could interleave more plastic or bituminous sheeting under adjoining shingles for further waterproofing.

At the apex, the shingles will reduce to quite narrow triangles. Take them as close as you can to the top, then use a hexagon of lead or copper sheeting about 12 inches across to cover the meeting of the six sets of shingles. Finish it to the roof shape and nail it down closely.

There will be a gap between the wall plates and the underside of the roof. This gap might be left as ventilation, but if you prefer it closed, fit pieces between the rafters.

The entrance is a few inches above the surrounding ground. Fit a step under the sill and make it the full width of the doors. It will be convenient and improve the appearance of the gazebo.

Arbor

If you make a pergola structure with a seat, it becomes an arbor. Foliage grows over and around it and makes it a shelter. The foliage may be quite dense, except at the front, or it may just form a roof. Roses particularly are associated with an arbor, but you can use any type of climbing plant. You could build a pergola and place a seat under it, but it is better to build the seat in. Because this is a permanent structure and it is exposed to all kinds of weather, you must make the seat of wood. Any softening must be with portable cushions. This fact does not mean the seat cannot be at a comfortable angle for use without cushions on occasions.

Materials List for Arbor

4 legs	2 × 4 × 84
2 struts	2 × 3 × 70
2 tops	2 × 4 × 74
2 bottoms	2 × 3 × 66
2 seat supports	2 × 4 × 48
6 beams	2 × 4 × 120
4 seat rails	2 × 2 × 84
2 seat dividers	2 × 2 × 20
12 seat slats	1 × 4 × 20
2 seat boards	1 × 6 × 84 or slats
4 platform strips	1 × 4 × 74
6 platform supports	2 × 2 × 22

The arbor shown in FIG. 6-29 has inverted V legs supporting a flat top similar to a pergola. At each end, a strut parallel with a leg slopes up to give additional support to the top. This strut sets the angle of the seat-back, which has vertical slats. You can make the bottom of the seat solid or slatted. The legs go into the ground, and crosspieces prevent them from sinking too far. The suggested sizes

Fig. 6-29. *Make an arborlike pergola so foliage can form a roof over a seat.*

(FIG. 6-30A) are for an arbor 6 feet high and about 7 feet long, but you can alter these to suit your needs or available space.

You can use softwood treated with preservative or a more durable hardwood. Remember that once you erect the arbor and foliage is growing over it, you cannot do much to treat or repair it. Its original construction must be strong enough to have an expected life of many years. Bolts ought to be galvanized to minimize rust. Any glue should be a waterproof type, and screws should be plated or made of a noncorrosive metal. The main parts are 2-inch-×-3-inch or a 4-inch section.

Start by setting out an end. If you want to set tools, the angles are 15 degrees. From the ground line, draw a centerline square to it; then 72 inches up, mark the apex of a triangle with a 39-inch spread at the base (FIG. 6-31A). Draw the top across (FIG. 6-31B), and mark the widths of the wood. Draw the seat support across the legs (FIG. 6-31C). The seat top is symmetrical about the centerline of this seat support and the strut slopes up from the back of it, parallel with the front leg (FIG. 6-31D). This layout gives you all the shapes and sizes you need to start construction.

Notch the tops to take the lengthwise beams (FIG. 6-31E). Let the legs meet on

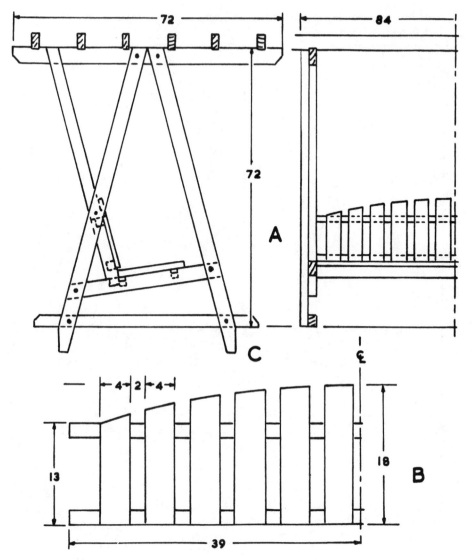

Fig. 6-30. *Sizes of the arbor.*

the beam and drill through for bolts. Spread the bottoms and secure them with the ground strips (FIG. 6-31F). On this framework, mark where the seat bearers come. Put these pieces across and add the long struts (FIG. 6-31G), marking where they cross and where you want to drill for bolts or cut joints.

On the seat bearers, mark and cut the notches for the lengthwise seat supports, not more than 1½ inches deep (FIG. 6-31H). The strut joins by halving. This halving is best cut with a dovetail shape (FIG. 6-31J). Cut the notches to take the lengthwise back supports (FIG. 6-31K). At the top, halve the strut into the top

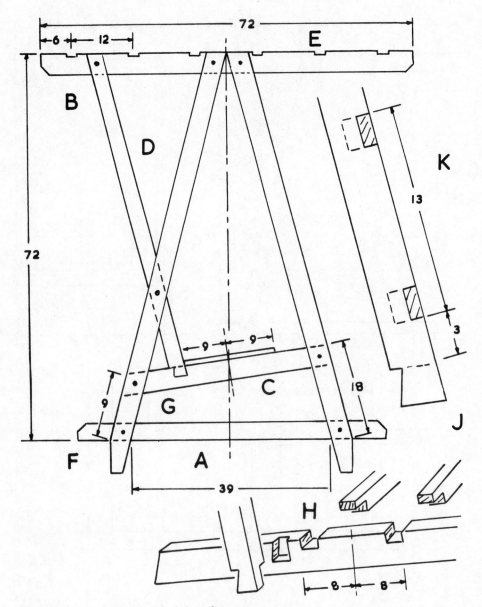

Fig. 6-31. Detail of one end of the arbor.

piece. Assemble the pair of ends, with bolts where parts overlap and glue and screws at the joints.

The seat back has vertical slats with a curve cut on their top edge (FIG. 6-30B). You might prefer some other shape. Make the two 2-inch-square rails, notching ends to fit the notches in the struts. Have the back slats too long at first. Fit them temporarily to the rails. Bend a batten over them and draw a curve on their tops.

Remove the slats to cut their curved tops and round all exposed edges. Glue and screw them in place.

Make the seat supports to the same length as the back supports. Put pieces between them—if you divide the length into three, that should be sufficient (FIG. 6-32A). The seat top could be solid and made up of any boards of convenient width (FIG. 6-32B), or you could use slats with gaps between them (FIG. 6-32C). In any case, round the front and top edges. Glue and screw the seat parts together.

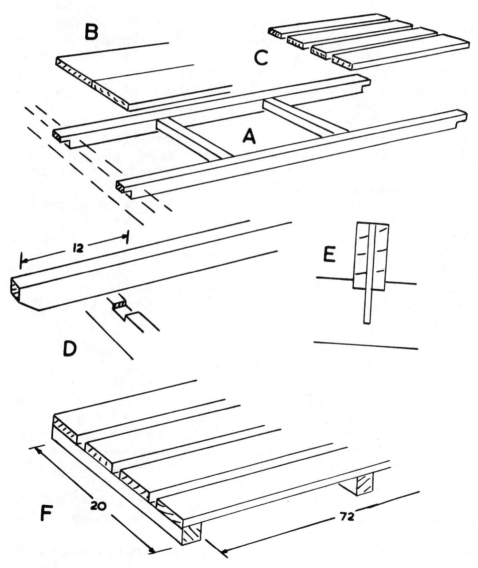

Fig. 6-32. Construction of parts of the arbor.

Glue and screw the seat rails into the end assemblies. With the aid of the top beams, the seat rails provide lengthwise rigidity to the structure. Check squareness, both upright and front-to-back. Because of handling problems due to weight, it probably will be advisable to erect the arbor in position before fitting the beams. The legs are shown with short points to push into the ground in FIG. 6-30C. If this design does not suit your situation, you could set the legs in concrete, or you might want to bury flat boards under the legs in loose soil. If the ground is not level, you might have to sink the boards by different amounts. Check with a level on the bottom crosspieces and on the seat or on a board between the bottom parts.

Make the top beams all identical. They should overhang by 12 inches or more on the ends (FIG. 6-32D). Bevel the undersides of the ends. Drill down through for a 1/2-inch steel rod to be driven in to act as a dowel at each crossing (FIG. 6-32E). To prevent the entry of water and the start of rot and rust, you could drive the rod below the surface and fill the hole with a wooden plug or mastic, or nail a thin piece of wood above it.

So plants will grow and engulf the arbor, there should be as much soil area around the base as possible, but you might want to lay a concrete slab in front of the seat to provide a clean, dry area for the feet. More in keeping with the arbor would be a platform of slats on crosspieces (FIG. 6-32F). Make it as a unit, so you can lift it occasionally.

If you paint or treat with preservative after you have erected the arbor, do it long before plants start to climb, so solvents will evaporate before the shoots come into contact with the structure. As plants climb, you might have to encourage them to go where you want by tying them to nails or by providing temporary strips of wood across the uprights. Ideally, you should have the arbor in position well before the start of the growing season, then you can watch progress, although it will be a few years before the foliage densely covers the roof and walls of your arbor.

Gateway

Something more than just a simple gate in the fence will provide character to your yard or garden and improve its appearance. It could be an access from the road on your boundary or between parts of the garden—opening up a new vista as you go from the vegetable plot to a flower garden. A gateway that has depth as well as width helps in maintaining privacy. Such a gateway is best made with a roof, which can improve the looks of the structure and offer shelter from sudden storms or excessive sunshine.

This gateway (FIG. 6-33) is a roofed shelter with picket-fence sides and a gate to match. You could alter the design to fit in with an existing boundary or dividing fence. With vines and other plants around and over it, it becomes a sort of arbor. You could build it with an open-topped roof if all you need is a framework for climbing vines.

Fig. 6-33. *A roofed gateway is attractive and gives shelter and privacy.*

Materials List for Gateway

4 posts	4	×	4	×	108
4 rafters	2	×	4	×	48
4 purlins	2	×	3	×	64
1 ridge	2	×	3	×	64
4 bargeboards	1	×	6	×	48
1 tie	2	×	4	×	54
2 roof panels	44	×	64	×	1/2 plywood
2 roof edges	3/4	×	1 1/2	×	64
4 side rails	2	×	4	×	60
2 gate rails	2	×	4	×	54
30 pickets	1	×	4	×	36
1 gate brace	2	×	4	×	66

The suggested sizes (FIG. 6-34) are for a gateway 5 feet square at the base, with an overall height of 8 feet and head room of 6 feet, 6 inches underneath. You might wish to adapt sizes to suit your needs. At the suggested size, the roof provides plenty of shelter. You could reduce the back-to-front size to 2 feet or less, if all you want is an arch. However, with a square ground plan, the gate can be made to swing inwards and fasten against a side, without anything projecting when you want a clear run through.

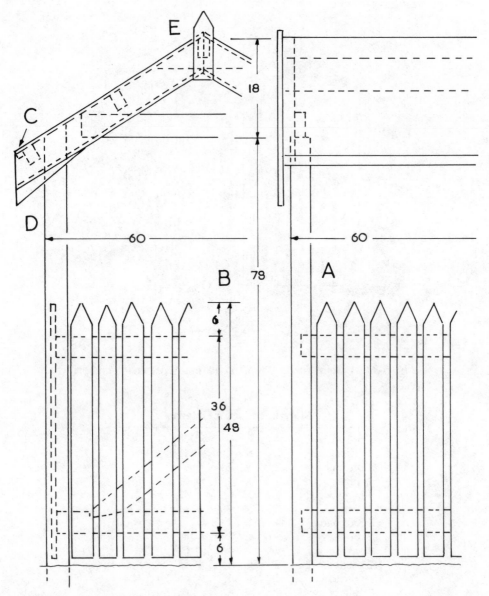

Fig. 6-34. Suggested sizes for the gateway.

The parts are mostly stock sections and could be hardwood or softwood. Treating with preservative is advisable. The posts could be made from 2-inch- × -4-inch pieces joined together if 4-inch-square wood is not available. The roof is 1/2-inch plywood covered with felt or other material. Besides serving as decoration, the bargeboards seal the roof ends and its supports. Most parts are notched into each other and nailed. You could also use waterproof glue, but that is not essential.

In the instructions, it is assumed that the posts will be sunk directly into the ground 18 inches, but in weak ground and for greater strength you could use concrete, as described for earlier projects. Instructions are for the gateway as drawn, but if you alter sizes and keep the slope of the roof similar, main construction will be the same.

The key parts, which control the sizes of many other parts, are the two pairs of rafters (FIGS. 6-35A and 6-36A). Set out the slope (FIG. 6-36B) full size. Mark a rafter to this angle. At the apex, it is cut vertically (FIG. 6-36C). At the eaves, make it extend enough to take a purlin and the overhang of the roof (FIG. 6-36D). Mark the position of another purlin (FIG. 6-36E).

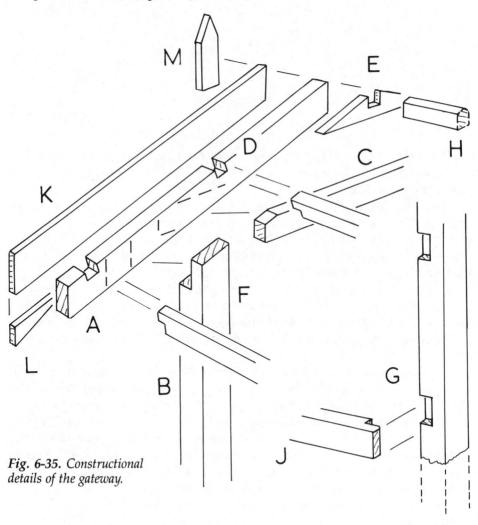

Fig. 6-35. *Constructional details of the gateway.*

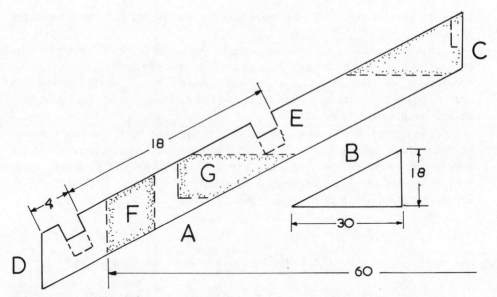

Fig. 6-36. Setting out a rafter for the gateway.

Draw on the positions of the posts (FIGS. 6-35B and 6-36F) and the tie (FIGS. 6-35C and 6-36G). Notch for the purlins half their depths (FIG. 6-35D). Cut the two pairs of rafters to match.

Assemble each pair of rafters together. Use a 1-inch-thick piece at the apex (FIG. 6-35E), notched to take the ridge piece. Put the tie across. Although all other parts can be nailed, this is best bolted because it has to resist any tendency for the assembly to spread. Two 2-inch bolts at each end would be suitable. Check the width across the marked positions of the posts.

Cut the two pairs of posts to size (FIG. 6-34A). Bevel and notch each top to take its rafter (FIG. 6-35F). Allow for the amount a post will go into the ground, and mark the positions of the fence rails (FIG. 6-34B). The rails could be notched right through, but you can avoid their ends showing with shorter notches (FIG. 6-35G).

Dig oversize holes for the bottoms of the posts so you can move them to get them plumb and correctly located during assembly. Join the posts to their rafters, so you have two end assemblies ready to erect. Cut at least two purlins to length. Stand the end assemblies in their holes and put a purlin across at each side. Check squareness and that the posts are upright. Stand back and look at the gateway from several angles to see that it looks right. Tamp some earth loosely into the holes to prevent movement. Fit all purlins. Make the ridge (FIG. 6-35H) to fit into the end supports. Bevel its top edge to match the slope of the roof.

Your assembly should now be reasonably rigid, but it will help to nail on the roof plywood. Thicken underneath at the eaves (FIG. 6-14C) to give a strong edge for tacking the covering felt. Cut the plywood level at the outside edges of the rafters.

Make a final check of squareness, then fit the fence rails (FIG. 6-35J) to hold the posts, and tamp down the earth around the bottoms of the posts.

Cover the roof with felt or other material, taken across from eaves to eaves, turned under each side, and nailed down onto the rafters at the ends. Cut barge-boards (FIG. 6-35K). They meet at the top, but should extend about 1/2 inch at the eaves and be arranged to come equally above and below the roof ends. You could leave these as plain parallel boards, but they are shown with tapered pieces added (FIGS. 6-34D and 6-35L) and with finials at the ridge (FIGS. 6-34E and 6-35M). Plain strips are shown, but you could turn pieces for a different effect. Nail on the bargeboards closely to limit the amount of rainwater running into the joints.

The picket pieces for the fence and gate are the same. You can use your own ideas for the treatment of tops. Some possible shapes are suggested (FIG. 6-37).

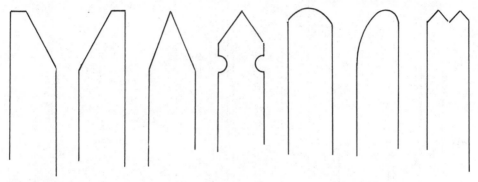

Fig. 6-37. Tops of palings can be cut in several ways.

Any points should not be taken to an acute angle, but should be square across or rounded. If you choose hollowed sides, you can drill half-holes with a Forstner bit or hold rails against each other to drill with an ordinary bit.

On gate and fences, allow for 4-inch strips about 1 inch apart, but adjust them in the available spaces to give even gaps. Nail the pickets to the fence rails, so their bottom edges are clear of the ground by about 1 inch.

Cut the gate rails (FIG. 6-38A) to fit between the posts with 1/2-inch clearance. Cut all the gate pickets to size and shape. Mark on them where the rails will come. Allow ample clearance at ground level. Put the pickets on a flat floor with the rails in position over them. Check squareness by comparing diagonal mea-surements. Arrange the diagonal brace to slope upwards from the side that will be hinged, as it has to resist any tendency of the gate to sag.

Put the wood that will make the brace over the rails so it crosses 3 inches in from the ends. Mark on the rails where this comes. Notch the rails (FIG. 6-38B)— 3/4 inch at the deep point will be satisfactory.

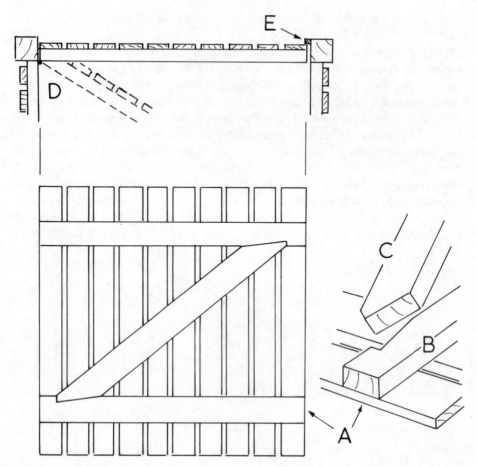

Fig. 6-38. Design for a gate.

Nail the outer pickets to the rails. Try the gate in closed and open positions between the posts. Again check squareness, then nail on all pickets securely. Mark the ends of the brace from the rail notches (FIG. 6-38C). Cut the brace so its ends are a tight fit. Nail it in and the pickets to it.

Hinge the gate with its rails level with the inner surface of a post (FIG. 6-38D). You could use 4-inch butt or T hinges. At the other post put a stop piece the full depth of the gate (FIG. 6-38E). Arrange a catch to hold the gate closed. If this is at the top rail level, you can reach over to operate it. The gate will swing inwards to rest against the side fence. It might be sufficient for it to just rest there, or you could provide a hook or catch to stop the gate swinging closed unintentionally.

A-Frame Canopy

A roof without corner supporting posts has a lighter and often more attractive appearance. You might need a canopy or awning to provide shade or protection from rain with a fairly clear view all around and access from any direction. This might be in a place where you have open-air meals, serve refreshments at a sports field, want to entertain guests outdoors in any weather, or just need an attractive canopy permanently on your property.

This canopy (FIG. 6-39) has a ridged roof with scalloped edges and two A-frames providing support at the ends. The suggested sizes (FIGS. 6-40 and 6-41) are for a roof 8 feet wide and 12 feet long, supported high enough to give ample head room and a total height of 9 feet. There are strong supports, and stiffness is provided by diagonal braces inside the roof. The suggested roof is plywood covered with tarred felt, but you could use other materials. Sizes might be altered, but too great a difference could affect strength and the sizes of wood required.

Fig. 6-39. A canopy supported on A-frames provides shelter without sides or corner posts.

The important sizes are those of the end assemblies (FIG. 6-40). Draw the main lines of half an end, preferably full-size, on the floor. This will show you the lengths of sloping parts and angles to cut at joints. Note that there is a ridge piece passing through the end trusses (FIGS. 6-40A and 6-43A and B). At the eaves, the rafter and tie fit onto lengthwise eaves strips (FIGS. 6-40B and 6-42A and B).

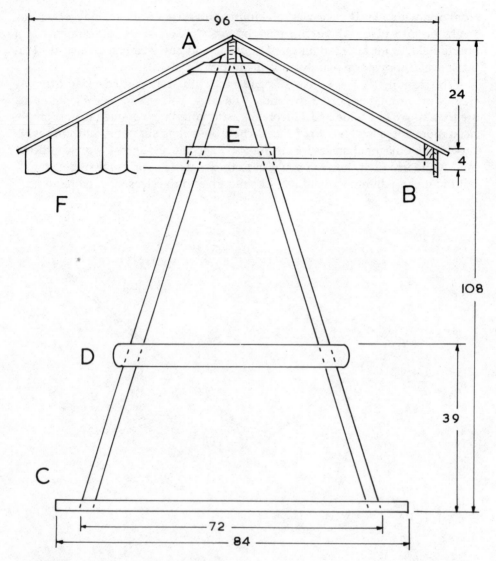

Fig. 6-40. End view of the A-frame canopy.

Measure the exact sections of these parts before making the trusses. Planed wood will be at least 1/4 inch less than the specified sizes, which will not matter if you allow for the differences in joints.

Make the two trusses. The rafters will be linked below the apex with the support for the ridge strip (FIG. 6-43C). At the eaves you can put the end covering piece on the joint (FIG. 6-42C) or nail on a temporary piece of scrap wood until the roof is assembled.

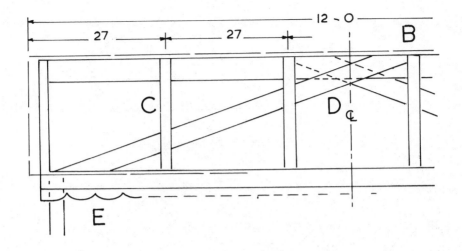

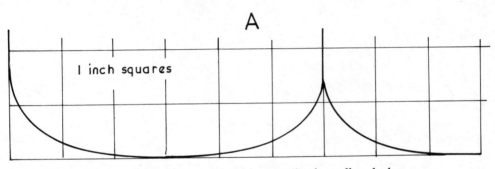

Fig. 6-41. Side view, showing internal bracing. Details of a scalloped edge.

**Materials List for
A-frame Canopy**

12 rafters	2	× 2 ×	60
2 ties and pads	2	× 2 ×	30
2 ties	2	× 2 ×	100
4 legs	2	× 4 ×	120
2 feet	2	× 4 ×	86
2 rails	1	× 5 ×	60
1 ridge piece	2	× 6 ×	144
2 eaves strips	2	× 4 ×	144
2 fascia boards	1	× 6 ×	144
2 braces	1	× 6 ×	96
End covering	1 × 6 boards or 3/4 plywood		
Roof	1/2 or 3/4 exterior plywood		

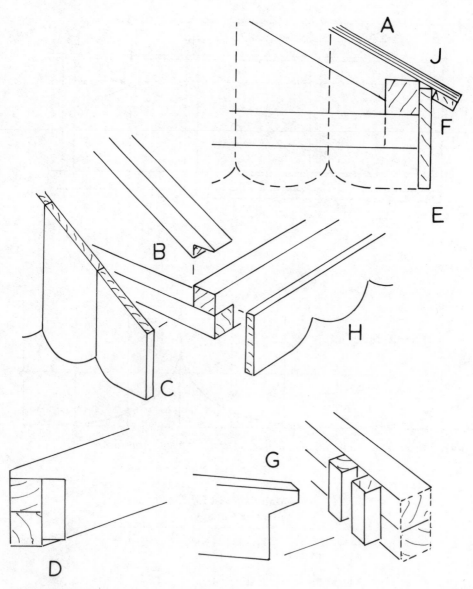

Fig. 6-42. Roof details for the A-frame canopy.

The A-frames fit inside the trusses. Cut the tops so they will notch under the ridge piece (FIG. 6-43D). Where the A-frame sides cross the truss horizontal parts, it will be stronger to use long screws than to depend on nails.

The foot of an A-frame is shown extending 6 inches (FIG. 6-40C). The foot has to provide stability. It must be securely fastened to the legs and firmly fixed to the ground. You could notch the legs into the foot (FIG. 6-43E and F), then nail upwards and diagonally downwards. It would be stronger to tenon the legs (FIG.

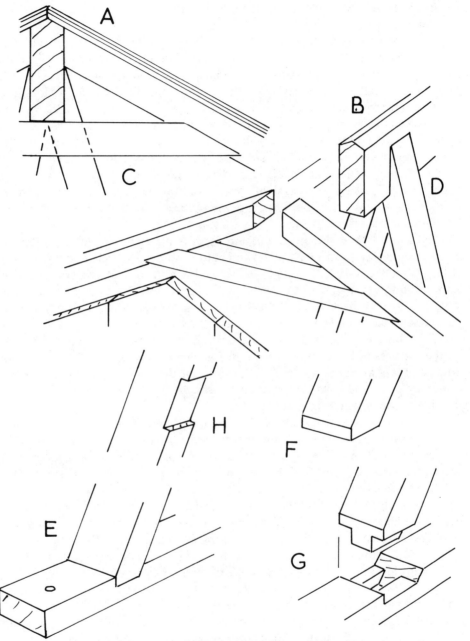

Fig. 6-43. *A-frame and roof truss details for the A-frame canopy.*

6-43G). You could fasten the feet to the ground with stakes or metal spikes. It would be strongest to make concrete pads to extend a few inches around each foot, let in level with the surface of the ground, then bolt the feet to them.

A rail (FIG. 6-40D) stiffens the assembly and acts as a barrier. Fit each rail into shallow notches (FIG. 6-43H) in the legs. You can cut them level with the legs or round the extensions, as suggested.

Put a strip across the legs above the truss tie (FIG. 6-40E) to form a pad for the diagonal bracing (FIG. 6-42D). The trusses are intended to be enclosed. You could use plywood, but vertical boards about 6 inches wide are suggested (FIG. 6-40F). They have a scalloped pattern along the bottom, and this is carried along the sides with fascia boards. Check on the width of the wood for the fascia boards (FIG. 6-42E) and trim the truss-covering boards to come level when finished. You could leave the bottom edges straight, but if you use the scalloped pattern, it is important that you make uniform shapes if the canopy is to look attractive. Parts of ellipses look better than parts of circles. Make a template (FIG. 6-41A) long enough for at least 1¹/₂ curves, then you can put the part curve over an already-marked curve on a fascia board to get the next curve marked uniformly. Cut and fit all the boards on the trusses.

The roof is intended to overhang only far enough for the thickening piece on its edge, both at the eaves (FIG. 6-42F) and at the ends. An overall length of 12 feet is suggested (FIG. 6-41B). You might want to adjust this to suit available space or for economical cutting of plywood. Cut the ridge and eaves strips to suit the length of the roof. Bevel the top of the ridge strip to match the slopes of the roof. Fit the eaves strips ends into the framing of the trusses.

There have to be some intermediate rafters. How many you make depends on the stiffness of the plywood. Four each side are shown (FIG. 6-41C). You can arrange others to suit joints in the plywood. Fit the rafters to the eaves in the same way as the end ones. At the ridge you can merely cut the rafter to fit against the side of the ridge piece or notch it in.

Assemble the end trusses on the A-frame and join them with the ridge and eaves pieces. Check squareness and that the sides are vertical. The whole assembly should stand firm, but it is important to add diagonal bracing to withstand wind and unusual loads. The braces go from the pads on the truss ties (FIG. 6-42G) to cross at opposite sides of the ridge piece (FIG. 6-41D). Put cleats each side on the truss ties. Nail the braces there and nail or screw them to the ridge piece. In the event of shock loads, one brace will receive compression and the other tension. Fastenings at each end should be strong enough to resist these loads.

Cut and fit the fascia boards (FIGS. 6-41E and 6-42H). Arrange the top edge of each board low enough to miss the slope of the roof covering (FIG. 6-42J).

Cover the roof with plywood, edged underneath to allow for turning felt under and nailing. Put a strip of tarred felt about 12 inches wide along the ridge. Put tarred felt over the roof from one eaves to the other, with ample overlap between sheets. Tack securely underneath. Put battens over the felt at about 18-inch intervals (FIGS. 6-39 and 4-23).

Painting will depend on the situation. You might have to fit it in with a background and the surroundings. If bright colors would be welcomed, you could paint alternate end boards in contrasting colors and use bright colors for other exposed parts.

Covered Bridge

Covered bridges in many sizes are traditional in many parts of the country. You can carry on the tradition by building one in your yard or garden. If there is a stream or just a hollow, you have an excuse for building a bridge. Even without water, a bridge to take a path across a hollow can be a scenic feature. You might be able to divert water to make a pond for the bridge to cross if you feel water is necessary to the feature. After all, the mighty imported London Bridge re-erected at Lake Havasu City, Arizona, had to have water brought in to justify its existence!

Materials List for Covered Bridge

8 posts	4	×	4	× length as needed
16 rafters	2	×	4	× 36
4 ties	2	×	4	× 30
2 beams	2	×	6	× length as needed
8 rails	2	×	4	× 160
12 rails	2	×	4	× 30
2 hand rail tops	1	×	4	× 160
30 palings	1	×	5	× 36
12 floor boards	1 1/2	×	12	× 54 or as needed
Roof trim	3/4	×	4 or	5
Roof			3/4 inch plywood and shingles	
4 roof ends	1/2	×	2	× 48

The size of bridge will have to be arranged to suit your situation and the design adapted, but this bridge (FIG. 6-44) has a 42-inch-wide footway and 75 inches minimum head room, and is 12 feet long. Its length is divided into bays of about 48 inches. You could arrange your own bridge length in steps of 48 inches to suit the span you wish to cover.

It would be advisable to make the whole structure from a naturally durable wood, but with modern preservatives you can expect a long life from other treated woods. Cedar shingles would be appropriate for the roof of this covered bridge, and they could be laid over exterior grade plywood.

The design of the bridge will be controlled by the hollow you will be building over. Experiment with the beams that will support the floor or some temporary long straight boards. The beams will have to be let into the ground at one or both sides, or they can be arranged with steps up or down. The footway should be level across, so use a spirit level while testing the positions of beams. A width of 54 inches over the posts is shown as an example (FIG. 6-45A), but you can alter this to match the approach paths.

What you do at the ends of the beams will depend on the soil. They might have to be supported on concrete, although if they do not have to project much from the ends of the framed parts, tightly packed earth might be all you need.

Fig. 6-44. *A covered bridge on a path adds a traditional touch to your yard or garden.*

With the beams set parallel and level, you can lay out the rest of the bridge. If you want to make the walkway much wider, there would have to be a central beam, but anything up to the width shown should be satisfactory with the suggested 1¹/₂-inch crosswise boards. A few boards could be attached temporarily to steady the beams while you deal with the posts.

The drawn sizes (FIG. 6-45B) allow for handrails at a convenient height and the minimum headroom of 75 inches, which you might wish to adjust. Lengths of posts will depend on the hollow to be spanned and the firmness (or otherwise) of the ground. With reasonably compacted soil, you could allow a penetration of 18 inches. With loose or soft soil, you might have to concrete the bottoms of the posts. The beams will provide some support for the posts, but strength has to be shared and the posts must be firmly held in the ground.

Notch the posts ³/₄ inch deep to take the beams, the floor thickness, and the

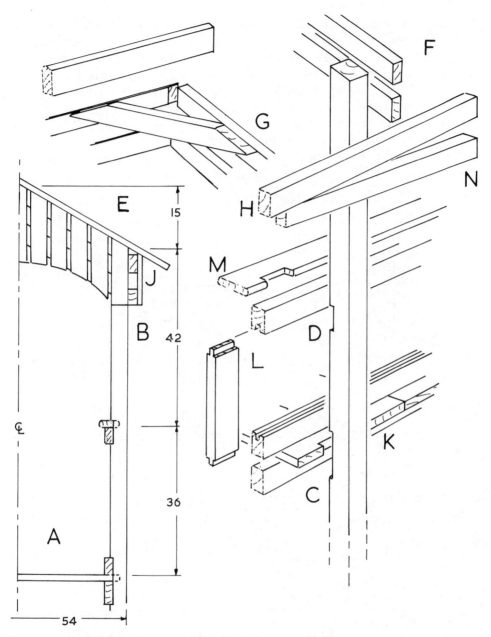

Fig. 6-45. *End view and structural details of the covered bridge.*

railing frame (FIG. 6-45C). Also notch to the same depth for the handrail (FIG. 6-45D). All posts are the same above the beams, but you will have to allow suitable lengths below.

Set out the angle of the roof full-size (FIG. 6-45E). Cut the tops of the posts to this angle. For each position, make a rafter and a piece parallel to it at each side (FIG. 6-45F), and leave a gap at the top for a ridge piece. These pieces can be nailed or screwed on the surfaces of the posts without notching. Put a tie across to support the ridge piece (FIG. 6-45G). This will also hold the lower parallel pieces.

Assemble all the posts to the beams. Check all levels and see that the posts are upright and parallel when viewed from a distance. When you are satisfied with the accuracy of the assembly so far, add the top side rails (FIG. 6-45H) to steady the assembly. Fit these rails low enough to clear the slope of the roof (FIG. 6-45J). Add the roof crosswise parts. You can fit in the ridge piece. Let it extend 6 inches at the ends (FIG. 6-46A). Bevel its top edge to match the roof slopes.

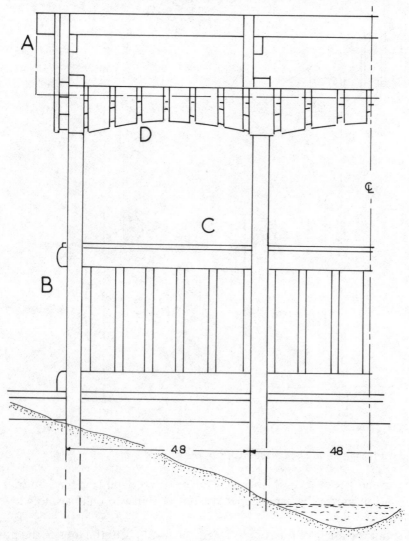

Fig. 6-46. *Side view of part of the covered bridge.*

Nail floor boards to the beams. Let them extend a little each side, and notch them around the posts (FIG. 6-45K).

The side railings consist of upper and lower rails with palings between. You could fit the palings into individual mortises, but it is simpler to let the paling tenons fit into plowed grooves (FIG. 6-45L). The grooves can be $1/2$ inch wide and $3/4$ inch deep. Make the rails to extend past the outer posts with rounded ends (FIG. 6-46B). Make enough paling to fill the available spaces with gaps not more than 2 inches between (FIG. 6-46C). Glue and nail them into place. Cover the top rails with overhanging pieces with rounded edges to provide comfortable hand grips (FIG. 6-45M).

Many traditional bridges have vertical pieces at the sides and ends cut to hollow curved outlines. This bridge is decorated in the same way. The pieces parallel with the rafters at the ends will support the decorative strips there. At the sides, cut pieces to slope up to the top side rails (FIGS. 6-45N and 6-46D).

You can draw neat curves to cut the lower edges by putting the strips in place or in an equivalent position on the ground, so you can spring a lathe to a curve and draw around it (FIG. 6-47A). Take care to get even spaces when you nail these strips into place.

The purpose of covering a traditional bridge was to protect the wood from which it was built from extremes of weather, so the roof was given a good overhang. On this small bridge you should allow an overhang of 6 inches. If you have been working to the sizes given, $3/4$-inch plywood should not need any intermediate rafters or other supports. Nail the plywood to everything it crosses. If you want to cover the roof with tarred felt, thicken under the edges all around, but if you intend to use shingles, that should not be necessary. You could add bargeboards to a felted roof, but they should not be very wide or they would detract from the decorative strip below.

If you wish to cover the roof with shingles or shakes, put a strip of tarred felt along the joint at the ridge. You could protect the plywood with a coat of paint.

Shingles or shakes might come with instructions. If so, follow them; otherwise, allow for a double thickness at the eaves, with staggered joints and an overhang of $1^{1}/_2$ inches (FIG. 6-47B). Arrange rows of shingles to overlap to expose one-third of the row below each time (FIG. 6-47C). For economy you could reduce the amount of overlap (FIG. 6-47D). Cover the ends of the roof with strips like narrow bargeboards (FIG. 6-47E).

Cut the meeting shingles to fit close at the ridge. You could use a manufactured ridge piece as a cover or trim shingles so one side overlaps the other along the ridge line.

Any finish you apply will depend on circumstances. Natural rot-resistant wood could be left to weather. If you have used wood soaked in preservative, that might be all the treatment needed. Cedar shingles are not normally treated in any way. You could paint a light color under the plywood roof. Any untreated wood should be protected by painting, probably in a color to match other woodwork nearby.

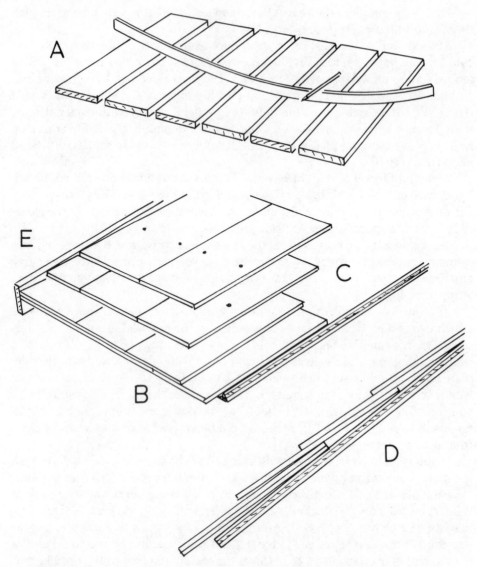

Fig. 6-47. Marking shaped boards and covering the roof with shingles.

Deck with Pergola

Decks are usually associated with houses, but you could make an independent one to take advantage of uneven ground. If you have land that slopes, you could make a deck projecting from a high part, possibly to give you a view of a garden or a piece of natural scrub or trees. If the deck can be arranged with a southern aspect, it will face the sun for most of the day and will be a suitable place for lounging in the right weather.

Materials List for Deck with Pergola

10 posts	4	×	4	× lengths as needed	
2 beams	2	×	8	×	118
2 beams	2	×	8	×	90
5 joists	2	×	6	×	124
2 joists	2	×	6	×	48
4 rails	2	×	4	×	90
2 rails	2	×	4	×	118
2 rails	2	×	4	×	48
2 cappings	1	×	4	×	90
2 cappings	1	×	4	×	118
1 capping	1	×	4	×	48
2 pergola beams	2	× 10		×	150
7 pergola beams	2	×	4	×	120
Decking	1 1/2	× about 12			
2 stair stringers	1 1/2	×	9	×	70
1 stair top	1 1/2	×	9	×	32
3 stair treads	1 1/2	× 12		×	30
7 stair cleats	1 1/2	×	1 1/2	×	14

A deck alone can be attractive, but it will be improved if it has an open covering over which vines and other plants can be trained. Besides improving appearance, this will provide shelter and shade. You will have to design the deck and pergola to suit your situation, the slope of the land and available space, but an example is offered (FIG. 6-48) so methods of construction can be shown. It is assumed that the rear of the structure meets level land or there can be a path or steps cut in a bank down to it. You might not need stairs, but some are shown as an example of the method of construction. They give access to and from the lower ground without the need of scrambling on a bank.

Sizes are suggested (FIGS. 6-49 and 6-50). As you adapt the design to suit your needs, choose wood of about the same sections and arrange spacings close to those suggested. The wood should be naturally durable. California redwood would be suitable. If you have to use a less-durable wood, it should be treated with preservative. You can paint wood, but some parts will become inaccessible, particularly as foliage grows over the framing. It will be better if the wood has its own resistance to decay.

For similar reason, fastenings should resist corrosion. Nails and bolts could be stainless steel or provided with a corrosion-resistant coating, such as galvanizing. Load-bearing parts are best bolted through. You could notch some crossing parts into each other so the wood complements the strength of bolts. For the best appearance, all exposed wood surfaces should be planed.

The datum you have to work from is the surface of the deck, which has to finish level in all directions. Unless you are dealing with a simple, even slope, it will be advisable to use some scrap pieces of wood and assemble a mock-up of the outline of what you propose building. Use a spirit level and get the deck line

Fig. 6-48. You can build an independent deck over sloping ground and erect a pergola roof over it.

correct. This will show you the extent of posts below the deck. It might show you how construction and appearance would be better if you moved the deck or altered its size. You might wish to build the deck out of square to suit the land, but this will complicate construction. It is better to have at least some parts square. The pergola section looks better if its parts are square.

In the example, there are ten posts (numbered in FIG. 6-49). Posts 1, 4, 5, and 8 support the pergola. Posts 2 and 3 are under the deck. Posts 6, 7, 9, and 10 are at handrail height. You will have to allow enough length for letting into the ground. Leave a little extra at the tops for trimming during assembly.

Figure 6-51 shows how parts are arranged in relation to each other. Main support comes from four beams (FIG. 6-49A) from back to front and held with two or three 1/2-inch bolts to each post (FIG. 6-51A). Over these there are joists (FIGS. 6-49B and 6-51B), spaced 15 inches to 18 inches apart (FIG. 6-50A). Beams and joists

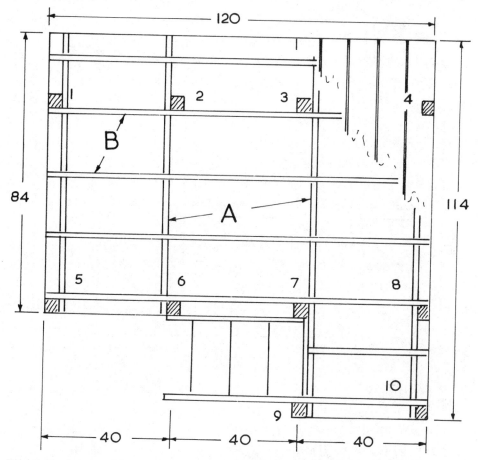

Fig. 6-49. Suggested layout for a deck to be covered by a pergola.

could be let into 1/2-inch notches where they cross posts, if you wish. The ends of joists and beams should reach the outside line of the posts. Nail joists to beams with diagonal nails. Decking is laid across the joists and taken to the outside lines of the posts (FIG. 6-51C). Leave gaps between the boards. If the rear of the deck has to fit into uneven ground, you will have to trim decking boards to suit. A handrail (FIG. 6-51D) goes around the sides and front, except the space for the stairs. One rail below it should be sufficient, but you could put two lines of rails if you are concerned with the safety of children.

Posts must be adequately supported in the ground. Accurate positioning could be difficult with very uneven ground. Mark post positions, but dig holes that will allow movement. You could put concrete in the bottom of a hole and let it harden so you will be able to move the post about to get it correct in relation to the deck (FIG. 6-52A). When you are satisfied with the assembly, fill the hole with concrete, sloping the top so water runs away (FIG. 6-52B). Get all posts upright

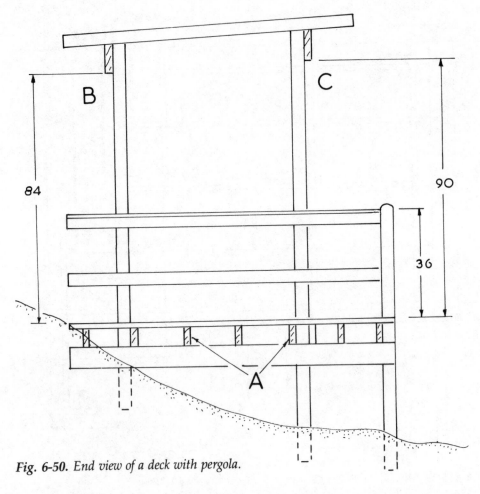

Fig. 6-50. End view of a deck with pergola.

and in line. Slight differences in measurements will not matter, providing posts are in line and square to each other. Nail on temporary braces between posts and to the ground to hold the posts in position.

You will probably find it simplest to fit the beams to the posts and position at least a few of the joists before completing the concreting of the posts. Clamp or temporarily nail beams to posts as you check levels before drilling for bolts. This is the stage that settles the accuracy of the assembly.

When all beams and joists are fixed, you can lay the decking. To keep gaps between boards even, use a strip of wood 1/2 inch thick as a gauge. You should avoid having to cut down the width of a board at the top of the stairs. Try putting a few boards across at that end of the deck to see what adjustment might be needed. If a board will have to be cut down, you could put the first board across at the top of the stairs, then space boards towards the long side and adjust the

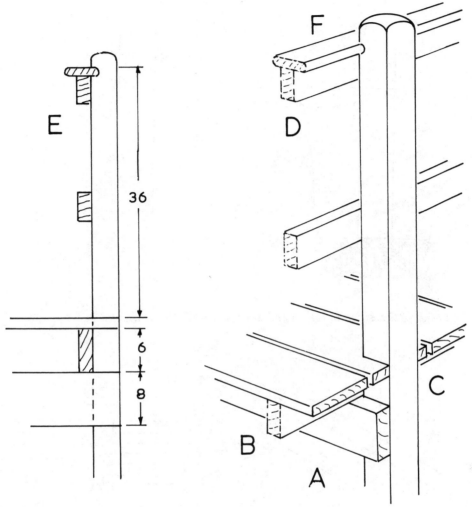

Fig. 6-51. Arrangements of parts for the deck and handrail.

width of the last board as necessary. Continue laying to the other side of the first board and adjust the width of the final board at the short edge, if necessary.

Mark the heights of the handrail and lower rail on all posts (FIG. 6-51E). Bolt the rails in place. They will meet with an internal angle on posts 5 and 10, where the best joint will be a tenon from one rail into the other (FIG. 6-53A). The capping is notched around the posts. It could be flat with rounded edges (FIG. 6-53B) or you might be able to get a special section (FIG. 6-53C). In any case, you will make the neatest finish if you attach it with counterbored screws covered with wood plugs (FIG. 6-53D).

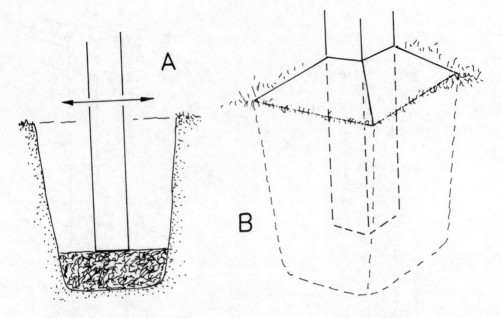

Fig. 6-52. *Post position in the ground can be adjusted, then concreted in.*

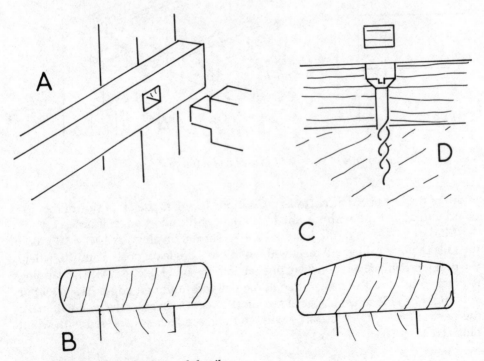

Fig. 6-53. *Handrail sections and details.*

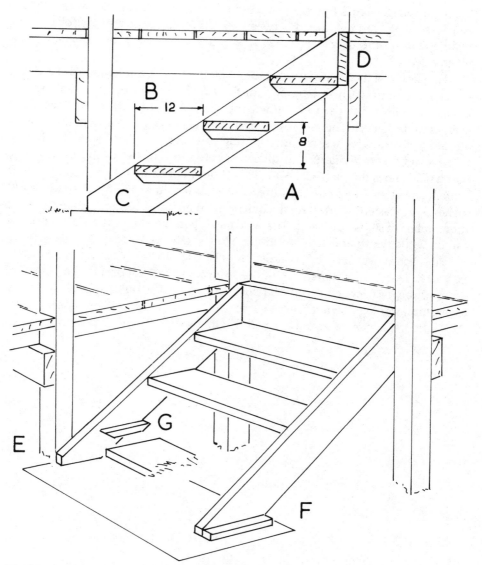

Fig. 6-54. Construction of a staircase for the deck with pergola.

Posts 6, 7, 9, and 10 could be cut square and an overhanging square capping should be fitted or rounded (FIG. 6-51F). Avoid a plain exposed square cut, as that might encourage rainwater to enter the end grain.

The pergola roof is supported by two beams (FIG. 6-50B and C). They could be the same height, but a slight slope looks better. Bolt them to posts 1, 4, 5, and 8. They could be cut level, although a short overhang looks better. How many and how long you arrange the strips across the top depends on appearance in the particular situation. If there will be vines or anything else with spreading and luxuriant foliage across the top, you could arrange the strips 12 inches or more apart, so foliage can be draped between. If you do not expect much foliage, but will depend on the pergola itself as shade and decoration, the strips could be much closer.

The design of the staircase will depend on the type of land and how far down the stairs have to reach. It is important for safety and convenience that anyone using the stairway steps up or down the same amount with each tread from ground to deck level. The amount of each step is its *rise* (FIG. 6-54A). This is usually fairly close to 8 inches, so the first thing you have to do is measure the height to be covered and divide it into divisions between 7 inches and 9 inches. The width of a step is its *run* (FIG. 6-54B). This should not be less than the rise, and it actually is better if it is more. In this case, you will have plenty of space, so 12 inches is suggested. Mark out 8 inches by 12 inches and continue doing this for the number of steps you need. That will show you the run of the stairs and you can draw the width and size of the stair *stringer* (FIG. 6-54C).

Fit a board over the deck boards and joist (FIG. 6-54D). Make a level concrete pad for the foot of the stairs. Mount the stringers inside the posts. The inner one can probably be fastened to the next post (FIG. 6-54E). The outer stringer will need a cleat for fastening down to the concrete (FIG. 6-54F). Support the treads on cleats (FIG. 6-54G). You can also screw or nail through the stringers.

7

Animal Houses

If you have pets, breed birds, raise poultry, keep farm animals, or own a pony or horse, you need housing for them, which might range from the simplest shelter to a structure at least as large and strong as a workshop or garage.

In many cases, these shelters are quite crude, which might be satisfactory if all you need is temporary shelter. Usually it is better to give almost as much thought to this building as you would to a place for your own use. Even if what you build will be standing in a field, you should consider its appearance. If it will be in your yard or near your house, something less than well-made will offend your craftsmanlike instincts every time you look at it. The building should also be fit for its purpose: to provide the animals with shelter, protect them from predators, and keep them within the limits you have set.

You can partially prefabricate smaller animal or bird houses, but most of their assembly will have to be on-site. You can make the smallest buildings completely in your shop, or alongside it, then take them to their permanent location. You will have to make the biggest buildings in sections to fit together on-site, in the same way as many other buildings already described.

Many buildings need to be portable, at least to a limited extent. If they are open to the ground, you will want to move them to another position after the ground underneath has been fouled or usefully manured. Handles at the ends or corners might be all you need, or you might have to fit wheels at one end so you can lift the other end and push or pull. You might have to fit an even larger building with four wheels. If you can arrange three wheels, that makes moving in any direction easier.

Ark

A small shelter light enough for two people to carry is useful for small birds and animals, such as ducks, which might wander freely during the day, but which need a closed shelter at night. An ark is a simple, V-roofed building. You can vary sizes to suit the animals. Pigs will need a much bigger ark than ducks or other domestic birds. The ark shown in FIG. 7-1 measures 60 inches in all directions and will suit a small flock of ducks or hens. It does not have a bottom, and you can move it to a new position every day, if necessary. One end has a lifting door. This shelter needs to have an opening big enough for the birds or animals to pass easily, but it should not be any larger. It is shown in FIG. 7-2A about 18 inches high and 16 inches wide.

Fig. 7-1. *You can move this light ark for small animals or birds easily.*

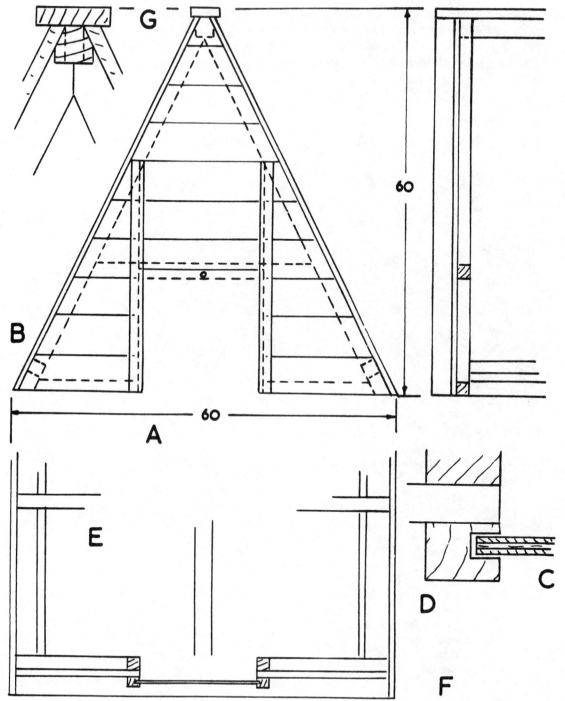

Fig. 7-2. Sizes and sections of the ark.

Make the door end first. Halve the bottom corner joints and the end of the bar above the opening with its door uprights. At the top, cut down for a 1-inch-thick capping and notch to make a tenon on a ridge piece (FIG. 7-3A). To avoid the complication of a three-way, sloping-bottom corner joint, notch the roof framing for lengthwise pieces above the corner joint (FIGS. 7-2B and 7-3B).

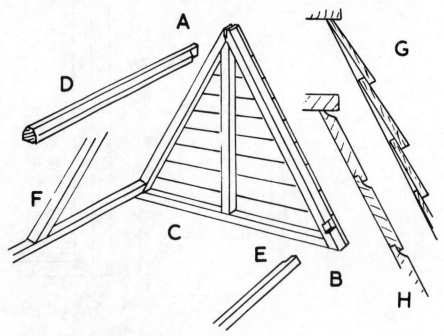

Fig. 7-3. Constructional details of the ark.

Materials List for Ark

6 rafters	2 × 2 × 70
1 bottom	2 × 2 × 6
2 bottoms	2 × 2 × 24
1 rail	2 × 2 × 48
1 post	2 × 2 × 60
2 door sides	2 × 2 × 40
2 side rails	2 × 2 × 60
1 ridge	2 × 2 × 60
1 capping	2 × 4 × 64
1 door	18 × -18- × -½ plywood

Covering 1- × -6 boards, plain, shiplap, or tongue-and-groove

Cover the framing with horizontal boarding. These boards could be plywood, shiplap boards, tongue-and-groove boards, or just plain boards. The door might be a piece of 1/2-inch, exterior-grade plywood (FIG. 7-2C). Make guides with grooves (FIG. 7-2D). These guides will keep the door 1/4 inch forward of the covering boards and allow it to slide very easily. With a hole at the top of the door, you can use a cord or wire to a hook or nail to hold the door up. You cannot lift the door out, so it is unlikely that you will lose it during the day. You can remove it if you lift the end of the ark off the floor.

Make the opposite end to match. It could also have a door, but it is shown closed in FIG. 7-3C. Take the bottom rail right across and include a central post if your covering needs stiffening. In both ends, finish the covering boards level with the framing all around, including the doorway edges.

Make the ridge piece (FIG. 7-3D) with its edges matching the slopes of the sides and with tenons to fit in the slots in the tops of the ends. Make the two bottom side rails with their ends halved to fit in the notches in the ark ends (FIG. 7-3E).

Whether you should include any other framing or not depends on the stiffness of the covering boards and the length of the ark. For a length of 60 inches, it probably will be advisable to include central rafters (FIGS. 7-2E and 7-3F) between the bottom rails and the ridge piece.

The roof covering might be exterior-grade plywood, simple, overlapping weatherboarding (FIG. 7-3G), or shiplap boards (FIG. 7-3H). Let the boards extend about 3 inches past the ark ends (FIG. 7-2F). At the ridge, flatten the edges of the boards and nail on a capping (FIG. 7-2G).

Mini Hen House

If you want to keep just a few laying hens, you do not need a large house for them. This poultry house is intended for four hens or maybe six bantams. You could use it for ducks, but you would have to fit it with a solid floor instead of the slats. The mini hen house shown in FIGS. 7-4 and 7-5 is without a run, but if you want to stop your little flock from wandering too far, there is a suitable run described after this project.

Construction may be quite light, and a skin of plywood on 1-inch-×-2-inch strips is suggested. There is a pop hole with a sliding door. One perch is provided, and there is a single nest box opposite it. The roof hinges open for access to the entire house, which you can move easily to a different position.

Make the front (FIG. 7-5A) with the framing having its 2-inch side against the plywood for top and sides, but having the 1-inch side towards the plywood across the bottom. The hole is 11 inches wide and high.

Make the door and its guides in the same way as for the ark (FIG. 7-2). Frame the back in the same way as the front, but make it 24 inches high. Drill 2-inch ventilation holes high in each part.

Make the pair of sides (FIG. 7-5B). Use the framing strips in the same manner

Fig. 7-4. A mini hen house made of plywood and suitable for a few laying hens.

as the back and front, but at the corners, allow for the plywood to overlap (FIG. 7-5C). Bevel the top edge of the front to match the slope of the sides. There is no need to bevel the top edge of the back. Notch the corner strips over each other at the bottom, when you nail the walls together.

The roof is a single piece of plywood overhanging 3 inches all around (FIG. 7-5D). Frame around the underside to fit very loosely inside the walls—this prevents roof warping since you do not make a close fit in the walls. At the front, where you are to place the hinges, put a strip across above the plywood (FIG. 7-5E) to take the screws. Two 3-inch hinges should be adequate. You could have a fastener at the back, but its weight will hold the roof closed.

Put supports for the perch (FIG. 7-6A) at both ends, about 6 inches from the bottom and side. The perch is a square section, but take sharpness off the edges. Make the slatted floor (FIG. 7-5F) of 1-inch-square strips with rounded edges.

Make the slatted floor (FIG. 7-5F) of 1-inch-square strips with rounded edges, nailing them 3 inches apart (FIG. 7-6B) to the bottom strips on the sides. If the house is for ducks, put in a plywood floor in place of the slats, or on top of the slats if you might want to use the house for hens later.

Make the nesting box of plywood, with framing strips holding it into the corner (FIG. 7-6C). The sizes shown should suit one bird, but check your bird's needs. The only access to the nesting box is by lifting the roof. No feeding or drinking arrangements are in the house, since it is assumed it is only to be used for sleeping and nesting.

Materials List for Mini Hen House

7 pieces	1 × 2 × 38
6 pieces	1 × 2 × 44
6 pieces	1 × 2 × 32
4 pieces	1 × 2 × 26
1 perch	1 × 1 × 44
9 slats	1 × 1 × 38
2 sides	30- × -42- × -$\frac{3}{8}$ plywood
1 front	30- × -38- × -$\frac{3}{8}$ plywood
1 back	26- × -38- × -$\frac{3}{8}$ plywood
1 roof	42- × -50- × -$\frac{3}{8}$ plywood
Nest box and door	12- × -36- × -$\frac{3}{8}$ plywood

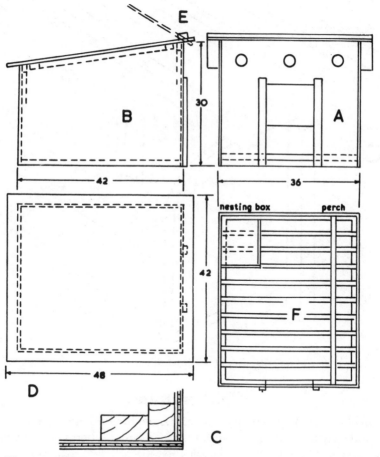

Fig. 7-5. Sizes and internal arrangements of the mini hen house.

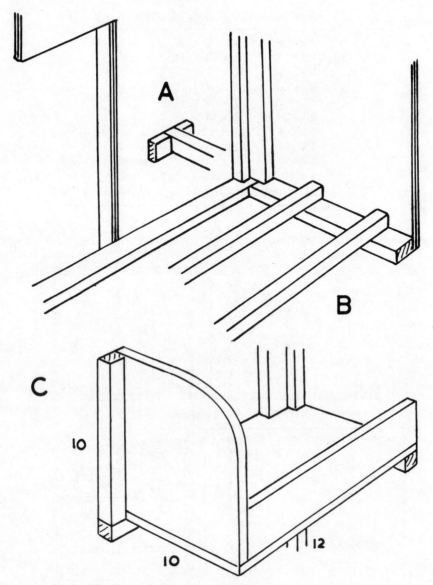

Fig. 7-6. Perches and laying box for the hen house.

Chicken Run

With a small poultry house or ark, you can allow the birds to roam freely during the day and only be shut up at night. Occasions exist when you need to restrict their movement. Some kinds of chickens require limited movement. Small animals, such as rabbits, need a restricted run. For the occasions when you require a small run, it is helpful to have one that you can put against any house with a door at ground level.

Materials List for Chicken Run

2 bottom sides	1 × 4 × 86
2 top sides	1 × 3 × 86
2 bottom ends	1 × 4 × 30
2 top ends	1 × 3 × 30
8 uprights	1 × 3 × 22
12 tops	1 × 3 × 30
1 spacer	9- × -30- × -¼ plywood

The run shown in FIG. 7-7 is intended to go directly on the ground and fit against a pop hole in a hen house, allowing you to operate the sliding door. This run has two side frames, an end, and three top sections, one of which might hinge upwards (FIG. 7-8A). Fit 1-inch wire mesh inside all parts. Construction is mainly 1-inch- × -3-inch strips, but the bottom rails are 4 inches deep.

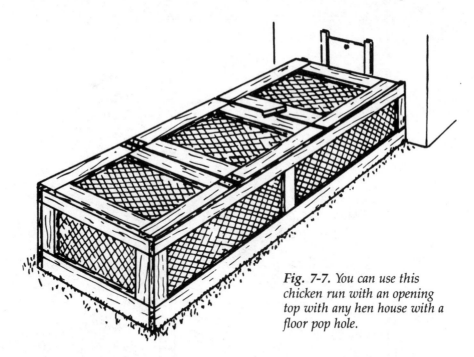

Fig. 7-7. You can use this chicken run with an opening top with any hen house with a floor pop hole.

Start by making the two sides. Various joints are possible, but we suggest you glue two ¹/₂-inch dowels each place (FIG. 7-8B). Match the two assemblies (FIG. 7-9A). Make the end the same height to fit between the sides (FIGS. 7-8C and 7-9B). To hold the other ends of the sides the same distance apart at ground level, make a thin, plywood spacer about 9 inches wide (FIGS. 7-8D and 7-9C), which you will fix between the sides, 3 inches from the end (FIG. 7-8E), when you assemble the run.

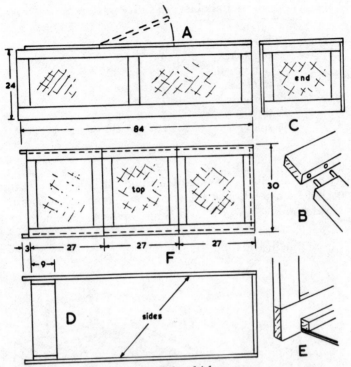

Fig. 7-8. Sizes and details of the chicken run.

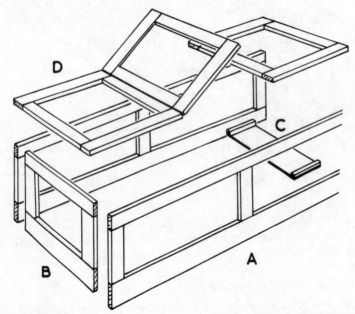

Fig. 7-9. Assembly arrangements of the parts of the chicken run.

The top sections (FIG. 7-8F) make a total length 3 inches less than the sides, leaving a gap to clear the pop-hole sliding door. Make the width and length of the top sections to match the assembled width and length of the sides and end.

Fit wire mesh inside all sections, with staples or nails bent over. Hammer any sharply cut ends of wire into the wood. Assemble the sides to the end with nails or screws, and fit the spacer at ground level near the other end. Nail or screw on the top section over the end to square the assembly (FIG. 7-9D). If the middle section is to lift, allow a little clearance for it and fix down the third section. Hinge the center section to one of the fixed sections and fit a turnbutton to secure it against pressure from inside.

Aviary Hen House

If you want to keep a few laying hens where they are unable to roam freely, you have to provide a run as well as a house. This run should be more lofty than one adequate for temporary use or for chickens.

This aviary hen house (FIGS. 7-10 and 7-11A) is intended to be as compact as possible for six or eight hens. Arrange extra run space by having the floor of the house above a part of the run, with a ramp from the doorway. If you want to close the door, hinge the ramp up and hold it with a turnbutton. There is a nest box long enough for at least three hens and doors to the run and the house.

Construction is light, with plywood that does not need to be more than 1/4 inch thick on wood that is mostly 1 1/2-inch-square section. Wire mesh is fixed inside all the run sections. The complete roof is plywood, although in a suitable climate you could have a solid roof on the house and more wire mesh over the

Fig. 7-10. The aviary hen house is a self-contained unit.

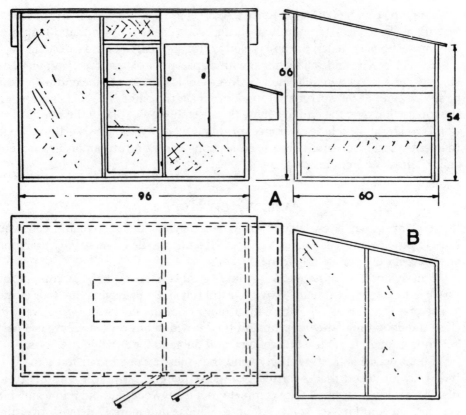

Fig. 7-11. *Sizes and layout of the aviary hen house.*

run. In an area where birds need protection from a strong prevailing wind, you can replace some of the wire mesh suggested with more plywood panels. Because of the fairly light construction, you will need to strengthen many corner joints with small, metal triangles by nailing them on one or both sides. Parts that might seem weak when you prefabricate them will gain strength when you assemble them to other parts that provide mutual support. Although you can make most sections away from the site, you should nail or screw them together since this is not intended to be a portable building.

You must match the three crosswise sections in their general outlines. At the house end, cover the frame with plywood, except for the gap for the nesting box and the wire below (FIG. 7-12A). At the other end is a matching open frame with a central upright, covered with wire mesh (FIG. 7-11B). Inside is a partition without the bottom crossbar (FIG. 7-13A). The back is a simple frame with plywood behind the house and wire mesh elsewhere. The front (FIG. 7-12C) has both doors.

You can make the aviary hen house either way around, and you can alter sizes. Decide how you want the assembly and make the house end first (FIG. 7-12A). Use it as a pattern for the outline of the opposite end (FIG. 7-11B), which

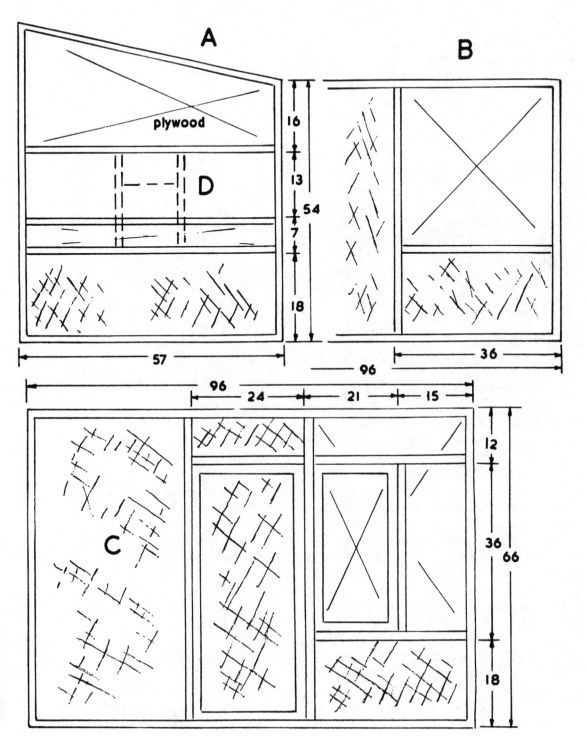

Fig. 7-12. Outside parts of the aviary hen house.

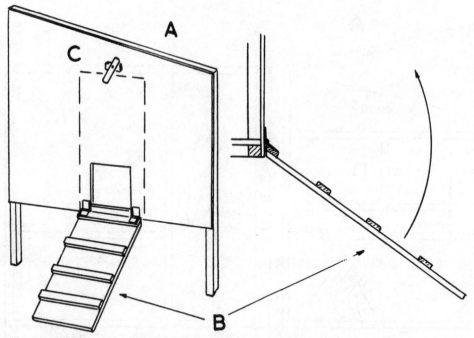

Fig. 7-13. House side and ramp for the aviary hen house.

you will cover entirely with wire. A central upright might be enough for stiffness, but you might wish to add a central, horizontal rail. For the partition (FIG. 7-13A), make the house end to match the other end. Make it in the same way, but leave out the lower nest box rail and put in two uprights at the sides of a 12-inch-square opening (FIG. 7-12D).

Make the back with pieces to match the house framing on the other parts (FIG. 7-12B). Include one or two uprights in the open part to stiffen it and provide attachment for the wire mesh. Cover the house back with plywood.

When you make the front (FIG. 7-12C), bevel the top pieces to match the slope of the roof. It is not as important to bevel the top of the back section. Fit framing to suit the house parts. Framing for the door openings should provide enough stiffness for this house without adding any additional upright in the run section.

The house door (FIG. 7-14A) is framed plywood. Arrange it to fit in the opening. Put a short or full-length stop inside. The hinges will hold the other edge, and a wooden turnbutton will keep the door closed.

Stiffen the run door with two strips across (FIG. 7-14B). Place three hinges and a stop and a turnbutton on the door similar to the house door.

Make the ramp (FIG. 7-13B) from a board that is 4 inches wider than the doorway and long enough to slope somewhere between 30 degrees and 45 degrees to the ground. Put slats across for the hens to grip. Cut the top slat to an angle that fits against the partition so you can screw hinges outside the opening, then you

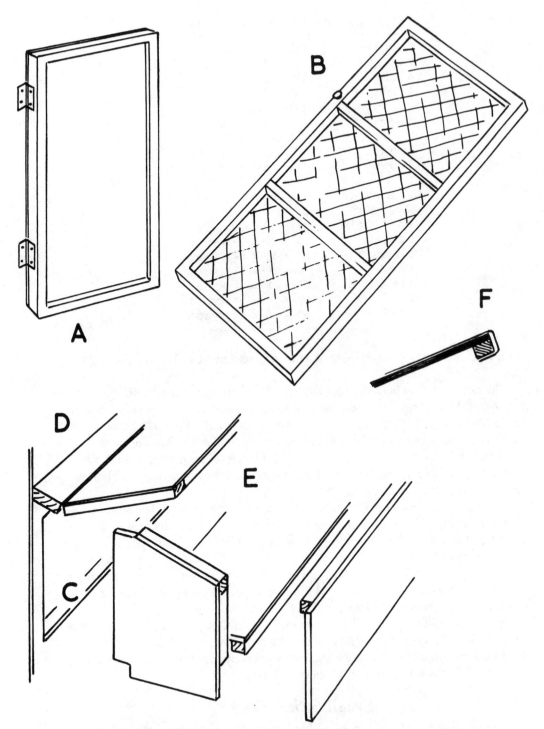

Fig. 7-14. Doors and nesting box details for the aviary hen house.

Materials List for Aviary Hen House

7 uprights	1½ x 1½ x 68
7 uprights	1½ x 1½ x 56
4 rails	1½ x 1½ x 98
14 rails	1½ x 1½ x 65
2 doors	1½ x 1½ x 56
2 doors	1½ x 1½ x 26
2 doors	1½ x 1½ x 36
2 doors	1½ x 1½ x 36
2 doors	1½ x 1½ x 23
1 ramp	16 x 26 x ¾
5 ramp strips	1 x 2 x 17
Nest box	1 x 1 x 240
1 nest box lid	1½ x 3 x 38
1 end	58- x -30- x -¼ plywood
1 partition	58- x -30- x -¼ plywood
1 front	50- x -38- x -¼ plywood
1 back	38- x -38- x -¼ plywood
1 roof	42- x -66- x -½ plywood
1 roof	66- x -66- x -½ plywood

can swing the ramp up and hold it with a block and turnbutton above (FIG. 7-13C).

The nesting box is held in place by its ends and bottom fitting into the frame (FIG. 7-14C). Frame the plywood with strips. For the lid, put a solid wooden strip against the wall (FIG. 7-14D) and hinge a framed plywood lid to it (FIG. 7-14E). You can fit all of these pieces to the end before you assemble the building.

Attach wire mesh to the insides of the frames—1-inch or 1¼-inch mesh should be satisfactory. Use staples or nails with their heads bent over. Hammer any cut ends of wire into the wood.

Level the ground where the aviary hen house is to be placed, leveling it completely or where the edges will rest so you can erect it without distortion. Screws are preferable to nails because you can join the parts tightly and there is no risk of damage from hard hammering.

Join the back and front to the partition, then the house end and the other end. Put in a sheet-plywood floor to the house part. This floor will square the whole assembly before you fasten it down.

If you use ½-inch plywood for the roof, it probably will be stiff enough without framing. Allow it to overhang at least 3 inches all around. A joint can be over the partition. You can stiffen the edges with strips underneath, which would be advisable if you want to cover the wood (FIG. 7-14F).

Small Stock Shed

Anyone keeping a variety of birds and animals will be able to use an adaptable building that can house a pig or goat or, at another time, hens. You also might be glad to use it for your own personal shelter in bad weather. When not used for animals, it would make a storage place for tools, feed, fertilizer, and many other things needed about a small farm.

The building shown in FIG. 7-15 is just high enough to stand in. It has a solid floor. A wire mesh window with a sliding shutter to adjust ventilation is shown. At the back is a slotted opening that could give access to a feed trough inside or a nest box.

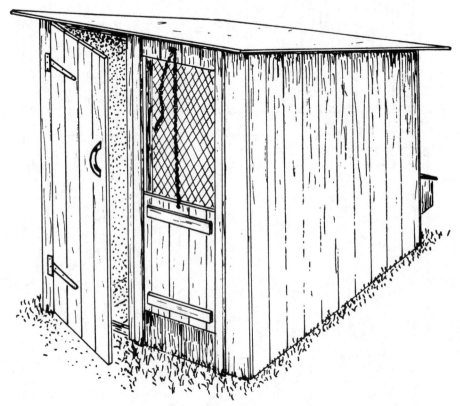

Fig. 7-15. You can adapt a small stock shed to many purposes.

Construction is sectional, so you can move the small stock shed to another site in pieces after releasing a few bolts. The drawing in FIG. 7-16A shows a covering of vertical tongue-and-groove boards, but you could use horizontal shiplap boards or exterior-grade plywood. Framing is mostly 2-inch-square wood.

Start with the pair of ends (FIG. 7-17A). Halve or tenon the frame joints. One horizontal rail might be enough, but if the skin has to withstand the antics of a lively goat or other animal, two rails might be better. The cladding should finish level with the framing all around.

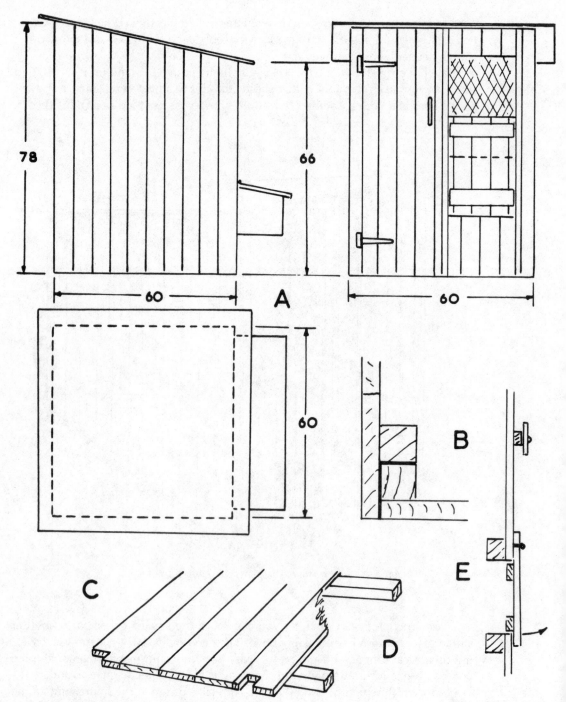

Fig. 7-16. *Sizes and details of the small stock shed.*

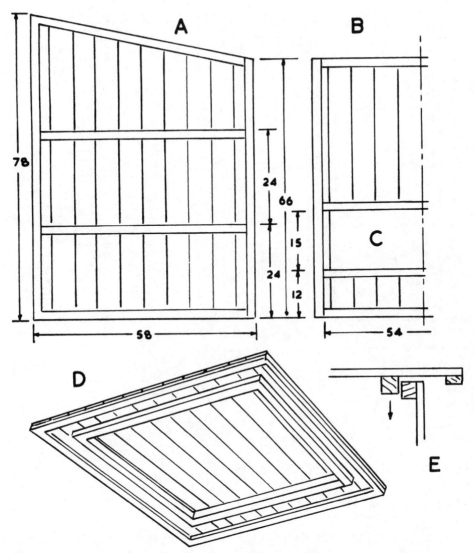

Fig. 7-17. *The sides and roof of the small stock shed.*

Make the back (FIG. 7-17B) with a height to match the ends and bevel the top to suit the slope of the roof. Fit two parallel rails for the gap at the back (FIG. 7-17C) and board over the rest of the area. At the side, allow for the boards extending over the ends (FIG. 7-16B) when you bolt the corners together.

The front has the door, the ventilating window, and the slide to cover it, but start by making the frame (FIG. 7-18A). Bevel the top edge to suit the slope of the roof. For the window opening, put strips inside the uprights between the rails (FIG. 7-18B). Cover with boards up to halfway over the upright at the doorway (FIG. 7-18C). At the other side, finish the board level with the doorway (FIG.

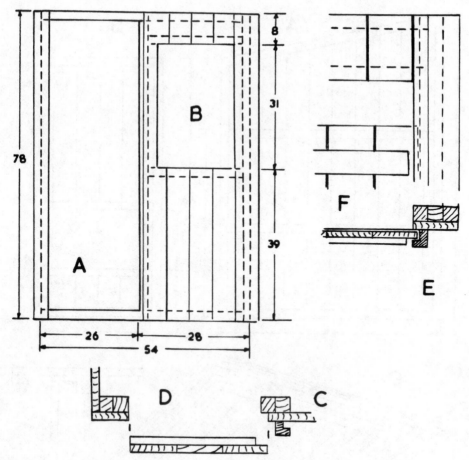

Fig. 7-18. Details of the front of the small stock shed.

7-18D). Do not fill in at top or bottom of the doorway, as the door will overlap there.

The guides for the shutter are the full height of the front. Cut rabbets to allow the shutter to slide easily (FIG. 7-18C,E). Fit them parallel at the opening width. Make the shutter from tongue-and-groove boards with ledgers across (FIG. 7-18F), keeping the ends of the ledgers clear of the guides. Fix a length of chain to the center of the top of the front, then you can hook the chain on to hold the shutter at the desired height. Nail or staple wire mesh inside the window opening.

Make the door with tongue-and-groove or plain vertical boards with three ledgers across. With the ledgers firmly attached, there should be no need for diagonal braces on this narrow door, but fit one if you think it necessary. Arrange the door to hinge on the outer edge and to overlap on the opposite upright, which will serve as a stop. At the top and bottom, allow for the door to overlap the frame with plenty of clearance, particularly at the ground. Use two or three

Materials List for Small Stock Shed

Ends

2 uprights	2 × 2 × 80
2 uprights	2 × 2 × 68
8 rails	2 × 2 × 62

Backs

2 uprights	2 × 2 × 68
4 rails	2 × 2 × 56

Front

3 uprights	2 × 2 × 68
2 rails	2 × 2 × 56
4 rails	2 × 2 × 32

Shutter and door

3 ledgers	1 × 6 × 26
2 ledgers	1 × 4 × 26
2 guides	2 × 2 × 80

Floor and roof

5 joists	2 × 2 × 60
2 roof edges	1 × 2 × 72
2 roof edges	1 × 2 × 76
4 roof frames	2 × 2 × 60

Cladding

Tongued-and-grooved boards	1 × 6

plain or T hinges, and you can hold the other side with a turnbutton, unless you want to fit a lock. Provide a wooden or metal handle.

Assemble the walls before making the floor or the roof. Coach bolts, 3/8 inch in diameter at about 18-inch centers, should be satisfactory for the corners. Have the heads outside and nuts over washers inside.

Have the assembly square and on a flat surface when you make the floor, which rests on the bottom framing and should not need to be anchored down. If it does not rest level, drive a few screws downwards. Cut boards to fit around the uprights and rest with a little clearance inside the covering boards (FIG. 7-16C). Nail these boards to joists the same height as the framing. Have one joist a short distance in from the frame and the others about 18 inches apart (FIG. 7-16D). The floor will serve to square the building when you erect it, but you have to drop it in place, so do not make it fit too tightly.

You can make a boarded roof that will lift off in one piece without covering it if you use tongue-and-groove boards, similar to those on the walls. It would be slightly lighter if you made it out of $1/2$-inch plywood. Allow for it to overhang the walls about 5 inches, and get the actual sizes by measuring the assembled building. Edge the roof with strips, which only need to be a 1-inch-×-2-inch section, since stiffening for the roof will come from the other pieces (FIG. 7-17D).

Fit 2-inch-square strips that will drop inside the walls. At back and front there might be an easy clearance, but at the sides, make the strips fit fairly closely (FIG. 7-17E), since there will be bolts through to hold the roof down. Try the roof in position, and drill holes for bolts into the side framing. The number of bolt holes depends on the situation—more are required if you experience high winds. In any case, there should be at least three $1/8$-inch coach bolts at each side.

At the back, make a flap that will hang down over the opening and swing up out of the way (FIG. 7-16E). You can make it with vertical tongue-and-groove boards, holding them with ledgers across that will clear the opening when you close them. Put a strip across to take the hinges. To hold the flap up, put two wooden turnbuttons on blocks. Fit two more to hold the flap in the down position.

If you want a nest box, make it in the same way as you made the aviary hen house (FIG. 7-14C,D,E), but use the flap just described, as the lid. Then if the box is taken away, you can still seal the opening. If the nest box is to be temporary, take its ends far enough inside for two bolts to be put through at each place.

Barn

If you need to house larger animals, the building has to be bigger and stronger than those described so far in this chapter. A horse or other large animal (or a group of animals) might put considerable strain on the structure, so it has to be substantial. You need a good barrier inside to spread any load on the walls. If the barrier is a strong, smooth lining, it reduces any risk of damage to the animals and makes cleaning easier. The building should be high enough to allow for good air circulation. These facts mean that if the building is to be adequate for its purpose, you have to be prepared to build fairly large.

The barn shown in FIG. 7-19 has a double-slope roof and double doors. It is 11 feet square and 10 feet high. Opening windows are high in the back, and shallow windows are at the sides above the lining. A building this size provides room for a horse to be stabled, with space for tack and feed. If you are concerned with smaller animals, you can accommodate two or more. The barn would also make a good place to store all the many things you would use on a small farm. The building has an attractive appearance, and you might wish to use it for many purposes in your yard. With different window arrangements, it would make a good workshop. You can alter doors to suit your needs. As shown, the doors are

Fig. 7-19. Make a strongly built barn of traditional shape with double doors and windows at the side.

big enough for small trailers or other wheeled vehicles. A motorcycle, trail bike, or even a small car could fit through them.

The drawings and instructions are for a barn framed with 2-inch-×-3-inch section wood covered with horizontal shiplap boards (FIG. 7-20). Suggested lining material is particleboard or plywood. Measure your available space. Allow for laying a concrete base larger than the barn area. You must securely bolt down a building this size. You may prefabricate the ends and sides. Roofing is done in position after you have erected the walls.

Start by making the ends (FIG. 7-21). The back (FIG. 7-21A) is closed, but the front has a 7-foot-square doorway (FIG. 7-21B). Assemble framing with the 3-inch way towards the cladding. Halve or tenon joints in the framing. Halve crossing parts of internal framing. The central rail is at the height intended for the lining. If that height does not suit your needs, alter its position. This height allows for shallow windows above the lining and under the eaves. Angles for the roof are shown (FIG. 7-21C). If you do not work exactly to these angles, it does not matter, as long as each end is symmetrical and they match.

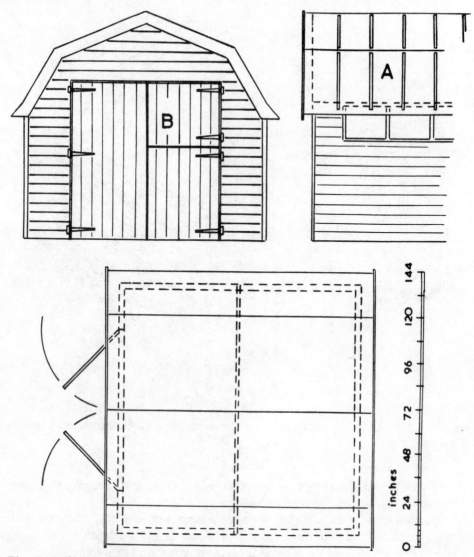

Fig. 7-20. *Suggested sizes for the barn.*

Make the back and use it as a pattern for the outline of the front. Make the bottom rail of the front right across (FIG. 7-21D), but after you have erected the walls and anchored them down, you can cut it away to give a clear door opening. You can improve appearance of the ends if you add a broad filler piece at each corner (FIG. 7-21E). To allow for this filler piece, stop the shiplap boards over the center of the corner posts. Take them to the edges of the roof slopes.

The two sides are the same (FIG. 7-22A), unless you want to fit a side door or alter the number of windows. The drawing shows four window openings on each side (FIG. 7-22B), but you could reduce this to two or none. The tops of the

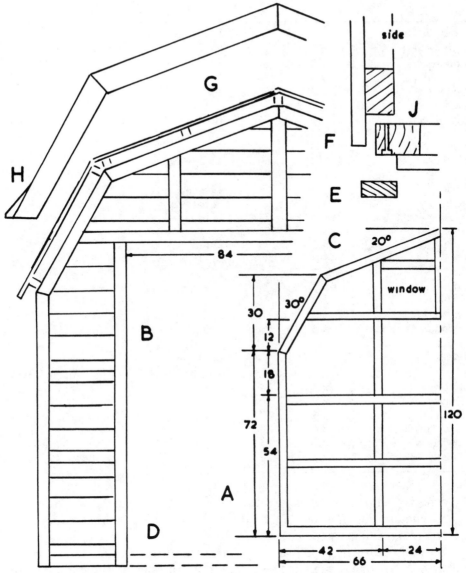

Fig. 7-21. *Details of the ends of the barn, which you should make first.*

windows are covered by the roof, so you cannot arrange them to swing outwards very much. They could open inwards, but it probably will be satisfactory to make them fixed.

Allow for the cladding boards extending at the ends to cover the end corner posts (FIG. 7-21F). Finish level at top and bottom. You do not have to bevel the top to match the slope of the roof.

You could add the lining at this stage or leave it until after erection. Take it to

Materials List for Barn

Front

2 corner posts	2	× 3	× 74
2 door posts	2	× 3	× 86
1 bottom rail	2	× 3	× 134
1 door rail	2	× 3	× 120
4 side rails	2	× 3	× 26
2 uprights	2	× 3	× 26
1 upright	2	× 3	× 36
2 rafters	2	× 3	× 84
2 rafters	2	× 3	× 60

Back

2 corner posts	2	× 3	× 74
2 posts	2	× 3	× 100
1 upright	2	× 3	× 36
3 rails	2	× 3	× 134
1 rail	2	× 3	× 12
1 rail	2	× 3	× 54
2 rafters	2	× 3	× 84
2 rafters	2	× 3	× 60
8 window linings	1	× 4	× 26

Sides

14 uprights	2	× 3	× 74
8 rails	2	× 3	× 130
8 window linings	1	× 4	× 24
16 window linings	1	× 4	× 18
8 window sills	1 1/4	× 5	× 24
4 corner fillers	1	× 2 1/2	× 74

Roof truss

2 rafters	2	× 3	× 60
1 tie	2	× 3	× 48
2 struts	2	× 3	× 120
3 gussets	2	× 3	× 60
	2	× 3	× 36

Roof

1 ridge	2	× 4	× 150
8 purlins	2	× 3	× 150
4 bargeboards	1	× 6	× 90
4 bargeboards	1	× 6	× 80
14 battens	1/2	× 1 1/2	× 84
14 battens	1/2	× 1 1/2	× 60

Doors

7 ledgers	1	× 6	× 42
4 braces	1	× 6	× 70
Covering boards	1-×-6 tongued-and-grooved boards		
3 door linings	1	× 5	× 86
8 edges	1	× 3	× 40

Cladding

ends and sides	1-×-6 shiplap boards or equivalent
roof	1-×-6 plain or tongued-and-grooved boards
doors	1-×-6 plain or tongued-and-grooved boards
lining	1/2 or 3/4 particleboard or plywood

the window line (FIG. 7-22C). Cover it there with a sill extending outwards (FIG. 7-22D). Line the tops and sides of the openings (FIG. 7-22E). The roof will provide protection to the upper parts of the windows.

The roof needs a truss halfway along. This truss must match the ends of the building, so use one of the ends as a pattern for the shape. The outline is the same down to the top of the side panels. As no boards are across to strengthen the framing, securely nail or screw gussets under the angles (FIG. 7-23A). The tie is the same height as the rail above the doorway. From its center, take struts at 45 degrees to it, up to the rafters (FIG. 7-23B). Cut the rafters to rest on the tops of the side frames, with locating blocks there (FIG. 7-23C). The purlins are 2 inches × 3 inches, and the ridge is from 2-inch-×-4-inch stock. Bevel the top of the ridge piece to match the slope of the roof (FIG. 7-23D). These slopes have to match the tops of the purlins. Measure their heights, and cut down the tops of the ends

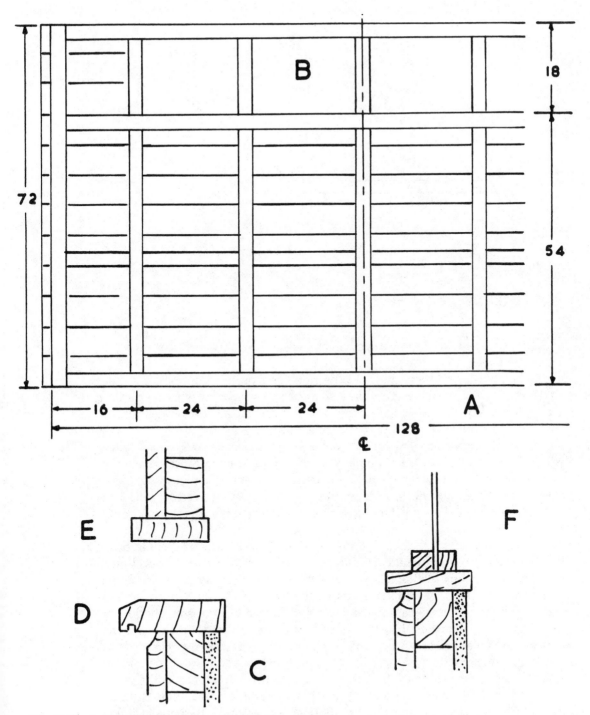

Fig. 7-22. A side of the barn and sections at the windows.

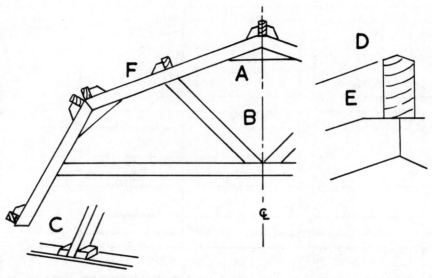

Fig. 7-23. Details of the barn-roof truss.

and the truss so the roof at the ridge will be the same height from the framing as it is at the purlins (FIG. 7-23E).

Make cleats to position and hold the ridge and purlins (FIG. 7-23F). At the angle of the roof, put the purlins as close together as possible. The top purlins are midway between the angle of the roof and the ridge. The lower purlins should come close to the joint with the sides.

Assemble the walls, using 1/2-inch bolts, sink their heads so the cover strips will hide them (FIG. 7-21J). For ample strength in any circumstances, have the bolts at about 12-inch centers. Check squareness and fasten down to the base. Cut out the bottom of the end frame under the doorway. If necessary, nail on temporary braces to keep the building square and to hold the truss upright until you fit the roof.

The purlins and ridge should extend 6 inches at each end. Fix them in position. The roof covering could be shingles over 1/2-inch plywood, but 1-inch boarding, covered by roofing felt or any of the sheet-roof material supplied in a roll, taken over the ridge and turned under the roof boards as described for several other buildings, is suggested. Cut the board ends to meet reasonably close at the ridge and at the angles. Take the ends of the boards to about 1 inch below the tops of the building sides. A gap will be all around under the roof boards. You can leave the gap entirely or in part for ventilation, or you can fill the narrow spaces against the lower purlins or the wider gaps between purlins at the ends.

Make bargeboards at the end (FIG. 7-21G). Take the ends a short distance below the roof edges. You can give a traditional appearance with triangles if you turn the board line outwards (FIG. 7-21H). Put battens down the slope of the roof over the covering at about 18-inch intervals (FIG. 7-20A).

The double doors are ledgered and braced, but because of their size and weight, you must double them around the edges (FIG. 7-24A). Put lining strips around the door opening, covering the wall lining as well as the cladding (FIG. 7-24B). Make the doors with vertical tongue-and-groove boards. Put braces across, level with the board ends, and fill in to the same thickness at the edges (FIG. 7-24C). So the diagonal braces take any compression loads that come on

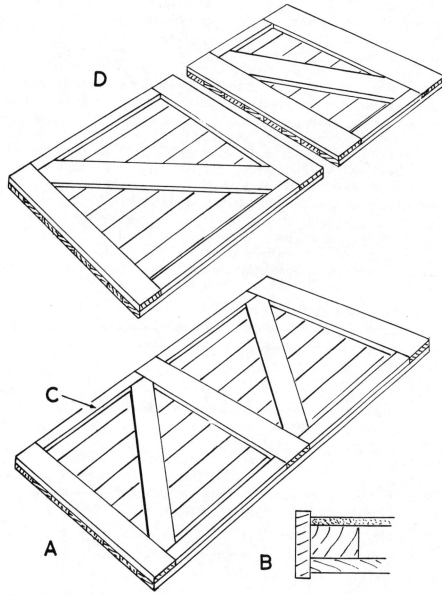

Fig. 7-24. Construction of the barn doors.

them without allowing movement, fit them closely at their ends, making sure there are no gaps which might cause the door to drop.

You could make one half in two parts for the usual stable door pattern (FIGS. 7-20B and 7-24D). A height of 48 inches would give a horse about 36 inches to put its head through, but the gap would not be big enough for most animals to jump through. Make each door part similar to the large door, with bracing upwards from the hinge side.

T hinges about 18 inches long would be suitable for hanging the doors. Notch the lining strips around the doorway for the hinges, which should come over the ledges on the doors and be held with long screws in both parts. You can take bolts right through to nuts instead of using screws. Arrange bolts upwards and downwards on the inner edge of one door, and place a lock on the other door to close it or a hasp and staple for a padlock. Put handles on the outside of both doors. If you make one door in two parts, put a bolt inside to hold them together when you want to use the parts as one.

How you make the windows depends on the use of the barn. If you want it to be weathertight, the windows should be made closely. The overhang of the roof, however, gives partial protection to the windows, and you can use a simple construction if a slight risk of leakage is not important. With the window openings lined, you can hold glass in between double strips (FIG. 7-22F). You could embed the glass in jointing compound, but another way would be to put single strips around the glass and putty the glass against them.

For better windows, frame them separately to fit in the openings (FIG. 5-4). If you want any windows to open by being hinged at the top, make them this way.

Stable

You could use the barn just described for a horse, but it is a general-purpose building with several other uses. If you want to build a stable, you can include features to suit that purpose only. This stable is designed to suit one fairly large horse, with an adjoining storage space for feed, tack, and all the equipment associated with keeping a horse. For more than one horse, you can extend the building two or three times. For a pony, you can reduce the sizes slightly.

The stable shown in FIGS. 7-25 and 7-26A has accommodations that are 11 feet × 12 feet, and there is a separate section built in alongside which is 6 feet × 11 feet. Both parts are under the same roof, which extends to make a 4-foot-wide canopy at the front, so the area covered by the building is about 17 feet square. A concrete base should extend several feet beyond this, and you must make provisions for anchoring the building securely. Besides any effect of wind, a horse that throws its weight against a wall could move an insecure building. You may bolt down through the bottom rails. An alternative is to leave gaps in the concrete base for bars extending downwards, which you can concrete in after you have erected the building (FIG. 7-26B).

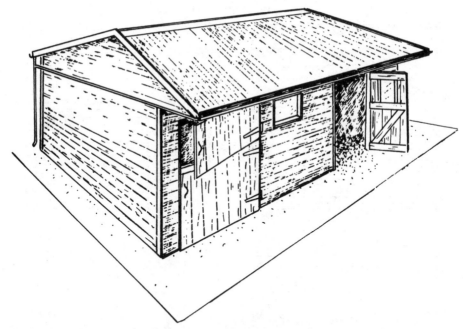

Fig. 7-25. *This stable has a store or tack room built in alongside.*

Most of the structure is 2-inch-×-3-inch-section wood, with shiplap boards outside and 3/4-inch plywood as high as a horse might kick and a thinner lining above that. You can board and cover the roof similar to many earlier buildings, but corrugated metal or plastic is suggested, with gutters at the eaves. The instructions only cover the making of the building. You will want to add a manger, hay rack, bucket holder, tie ring, and other stable equipment. The tack room will require various racks and a table, much of which you can build in. You can leave the roof area unlined with gaps at the edges for ventilation, or you could seal it only, or you could attach lining sheets as well under the purlins. You can use the roof area for storage, or you could fit a flat ceiling in the tack room for comfort.

Although the building is large and some sections are heavy enough to require help in making and erecting them, construction is simple and very similar to some of the smaller buildings. If you can make sections flat on the concrete base, they should be easy to move into place for erection.

The building is shown without windows except at the front, which is what many horse owners prefer. You also could have windows high in the back or end of the stables and above bench level in the tack room, fitting them into spaces in the framing and making them as described for the barn and other buildings. The following instructions allow for a window beside the stable door and one in the door of the tack room.

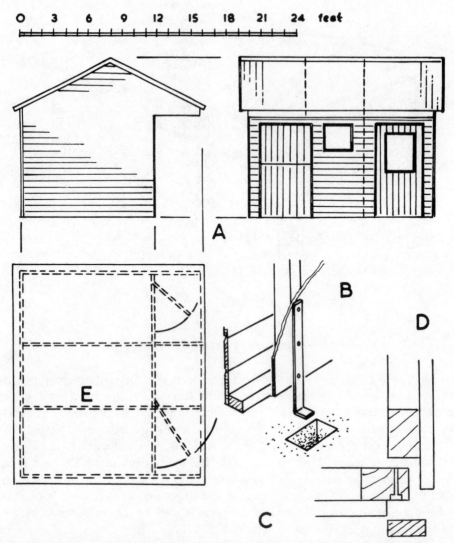

Fig. 7-26. *Sizes and layout of the stable with details on how to attach the foundations and assemble corners.*

The pair of ends and the division between the stable portion and the tack room are almost the same. Make one end and use it as a guide when making the other parts. Also use it to check the height of the back. All framing is 2-inch-×-3-inch wood with the 2-inch side towards the cladding.

Make the framing with halved joints where parts cross, but at the outside, you could notch or use tenons. Space uprights evenly in the width (FIG. 7-27A) and in the height to the eaves. This spacing should suit cladding with shiplap boards or vertical tongue-and-groove boards. At the eaves, drop the main horizontal member 4 inches (FIG. 7-27B). Mortise-and-tenon joints are advisable here,

Ends and division

3 uprights	2 × 3 × 104
6 uprights	2 × 3 × 130
6 uprights	2 × 3 × 145
9 rails	2 × 3 × 146
3 rails	2 × 3 × 194
6 rafters	2 × 3 × 112
6 braces	2 × 3 × 50
4 corner fillers	1 × 3 × 104

Back

7 uprights	2 × 3 × 104
4 rails	2 × 3 × 200
2 braces	2 × 3 × 55

Front

4 uprights	2 × 3 × 100
3 uprights	2 × 3 × 90
2 uprights	2 × 3 × 30
1 upright	2 × 3 × 70
2 braces	2 × 3 × 80

Roof truss

1 tie	2 × 3 × 194
2 rafters	2 × 3 × 112
1 post	2 × 3 × 52
2 diagonals	2 × 3 × 56

Window

4 linings	1 × 6 × 30
8 fillets	1 × 1 × 30

Canopy

1 rail	2 × 4 × 210
1 fascia	1 × 6 × 210
5 joists	2 × 3 × 56
1 fillet	1 × 1 × 210

Roof

10 purlins	2 × 4 × 220
4 bargeboards	1 × 6 × 120

Stable door

10 boards	1 × 6 × 60 tongued and grooved
10 boards	1 × 6 × 45 tongued and grooved
4 ledgers	1 × 6 × 56
2 braces	1 × 6 × 72
2 linings	1 × 6 × 90
1 lining	1 × 6 × 56

Tack room door

7 boards	1 × 6 × 90 tongued and grooved
3 ledgers	1 × 6 × 44
2 strips	1 × 3 × 40
1 brace	1 × 6 × 50
2 linings	1 × 6 × 90
1 lining	1 × 6 × 44

Covering

cladding	1- × -6 shiplap boards
lining	½ or ¾ plywood or particleboard
canopy	½ plywood

even if you use other joints elsewhere. This arrangement allows simpler and stronger eaves joints than if the parts met at the same level, and it provides for a board at the edge of the canopy.

Although firmly fixed cladding will help to brace the assembly, it might be advisable to include sway bracing (FIG. 7-27C) in two panels.

Fit the cladding on the ends to the edges of the roof portion. At the corners, stop it at half the thickness of the uprights to allow for filler strips (FIG. 7-26C).

You can line the ends now, allowing for where the other uprights have to fit,

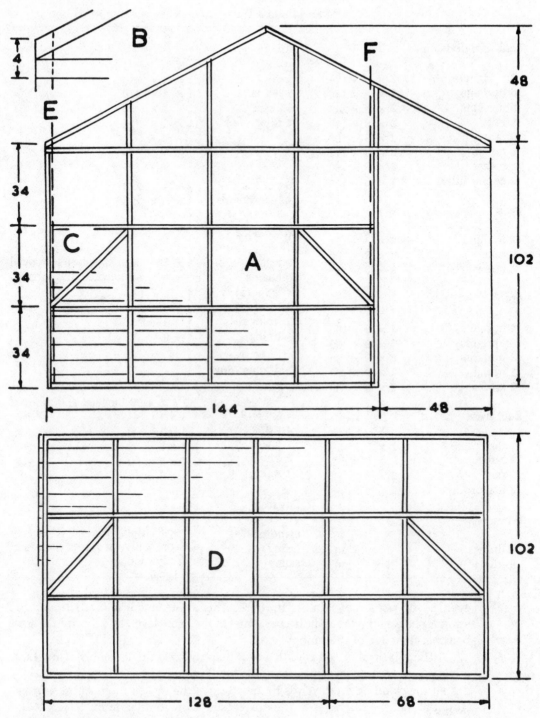

Fig. 7-27. An end and back of the stable.

or leave it until after you have erected the building. Use 1/2-inch or 3/4-inch plywood or particleboard from the floor level to the rail, 68 inches up. If you intend to line with lighter material above this point, stop the thick lining at half the thickness of the rail to allow space for nailing the additional lining above it. Stop the lining on the edges of the corner uprights.

The framing of the division is the same as an end, except you must cut the rear edge back by the thickness of the back framing (3 inches) to fit inside (FIGS. 7-27E and 7-28A) and the front upright must fit similarly (FIG. 7-27F). Line the framing on both sides. Although you could add some of the lining at this stage, you should fit it into the back and front for the best finish (FIG. 7-28B). It is easier to fit the lining after erection when you have the parts bolted together.

The back (FIG. 7-27D) settles lengthwise arrangements. If you want to alter them, do it now. Fit one upright against the division. Space other uprights evenly. Include some sway bracing. Height should match the ends, but you do not need to bevel the top edge to match the slope of the roof.

Make the cladding long enough on the back to overlap the end-corner uprights (FIG. 7-26D) behind the filler strips that you will put in after erection. It is better to line the back after erection so you can get at the assembly bolts and fit it closely to the linings of the ends and the division.

Place a roof truss over the center of the stable part (FIGS. 7-26E and 7-28C). If you increase the size of the stable, add two trusses. Use an end as a guide to the outline shape, but make the truss with the 3-inch direction of the wood upwards, for stiffness. Be sure the lower edge of the tie is at the same level as the bottom edge of the long rail, in the end.

The rafter part of the truss should follow the same lines as the ends. Notch it over the back (FIG. 7-28D). At the front, it finishes like an end frame so it holds the strip along the edge (FIG. 7-28E). At both ends, put fillers between the rafters and the tie. When you assemble the building, put blocks as cleats on each side of the truss end at the back and each side of the tie where it rests on the front.

The front (FIG. 7-28F) should be the same length as the back, to fit between the ends, but its height should be to the undersides of the main rails in the ends. You already made the undersides of the truss tie to suit this design. A height is shown, but check this against the parts which you must match. To keep the frame in shape, carry the bottom rail through in one piece. Leave this rail in place until after you have erected the building walls and attached them to the base. At this time, you might cut away the parts in the doorways, unless you prefer to leave them in. Leaving them in might be advisable if you will be putting a wooden floor on the concrete. Because of the doorways, much of the front framing lacks some lateral stiffening from the cladding and lining, so include the spray bracing shown in the only wide part of the covering.

Fit cladding to overhang the ends in the same way as the back (FIG. 7-26D). Leave lining until after you have erected the walls, so you can fit closely to that on the ends and division.

When you have erected the building, the roof truss comes directly over the

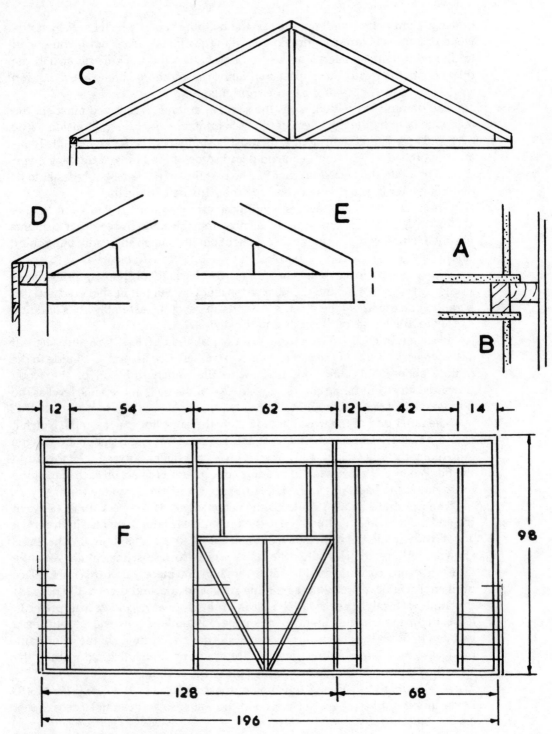

Fig. 7-28. A roof truss and front of the stable.

upright at the back, halfway along the stable section. Keep this truss parallel with an end so it will cross the front close to an upright, but not directly over it. Put cleats on the top edge of the front to locate and secure the truss.

Use 1/2-inch bolts through the corners and division at a spacing of less than 19 inches. It is advisable to assemble the walls and division, square them, and attach them to the base before fitting the roof and doors. Have the roof truss in position, and be sure the assembly is square in all directions, by checking diagonals. Use temporary struts, if necessary, to brace the structure until you add the roof.

The suggested roof is made of corrugated metal or plastic sheets on 2-inch-×-4-inch purlins, which overhang about 6 inches at each end. The arrangement of purlins will depend on the choice of sheet. For the length of slope shown, you can use sheets 60 inches long, with a 6-inch overlap on a purlin (FIG. 7-29A). For sheets of other lengths, you might have to alter the position of a purlin to get it under a joint. Purlins should be less than 25 inches apart, with the top ones as high as possible and the other one close to the eaves. Use cleats for location and fixing (FIG. 7-29B). Attach the sheets with large-headed nails or with the fastenings recommended by the sheet suppliers. Cover the ends of sheets and purlins with boards (FIG. 7-29C). Fit a ridge piece to match the sheets (FIG. 7-29D).

At the front of the canopy, fit a length of 2-inch-×-4-inch wood to the vertical ends of the rafters (FIG. 7-29E). You must fill the space between this wood and the front cladding. You can board it, but 1/2-inch or thicker exterior plywood is suggested. The existing horizontal projections are insufficient to provide enough support to keep the plywood flat. Put more joists in place at less than 31-inch intervals. At their outer ends, nail to the strip across (FIG. 7-29F). Take the inner ends over the front and secure them with cleats (FIG. 7-29G). Nail the plywood upwards and secure the inner edge with a strip (FIG. 7-29H).

Put a fascia board along the front (FIG. 7-29J) to cover the edge of the plywood. Fit a gutter with brackets to this board. This gutter might be led across an end to join the rear gutter at one downpipe, or it could have its own downpipe to a soakaway or a water barrel.

Fit lining pieces around the doorways and the windows to cover the cladding and lining (FIG. 7-30A). The canopy protects the window, so there would be no need for a wider sill.

Make the two-part stable door in the same way as described for the barn door (FIG. 7-24D), but line both parts in the same way as the walls. Hang it with similar T hinges, and fit a strong fastener or lock or hasp and staple for a padlock. Have a sliding bolt between the two parts. Fit a catch to hold the upper part, or the two combined, in the open position.

Some horses might chew the top edge of the lower door. Wrap and nail a piece of sheet metal over the edge (FIG. 7-30B) to protect it.

The tack-room door does not have to be quite as substantial, but it should be strong—if it is light enough to flex, you might crack the window. Make this door with three ledgers. Space two to suit the size window you want and arrange a

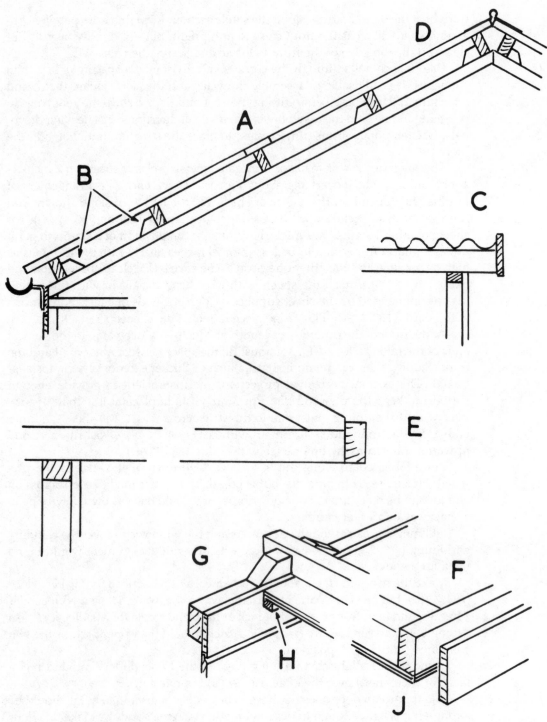

Fig. 7-29. *Roofing details of the stable.*

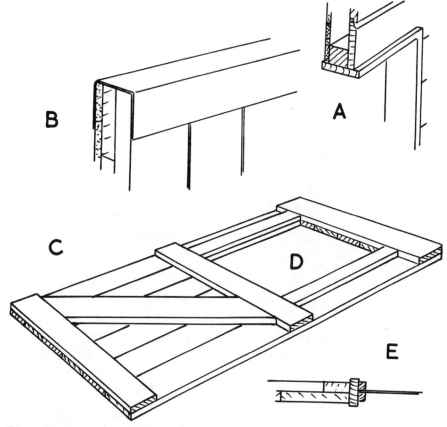

Fig. 7-30. Door and doorway details for the stable.

closely fitting brace in the panel below (FIG. 7-30C). Put a lining strip around the window opening (FIG. 7-30D) and mount the glass between two fillets (FIG. 7-30E). Nail them in so they can be removed easily if you have to replace the glass. Hinges could match those on the stable door and you probably will want to fit a lock.

You can fit the window in the stable in the same way, or you could arrange an opening window similar to those of the barn.

Dog Kennel

The common dog kennel with an end doorway does not provide much protection when the wind blows rain in the direction of the door. If you make it as a one-piece building, cleaning is difficult. The kennel shown in FIG. 7-31 has a porch, a raised floor, and a roof that lifts when you want to get at the inside to clean or for other reasons. The sizes suggested in FIG. 7-32 should suit a dog of

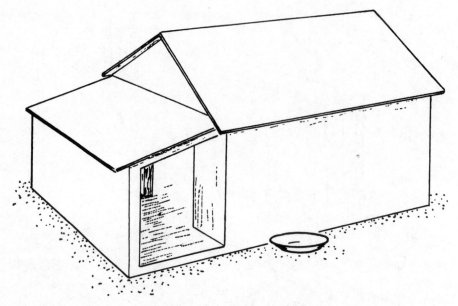

Fig. 7-31. A porch shelters the entrance of this dog kennel.

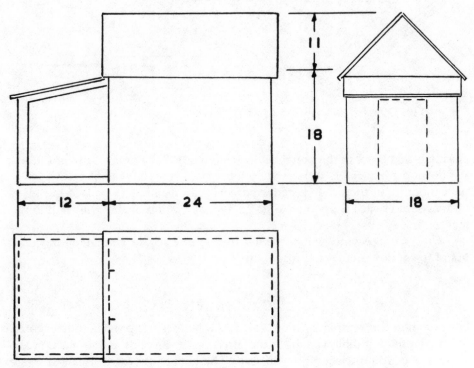

Fig. 7-32. Suggested sizes for the dog kennel.

medium size, but you can modify them easily if you think your dog would be happier with a different size.

Construction is with 1/2-inch exterior-grade plywood on a frame of 1-inch-×-2-inch strips. Covering could be with tongue-and-groove boards, or shiplap boards would look good on the walls. You could paint the roof, but it might be better if you use roofing felt or similar material on it.

It probably would be satisfactory if you merely nail all joints, but you can halve some. Use water-resistant glue between the plywood and the framing, with plenty of fine nails.

Start by making the closed end and the part with the entrance hole. At the entrance end (FIG. 7-33A), notch the bottom corners so the lengthwise rails can go through to the porch (FIG. 7-33B). You could do the same at the top corners, although it probably will be sufficient to rely on the plywood holding the lengthwise rail in place. Cut the plywood at the bottom notches. At the doorway, round all edges of the frame and plywood. Make the closed end similar to the end with the entrance, but without the door framing. Do not notch the plywood at the corners.

The gable ends (FIG. 7-33C) have a 45-degree slope and are as wide as the other parts over the plywood sides. Notch the framing and not the plywood for the lengthwise parts (FIG. 7-33D). Check that the width matches the other parts and that the two gable ends are a pair.

Make the two bottom side rails (FIG. 7-34A) with halving joints to match the ends. For the open side, join on plywood, extending enough to overlap the plywood on the ends, with a strip to fit between them at the top. You can halve this strip if you wish (FIG. 7-34B). Make a longer piece of plywood for the closed side (FIG. 7-34C), cut down by the thickness of its roof. You can do the framing of the edges of this part when you assemble the kennel by adding the porch end.

The porch end (FIG. 7-34D) is the same width as the main ends and is as high as the sloping side. Notch the bottom framing to match the lengthwise strips. Place the top-crosswise piece edgewise, and bevel the top part to suit the slope of the porch roof.

Assemble all the parts made so far. Add a stiffening piece to the top edge of the porch back and the porch front. Make a bottom of plywood to rest on the bottom frame strips. To get the bottom in, you will have to make a joint across the doorway. You can leave it loose so you can remove it for cleaning, but if you want to make it insect-proof, embed it in glue and nail it down. The gluing and nailing also will contribute to strength and keep the kennel in shape if the ground underneath is uneven.

Nail a strip above the entrance hole to support the inner end of the porch roof, with its top sloping to suit. Put on the plywood porch roof, placing it close to the main end and overhanging the walls by 1 inch. Notch it under the main roof. Round the exposed edges and corners, particularly if you will not be covering this roof.

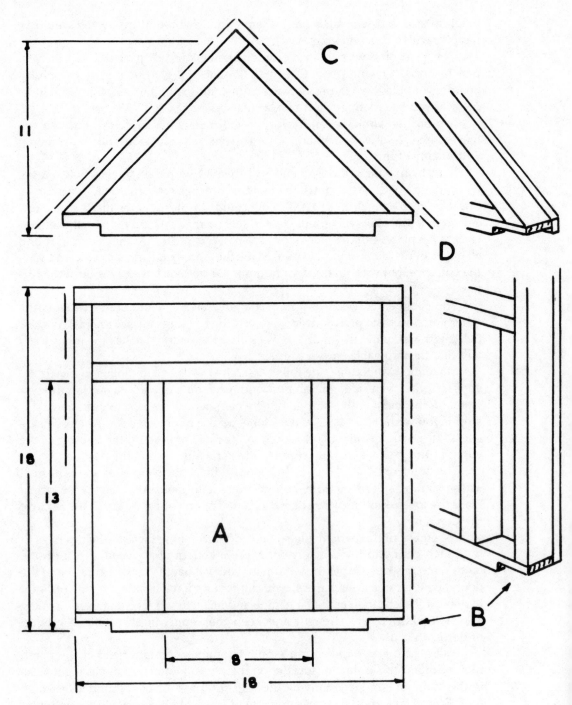

Fig. 7-33. End parts for the dog kennel.

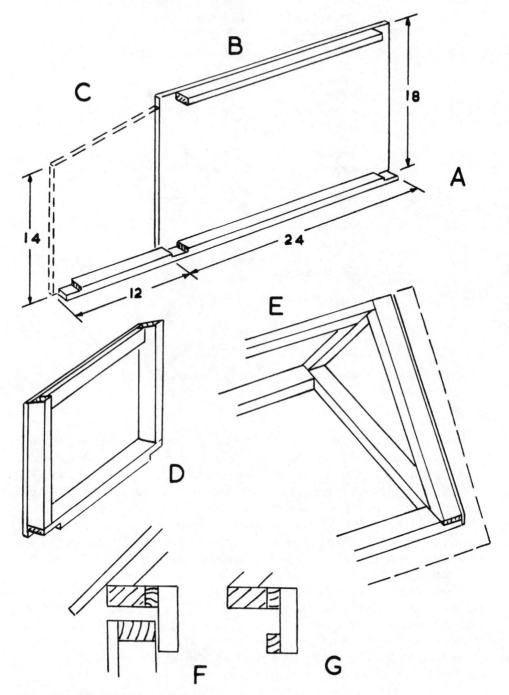

Fig. 7-34. Sides, ends, and roof of the dog kennel.

Materials List for Dog Kennel

Ends

9 strips	1 × 2 × 20
2 strips	1 × 2 × 16

Gables

2 strips	1 × 2 × 20
4 rafters	1 × 2 × 16

Porch end

2 strips	1 × 2 × 20
2 strips	1 × 2 × 15

Lengthwise parts

2 strips	1 × 2 × 38
2 strips	1 × 2 × 24
2 strips	1 × 2 × 14
3 roof strips	1 × 2 × 26

Covering	½ plywood

Make the two gable ends into a roof by joining their bases with lengthwise strips so they match the tops of the walls. At the apex, put in another lengthwise strip (FIG. 7-34E) to support the roof covering. The usual ¹/₂-inch plywood should be stiff enough to hold its shape on a roof of this size, without intermediate support, but if you think it needs stiffening, include some central rafters.

Cover the roof with plywood to overlap 2 inches at the ends and eaves. Round the edges and corners if you are not covering the roof. If you cover it with felt or other material, turn the edges under and tack them. Put light battens down the slopes, near the ends, and one or two intermediately.

Check the fit of the roof on the walls. It has to be given a positive location, and you might wish to fasten it down; otherwise, it might blow off. At each inside corner of the roof, screw 1-inch-×-2-inch strips projecting downward and packed out so they fit easily inside the top of the walls (FIG. 7-34F). At one side, add ends to hook under the top edge of the top strip of the wall (FIG. 7-34G). At the other side, on the outside, put screw hooks and eyes near each end to hold the roof down. You can use some lever-action clips and other fasteners there as alternatives.

Pole Barn

If you have poles of various sizes available, it is possible to make several types of buildings with them. You can make these buildings similar to the ones used by early settlers who had to adapt their needs to the available material—felled trees they used in the round if possible.

A pole barn can have a useful capacity, and it will blend into the scenery better than most other structures. Even if you are not a farmer, the building can have many uses on your property as well as being an example of traditional assembly which should be pleasing to the eye. The pole barn shown in FIG. 7-35 is of modest size, although you can use the technique for a barn of very different dimensions. In its width, you can divide it into three bays of about equal size. You can let the center bay open right through, but divide the side bays into stalls for cattle or horses, or use them for smaller animals. You can build walls which are full height or you can stop them at a lower level. Plenty of space is available for storage of feed, fertilizer, and other things, including some implements.

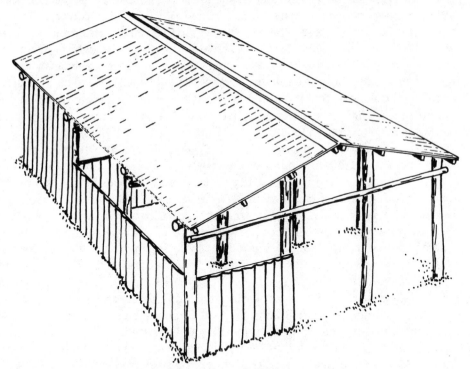

Fig. 7-35. This pole barn has many parts made from natural wood.

If you want to produce a barn of traditional appearance, walls and partitions should be of split poles, but you can back these with squared, wooden rails or even plywood, if the walls must be close-fitting and free from drafts. Although you can cover the roof in several ways, you have a choice of boarding or using plywood, which you would cover with shingles. Alternatively, you could use corrugated plastic or metal sheets. In this example, it is assumed that you will use corrugated sheets, but you can adapt the design to other forms of roofing.

The choice of poles will depend on what is available, but for uprights, the poles should be straight and about 6 inches in diameter, no matter what wood you choose to use. Lengthwise shakes are almost inevitable in many softwoods, and it does not matter if they are small. For rafters, you can use straight poles, if you have them. You can flatten poles slightly out of true on their upper surfaces, providing it does not weaken them too much. They should also have an average diameter of 6 inches. If suitable poles for rafters are not available, you might have to use sawn wood in 2-inch-×-6-inch sections. You might be able to use poles at the ends of the barn where they show and sawn wood intermediately. With modern facilities, it obviously makes sense to use modern materials and techniques, even if your aim is for a traditional external appearance.

The building could have some sway bracing, and any walls built in will help to maintain rigidity. Most of the stiffness of the barn is due to posts you will have buried in the ground. This type structure is not really a building you would want to mount on a concrete base. The concrete would destroy the traditional appearance. The site should be flat and should have compacted soil. Slight unevenness will not matter, but you might wish to bring the area to a reasonably level condition. If you decide to accept more unevenness, do not be tempted to let the building follow the slope—a roof that is not horizontal does not look right. See that the roofline in the length is level, even if that means the measurement from ground to eaves is 2 feet more at one end than the other.

The building used as an example in FIG. 7-36A is divided into three 8-foot bays across and into three 8-foot parts in the length. You could make the length as long as you wish, but you should not make cross members more than 8 feet apart, or additional roof trusses will be needed. Eight feet makes a reasonable division for many purposes, so you arrange walls or partitions at these points.

It is important to get the upright poles in line both ways and the layout square if the assembly is to look right. Start by laying out the post positions. A stretched cord will provide a straight line, and you can drive temporary pegs into the pole positions on one side (FIG. 7-37A). Use the 3:4:5 method to mark a line of pegs square to this first line. For 24 feet square, you can use an 8-foot unit, so the first side is 3 units. Measure 4 units (32 feet) from one end peg and 5 units (40 feet) from the other end peg to a meeting point (FIG. 7-37B). Stretch a cord through this point and mark the 8-foot distances with pegs on this line. For the lines of other pegs, measure parallel to these first square lines (FIG. 7-37C).

How deep you sink the posts depends on the soil, but for rigidity, they should go in at least 24 inches, even in the most dense soil. It might be possible to drive stones tightly under and around a post, but it will be better to embed a post in concrete, which will spread the load (FIG. 7-37D). The concrete could come to the surface, or it could just form a foot, with stones and soil compacted above.

Have the posts longer than they will have to be, so you can trim the tops to

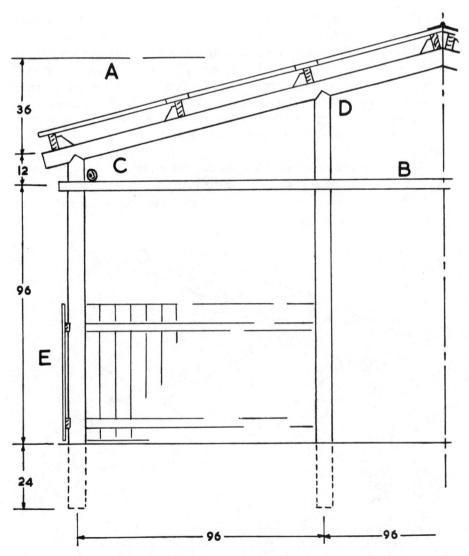

Fig. 7-36. *An end view of half the pole barn.*

match when they are all in position. At this stage, it is important to get each post as near upright as you can manage. Use a plumb level in several directions, but the best test is just to stand back and look at the poles from at least two directions. You might need some temporary props to hold a post upright while the concrete sets and until you attach other parts to it to keep it in shape.

When you have one corner post in position, it probably will be wisest to work the corner diagonally opposite it next, then the other corners. As you progress, you can sight one post against another. As you get more posts up to your satisfaction, it is easier to sight the remaining posts and get them true.

It will help to stabilize the assembly if you fit the horizontal ties next (FIG. 7-36B). They only need to be about 3 inches in diameter. They cross 8 feet from the ground, but if the ground is uneven, treat this as a minimum and keep the ties level. Use a cord across with the aid of a large spirit or other level and mark the crossing points of one set of uprights. At each place, make a flat surface, but do not go very deep (FIG. 7-37E). Make matching flats on the tie. If you do not have a pole long enough to go right across, you can make a joint over a post (FIG. 7-37F). Use a bolt which is at least ⁵/₈ inch in diameter at each crossing, with large washers under the head and nut.

To hold the assembly in shape lengthwise, put more ties on top of the first set close to the eaves joints (FIGS. 7-36C and 7-37G). Again, arrange meeting flats and bolt through. You will maintain stiffness on the inside uprights if you join

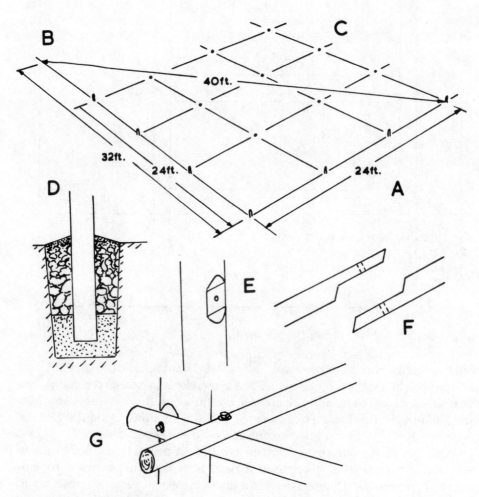

Fig. 7-37. The method of setting out the base of the pole barn. Details of pole joints.

partitions and other parts to them. If you think it advisable, fit more lengthwise ties near them.

It is important that the roof is straight, level, and without twist. If some of the lower parts of the building are slightly out of true, it might not matter and might add to the picturesque appearance of the structure. Errors in the roof will be more obvious and will detract from appearance, even if the roof is weatherproof.

Before cutting off any uprights, establish a horizontal line all around the building. The positions of the main ties will serve as a guide. The line can be near their level and about 12 inches down from where the eaves will be. Stretch a cord along the uprights of one side, and with the aid of your level, make it horizontal. Mark this line prominently on each post. Go around a corner and do the same across an end, starting at exactly the level of the first line. Place a similar line across the other end, then when you draw a line on the other side, these lines at the corners should be level. You might not achieve perfection, but if you are much more than 1 inch out, go back and check what you have done.

From the datum marks, measure up to where you will cut the tops of the outer posts. At one end, use two straight pieces of wood long enough to overlap at the apex of the roof. Put them in the rafters position, with their lower edges where you intend the lower edges of the pole rafters to be. Clamp their overlap and either clamp or temporarily nail to the posts. When you are satisfied with the shape, mark on the poles where the guidelines are to be, then remove these pieces.

You can use several methods to join the rafters to the posts. The simplest way is to put the rafters alongside the posts, with flat sides against the posts and bolt through them, similar to the joints of the ties. This method allows experiments with levels, before you drill through for bolts. The method shown has notched joints. Each post has a tapered top fitting into a notch in the rafter. Arrange this fitting to go less than halfway through the rafter (FIGS. 7-36D and 7-38A). At each joint, drill downwards and drive in a 3/4-inch-diameter steel rod as a dowel (FIG. 7-38B). At the apex, halve the rafters together, with two 3/4-inch bolts (FIG. 7-38C). At the eaves, cut off the rafters 9 inches outside the posts.

Assemble the rafters at one end, then use them as a guide when you erect the others. Sight along the top surfaces and check that they are as in line as is possible to get with natural poles. If there is a pronounced curve or kink in any rafter pole, you may cut it level, but do not take away too much wood. It might be better and easier to only cut away at purlin positions.

At the sizes suggested, it is possible to cover each slope with three rows of 60-inch, corrugated-metal sheets overlapping 9 inches. Locate the purlins to suit the sheet joints. With different length sheets, alter the purlin positions to suit. If you are going to board the roof, purlins may be 48 inches to 60 inches apart. On each rafter, arrange the top purlins quite close to the ridge. Position the lowest one within a few inches of the end of the rafter. The position of others is best found by experimenting with a row of corrugated sheets so the overlap will come where you can nail centrally into the purlin.

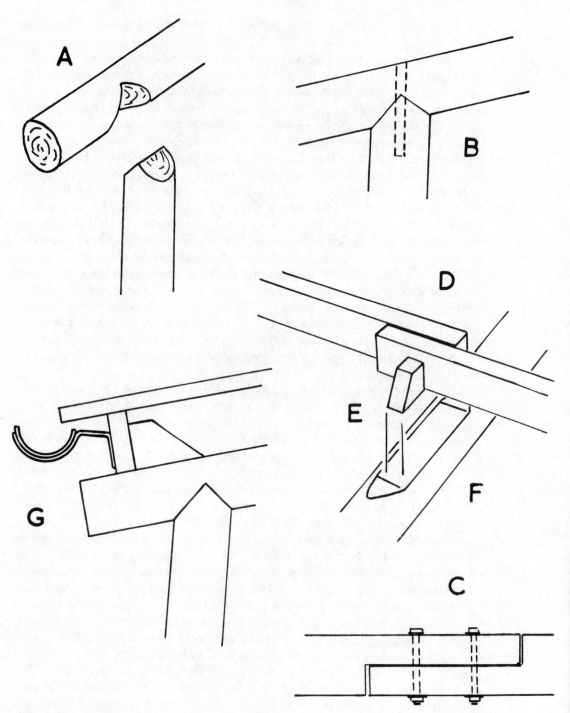

Fig. 7-38. Methods of joining parts of the pole barn.

The purlins could go right through, if you have wood long enough, but they will be easier to handle if you overlap them on the intermediate rafters (FIG. 7-38D). At the ends, they can project by whatever amount you want the roof to overhang—18 inches is reasonable. Where the purlins cross rafters, fit cleats. With 2-inch-×-6-inch purlins, each cleat should be at least 4 inches high (FIG. 7-38E). Flatten the rafter to make a good bearing for the cleat and purlins (FIG. 7-38F). If there are no problems with levels, this flattening can be quite slight, but if you need to make any adjustment to the purlin level, you need to cut deeper or put a packing between rafter and purlins.

Sway bracing will aid rigidity, particularly if the barn is in a windy position. In two bays on each end, nail diagonal pieces upwards into two rows of purlins. These could be 2-inch-×-3-inch sections. If you build walls into the barn, diagonals between rows of rails also will help resist wind loads.

Cover the roof and put a top on the ridge. At the eaves, extend the sheets a short distance below the purlin. You can then fit a gutter with brackets to the purlins (FIG. 7-38G). You could fit bargeboards to the ends, but you can finish this type of building without them.

How you arrange the accommodation of the building depends on your needs. In its simplest form, you can leave the building as it is, and use it as a shelter for implements and other equipment. At the other extreme, you may completely encase it and fit doors. You can put walls to the full height or only part way up the sides.

The arrangement of posts inside will allow the easy erection of partitions at 8-foot intervals, which should be right for horse or cow stalls, or storage compartments for grain, feed, and other things in containers. You do not have to treat the whole building in the same way. You could have walls to the eaves on one side and no walls, or just low ones, at the other side. Similarly, divisions could go to the roof or only part way up the inner posts. A useful arrangement allows the middle bays to be clear right through, with accommodation of various sorts to suit your needs along each side.

You can cover walls with plain boards, arranging them vertically or horizontally. If you want to maintain a traditional appearance, external walls should be split poles or the slabs that come off a log when it is squared in a saw mill. These slabs have the bark on. It is advisable to peel the bark off, as it harbors insects and might encourage rot. The natural outside of the wood still will have a suitable appearance. If you want the closest fit between slabs, cut the edges parallel (FIG. 7- 39A). Rails to support the covering pieces may be 2-inch-×-4-inch sawn pieces, notched into the posts (FIGS. 7-36E and 7-39-B). If you are making a wall extending over several bays, adjust the depths of notches so the rails are straight and parallel.

Make partitions the same way, but you can use plain boards. If animals are involved, the boards should be at least 1 inch thick. You might want to put boards on both sides of the rails for a smooth finish. Whatever the height of a wall or partition, rails should be less than 37 inches apart. Put boards over the ends of partitions, where appropriate, to cover roughness. Put capping strips on any low partitions. If there is to be an internal door, treat it as a partition, with suitable framing and a cutout for the doorway.

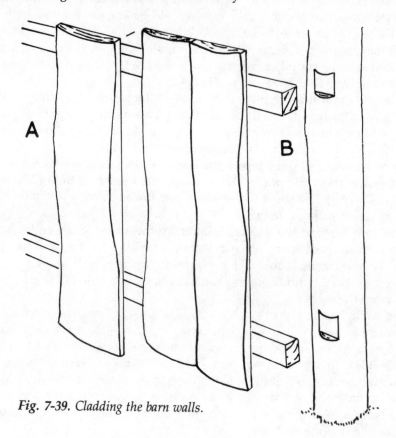

Fig. 7-39. Cladding the barn walls.

Hay Shed

Despite the name, it is unlikely that you will need a hay shed, but there are many other uses for this structure. In the days before combine harvesters and straw balers, hay and straw was gathered into ricks, which might have been thatched. The alternative was to put the hay under a permanent roof, such as this hay shed (FIG. 7-40). You might want to store produce of some sort in the shed or it could provide shelter for equipment, machinery or it might serve as a car port.

The shed could be made almost any size. Some hay sheds were very large. This one (FIG. 7-41) is drawn to cover a ground area of 14 feet × 18 feet, with an overall height just over 11 feet and a height to the eaves of 8 feet. You could alter sizes to suit your needs, but the sizes suggested give a roof slope of 8 feet, to suit standard sheets and the roof length is also easy to cover without cutting sheets.

Fig. 7-40. *A traditional hay shed can provide shelter for equipment, stock, or machinery.*

Materials List for Hay Shed
(all 2 × 4 unless marked)

16 rafters	96
4 ties	170
4 posts	42
24 cleats	10
16 columns	106
2 wall plates	220 (in parts)
6 purlins	240 (in parts)
12 struts	
end boarding	1 × 6 (as required)
roof	10 sheets 48 × 96 × ¹/₂ plywood
	(or corrugated sheets, as in text)

It is assumed the building will be erected on earth, with the columns let into concrete-filled holes. You could use a concrete floor. For the sizes suggested you can use 2-inch- × -4-inch wood for all the structural work. This would be suitable for a smaller shed, but you should use wood of larger sections if your shed is to be very much larger. The roof could be covered in several ways, as described later, but that does not affect the main construction.

There are four pairs of columns at 6-foot intervals (FIG. 7-41A), with a roof truss at each position. The end trusses might be closed by boarding (FIG. 7-41B), but start by making four identical trusses (FIG. 7-42A). The rafters are double, with the tie and post between them. It will help to set out full-size the shape of

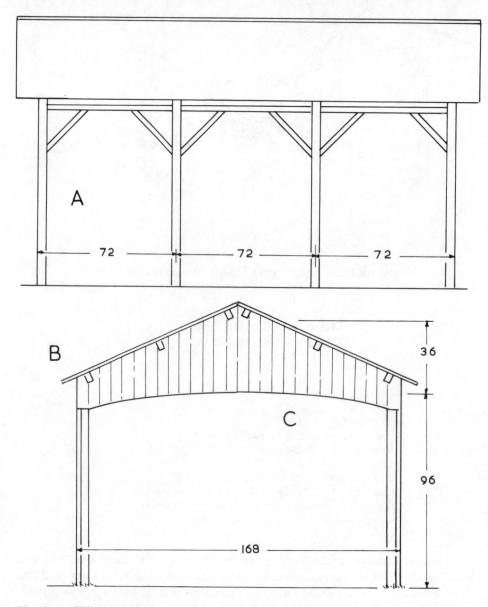

Fig. 7-41. Side and end view of a hay shed with suggested sizes.

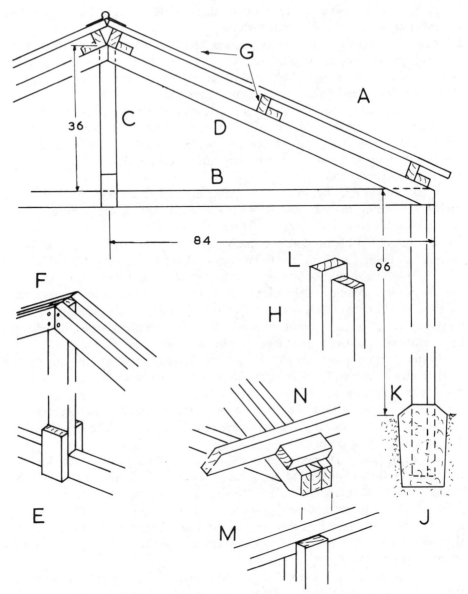

Fig. 7-42. Roof truss and supports for a hay shed.

half a truss on the floor. Make all parts for the four trusses at the same time, to ensure they match.

Make the four ties (FIG. 7-42B) to the width of the building. Make the post (FIG. 7-42C) to rest against the tie. Leave its top too long until the rafters (FIG. 7-42D) are cut and fitted over it. Join the post to the center of the tie with pieces each side (FIG. 7-42E), using nails, screws or bolts.

At the apex it will be best to put bolts through (FIG. 7-42F). You can use bolts or screws at the lower ends of the rafters.

Mark the probable positions of purlins (FIG. 7-42G) across the rafters. Three each side are shown, but you might have to modify their positions later to suit your chosen roof covering. Check that the trusses match each other. If there are slight variations, mark which way around gives the best match.

The columns are built up in a T section, with one piece of 2-inch-×-4-inch wood across another (FIG. 7-42H). Make sufficient columns, allowing some excess length at this stage particularly if you are dealing with uneven ground. Join the pieces with long screws at no more than 6-inch spacing. It will help if you can also use waterproof glue.

Mark out the ground, preferably using marked strips of scrap wood, and carefully squaring the corners. At each column position, dig a hole. Its size depends on the soil. In average soil you could dig about 18 inches deep and 12 inches square, but in soft soil you might need to cover larger areas. Allow for each column going in 15 inches, to be surrounded by concrete (FIG. 7-42J).

The columns should be treated with preservative, at least for the part entering the ground. Position each column in its hole, probably with stones underneath. Use scrap wood temporarily nailed on to hold columns upright and at the correct spacings. Be careful that crosswise distances suit the trusses. Slight errors in lengthwise spacings will not be so obvious. See that columns are upright when viewed from a distance. Fill the holes with concrete, and slope the top surfaces to shed water (FIG. 7-42K). Leave any temporary struts in place until after upper parts have been fitted.

Trim the column tops. The outer piece should extend 2 inches above the other (FIG. 7-42L). Check that a strip laid in any direction on the top will be horizontal, even if the ground slopes.

Put strips (*wall plates*) on the tops of the columns (FIG. 7-42M) for the length of the building. If there are any joints, arrange them over columns (FIG. 7-43A). You could join the columns to the wall plates with long nails driven both ways, or you might prefer angle irons or bent 1/8-inch steel brackets with bolts (FIG. 7-43B).

Put struts between the columns and the wall plates (FIG. 7-43C) at about 45 degrees. Cut shallow notches for the ends (FIG. 7-43D) to take the thrust. Fit the struts tightly and nail them in position.

Position the trusses above the columns. Attach them with long nails and bolted or screwed brackets similar to those suggested at the column tops. Put temporary scrap wood struts between the trusses to hold them until after attaching the purlins.

Make purlins to extend to the length of the intended roof. Arrange joints over trusses in the same way as suggested for the wall plates. As much as possible, let joints come on different rafters. Nail or screw cleats 9 inches long where each purlin will cross a rafter, then nail the purlins to the cleats (FIG. 7-42N). If you intend to board one or both sides, cut the cleats level with the outsides of the rafters there.

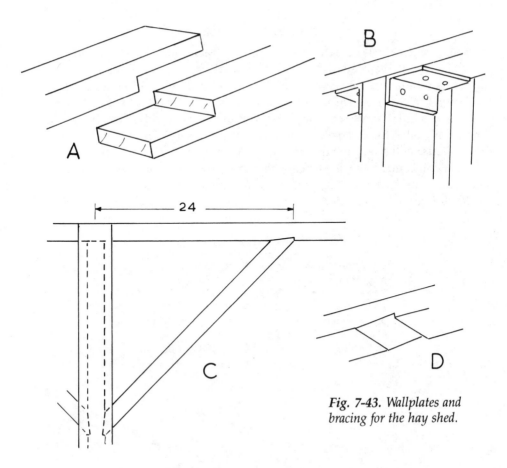

Fig. 7-43. Wallplates and bracing for the hay shed.

The roof covering could be corrugated galvanized iron, aluminum or plastic. If you can get standard sheets 8 feet long, they will extend for enough overhang without joints. If you have to use shorter lengths or want more overhang, there will have to be joints, and you might need to reposition purlins to allow for nailing through the overlap. There are standard apex pieces that will cover the meeting of sheets and nail through into the top purlins.

An alternative covering would be 1/2-inch plywood. This would provide enough overhang and the length could be made up of five widths to give 12-inch overhangs at the ends. The arrangement of purlins shown should suit plywood. Cover with felt or similar material, taken over the ridge without joints and turned under at the eaves. Allow adequate overlaps in the length.

If you wish to board an end, put wood outside the tie to build up its thickness to match the rafter. Use upright boards 1 inch thick and about 6 inches wide. Cut the top edges to come close under the roof. The lower edge could be level with the tie or you could shape it (FIG. 7-41C).

Animal Shelter

This shelter (FIG. 7-44) consists of a roof and a rear wall. Other arrangements are possible. It could be used to shelter farm animals from sun and rain, but it would have many other uses in yard or garden. It could provide a place for picnics or just sitting in the fresh air. It would serve as a place for a barbecue. If there is a prevailing wind the rear wall could be positioned on that side. The shelter shown has a rear wall to the full depth and the ends are closed in as far down as the rear eaves. You could board in any other way to suit your needs.

You could make the shelter any size, but as drawn (FIGS. 7-45 and 7-46), the roof suits standard 8-foot lengths of wood, metal, or plastic covering and the building length would suit three standard sheets of plywood. The instructions

Materials List for Animal Shelter

3 columns	4	× 4	× 108	
3 columns	4	× 4	× 96	
2 beams	2	× 6	× 134	
7 rafters	2	× 4	× 98	
3 roof sheets	48	× 96	×	3/4 plywood
Cladding	1 × 6 or 3/4 plywood			
20 brackets from	2	× 4	× 108 or offcuts	

Fig. 7-44. This simple shelter provides animals with protection from wind and rain.

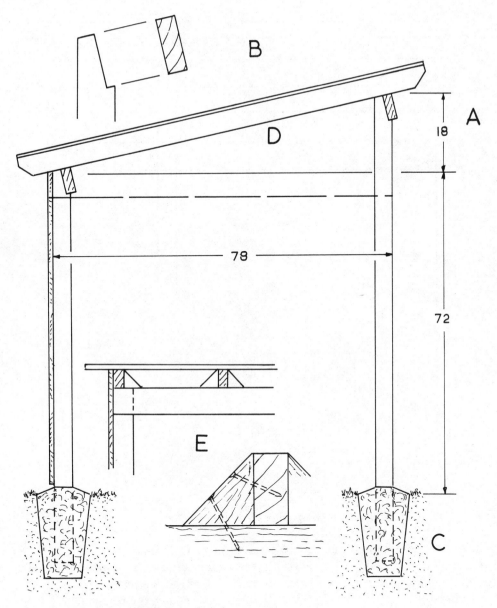

Fig. 7-45. End view of the animal shelter.

assume you will use ³/₄-inch plywood for the roof. The columns are 4 inches square. They could be wood cut to that size or you could use 2-inch-×-4-inch stock screwed together. The upright cladding could be plywood or you might use strips of solid wood laid horizontally.

Start by setting out, preferably full-size, the main lines of the upper part of an end view (FIG. 7-45A) to obtain the slope of the roof and the differences in

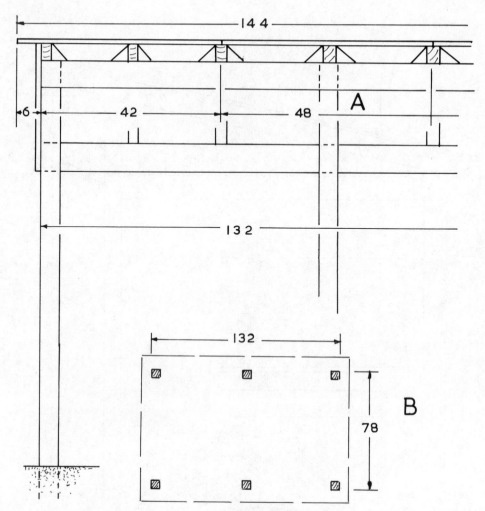

Fig. 7-46. Front view and ground plan of the animal shelter.

length of the columns. Cut the columns slightly overlong at first, particularly if the ground is very uneven. It is possible to let the columns into the ground with concrete in a similar way to that described for the previous project.

Bevel the tops of the columns and notch them to take the beams (FIG. 7-45B). Cut the beams to length and mark on them the positions of the intermediate columns and the rafters (FIG. 7-46A). Note that two rafters come under plywood roof joints.

Set out the positions of the columns on the ground (FIG. 7-46B) and dig the holes. Put the columns in the holes and clamp the beams to their tops. Clamp or temporarily nail strips of wood between rear and front columns to hold them upright. You could use wood that will later make rafters.

Check the levels of the beams and pack under the columns where necessary.

See that the assembly is upright and square. Concrete the bottoms on the columns (FIG. 7-45C).

When the concrete has set, nail the beams to the columns. Prepare the seven rafters (FIG. 7-45D). Bevel the ends for neatness. Attach them to the beams with triangular brackets (FIG. 7-45E). Cut these with their grain diagonally.

Nail the sheets for the plywood roof to the rafters, starting with the meeting edges over rafters. Cover with felt or similar material. You could put strips of about 3/4-inch-×-11/2-inch wood under the outer edges for stiffness and more security for nails through the felt.

Cover the rear wall with plywood or use strips of about 1-inch-×-6-inch section across. Cover the ends from under the roof down to the rear eaves line in a similar way. Finish with preservative or paint.

Larger Animal Shelter

If your animals are larger or there are more of them, you will need a shelter bigger and more substantial than the one just described. This shelter (FIG. 7-47) has an overhanging corrugated roof and walls giving full protection on three sides as well as a low wall across part of the front. As with the smaller shelter, you could have other uses for this type of shelter. It could cover equipment that does not have to be locked away. It could protect a barbecue or form a children's play area.

Instructions are for a shelter 8 feet wide and 12 feet long. This should suit all animals, except the largest horses. Sizes are not crucial, and even if you are working to these sizes and the finished building becomes a rather different size

Fig. 7-47. *If you have large animals or many of them, a shelter should be larger and offer protection in all directions.*

6 posts	2	× 4	×	120
6 posts	2	× 4	×	96
6 rails	2	× 4	×	98
3 rails	2	× 4	×	146
2 rails	2	× 4	×	78
3 rafters	2	× 6	×	132
Cladding boards about	1	× 6		

during construction, it will not matter. The only sizes you might need to keep in mind are the sizes of corrugated iron or plastic sheets used on the roof. For the suggested size of building the roof slope can be covered by overlapping 6-foot sheets, although a difference in total length of slope of 12 inches would not matter.

The shelter is intended to be built almost entirely on site. The posts could be natural poles, but they are shown as made up from 2-inch- × -4-inch pieces joined to make an L section. The posts are let into the ground. As designed, this is not a building to erect on a concrete slab. There are 2-inch- × -4-inch horizontal rails and the cladding is with vertical boards. You could use any available boards at least 1 inch thick. They could be plain or tongue-and-groove machined boards. Offcuts from a sawmill, produced when square-edge boards are cut from a log, would make an appropriate, natural-looking covering. Providing they have parallel edges, the irregular outsides will fit in with their surroundings.

Set out the positions of the posts on the ground (FIG. 7-48). It is important that this is arranged squarely, as any inaccuracy will make it difficult to fit the roof properly. You cannot arrange corrugated sheets on a skew—even slightly—without it being obvious to any viewer.

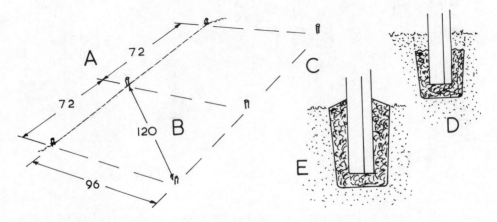

Fig. 7-48. Ground layout and post foundations for the larger animal shelter.

Use temporary pegs to mark post positions. Stretch a string to get the first three in line (FIG. 7-48A). Use the 3:4:5 method to mark one of the other post positions square to the first line. With 2 feet as the unit, you already have the 3 and 4 lengths, (6 feet between marked pegs and 8 feet to the new one), so if you measure 5 units (10 feet) diagonally (FIG. 7-48B) that gives you the new location. Stretch a string from this corner peg and get it parallel to the first line, so you can mark the positions of the remaining two pegs (FIGS. 7-48C and 7-51A).

How you let the posts in and how deep you take them depends on the ground. If it is tightly compacted soil and you have a post-hole borer, you could drive the posts in directly, possibly to a depth of 2 feet. In many soils it will be better to dig a larger hole and let each post into concrete. The amount of concrete will depend on the soil, but about 12 inches square is a probable size. You could use concrete to only enough depth to provide a base, then cover with soil (FIG. 7-48D) or bring the concrete above the surface and slope it so water runs off (FIG. 7-48E). Even if the whole post is not treated with preservative, the part that will be buried and up to a few feet above that should be soaked with preservative.

Consider the level (or otherwise) of the land. Use a long board and a spirit level to check slopes in all directions. You can build an animal shelter on sloping ground, but do not be tempted to let the building conform to the slope. All posts must be upright. The roof width must be horizontal and so must the lines of rails. You might have to take care of uneven or sloping ground with the bottom edges of cladding, but that has to be fitted upright on level rails. To get the roof level you will have to arrange posts projecting at different heights above the ground, even if variations are only a few inches.

Prepare the posts by joining strips together in an L formation (FIGS. 7-49A and 7-50A). Join with plenty of long nails. You could use waterproof glue as well. Allow ample length. Tops can be trimmed after erection.

Erect the six posts. Check that each is plumb. Sight along to see that the groups of three are in line. Stand well back and view from several directions. Comparing each post with the others will soon show if a post is leaning. If you are using concrete, do all this before the concrete begins to set. If necessary, put temporary struts from the ground to hold a post or link it to another post to maintain its position.

Other parts go on the outsides of the posts, being nailed in position without joints being cut (FIG. 7-50B). Put rails around the building. Ignore the ground and start at marked heights on one corner, then get the rails level as you extend them to other posts, even if the heights are different from uneven ground. If you fit one set of rails all around, further rails can be added parallel to them. Three lines of rails are suggested (FIG. 7-49B) on the main walls. Two should be sufficient on the partial front wall. Nail rails to each other as well as to the posts at corners.

With the rails attached you should have a very rigid structure. Stand back and view from a distance several times during assembly. Slight errors can then be put right. Make sure rails look level in relation to upright posts.

The rafters are nailed to the sides of the posts (FIG. 7-50C) in the same way as

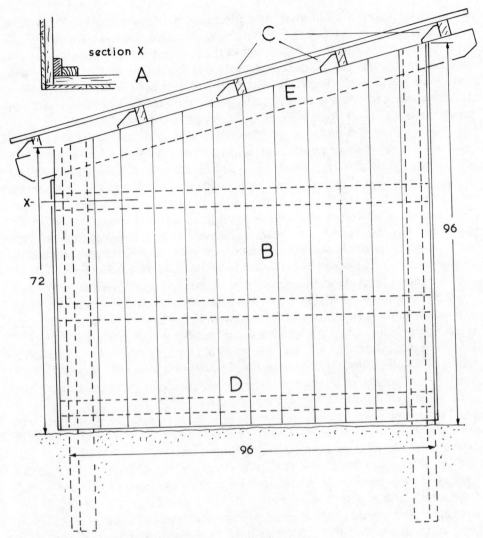

Fig. 7-49. An end wall for the larger animal shelter.

the rails. Try a rafter in position at one end. Clamp it there so you can stand back and check its appearance. It should extend up to 12 inches at back and front. Prepare three matching rafters and mount cleats on them (FIGS. 7-49C and 7-50D). With the arrangement shown, 6-foot sheets will overlap on the central purlin.

Attach a rafter at one end of the building. Put the other two rafters in position, held temporarily with clamps or nails. Put two purlins in place and check straightness. Measure up from rails. Sight along from one end. Use a spirit level on a purlin. When you are satisfied, permanently nail on the rafters and add the purlins, which should project about 12 inches at each end (FIGS. 7-50E and 7-51B)

Decide how you want to arrange the cladding. It will probably be best to leave a little clearance above the ground (FIG. 7-49D). Boards are shown taken to the top of the rafters (FIG. 7-49E) at the ends, but you could stop them at rafter level at the back or carry them up to the roof sheeting. Some ventilation space at this level is advisable. Overlap the boards at corners (FIG. 7-50F). Cut the boards level with the rail at the front (FIG. 7-51C). If the shelter is to have uses other than providing for animals, you could put a capping board on this wall, possibly wide enough to form a serving table at a barbecue.

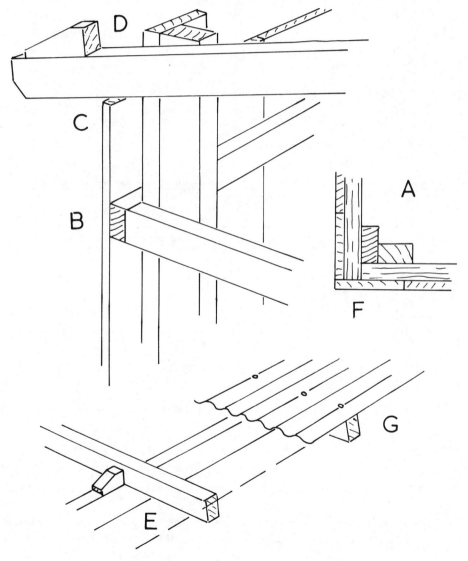

Fig. 7-50. Corner and roof details for the larger animal shelter.

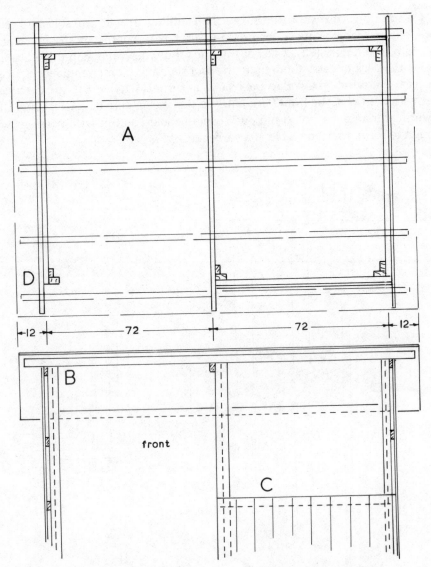

Fig. 7-51. *Roof layout and front details for the larger animal shelter.*

Arrange the roof sheets to extend about 12 inches all around (FIG. 7-51D). Nail through the tops of corrugations, preferably with washers under the nail heads (FIG. 7-50G).

In most situations you will let rainwater run onto the ground, but if you want to collect it, a gutter can be bracketed to the ends of the rafters then a downpipe led to a container.

Stock House

If you have a few poultry or animals that are allowed free range or spend their day in a fairly large enclosure, you will probably want to provide shelter, both for bad weather and to offer protection from predators at night. This small stock house (FIG. 7-52) could be used for poultry, including turkeys, geese and ducks, or many smaller animals. It is provided with handles so it can be moved, and there is a floor that can be lifted with the house or removed for cleaning. Animal or bird access is via an end opening that can be closed with a flap. There is a narrow door so you can get into the building, and there should be little risk of animals inside getting out, as your body will block the doorway.

Construction is intended to be of exterior plywood over framing, but it would be possible to cover with boards. This is not a take-down design, and it is assumed you will treat the house as a permanent structure, but it is small enough and light enough to be transported complete on a trailer or truck.

Fig. 7-52. This small stock house provides shelter and protection for birds or animals and is light enough to be moved about.

Materials List for Stock House

Ends

2 uprights	2	× 2 ×	74
2 uprights	2	× 2 ×	62
8 rails	2	× 2 ×	54

Front

4 uprights	2	× 2 ×	74
2 rails	2	× 2 ×	74
2 rails	2	× 2 ×	48
1 rail	2	× 2 ×	24

Back

4 uprights	2	× 2 ×	62
4 rails	2	× 2 ×	74

Slatted floor

30 slats	1	× 2 ×	48
8 slats	1	× 2 ×	36

Plain floor

8 supports	2	× 2 ×	48

Door

2 sides	1	× 2 ×	60
3 rails	1	× 2 ×	20

Flap

2 strips	1	× 2 ×	48
2 strips	1	× 2 ×	20

Roof

2 rafters	2	× 2 ×	52
2 edges	3/4	× 1 1/2 ×	84
2 edges	3/4	× 1 1/2 ×	62

Handles

2 pieces	1	× 3 ×	20
1 rail	2	× 2 ×	48
2 blocks	1	× 5 ×	9

Covering 1/2 or 3/4 exterior plywood

The sizes suggested (FIG. 7-53A) are intended to make economical use of standard 4-foot-×-8-foot plywood sheets. Most of the framing is 2-inch-square and 1-inch-×-2-inch strips. All wood should be treated with preservative or be thoroughly painted. Make the two ends (FIG. 7-54A) as a pair. Leave the hole open on the end that will have the flap (FIG. 7-54B and C). There should be ventilation in both ends. Arrange this high to keep out mice and other rodents. Drill a pattern of holes, 1-inch-diameter or larger (FIG. 7-54D). If you make the holes too large, you might be troubled by birds getting in. The plywood provides plenty of strength, and you might just butt the frame parts and securely nail them, but it will be strongest to use halving joints at the corners (FIG. 7-54E). Make up the skin thickness with strips alongside the hole (FIG. 7-54F).

When you make the front (FIG. 7-55A), arrange the full width of a sheet to come to the edge of the doorway, then cut it back so the piece above the door can be nailed on (FIG. 7-55B). At the corners, the framing uprights have to be arranged to come inside the uprights of the ends (FIG. 7-55C), so the front plywood covers the ends. Arrange two horizontal rails, equally spaced. Make the height of the front to match the edges of the ends. You might be satisfied with the top rail cut square, but for the neatest fit of the roof, bevel it to match the angle of the ends.

Make the back in a similar way at the lower height, with rails right across, as there is no doorway. Match the height to the ends and bevel the top rail, if you wish.

Join the four walls. You could drill the corner posts and bolt through. This

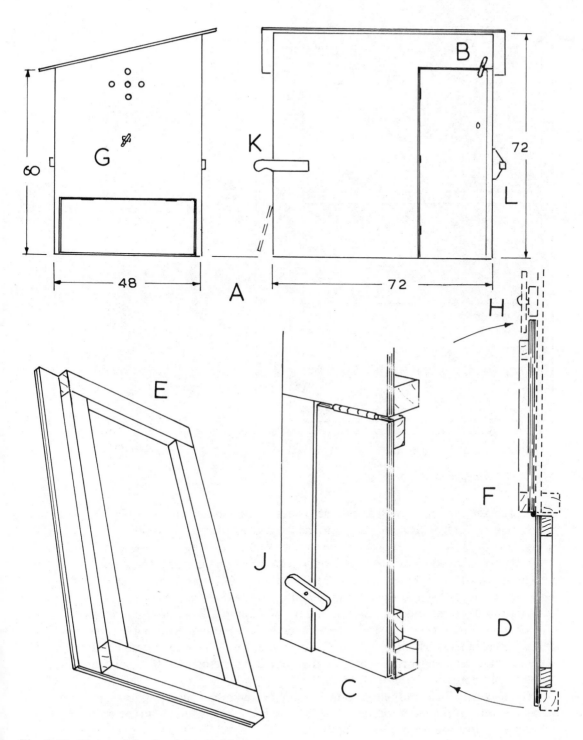

Fig. 7-53. *Sizes and details of the stock house.*

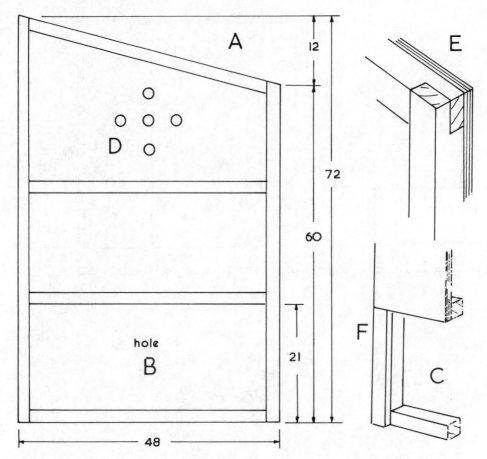

Fig. 7-54. Details of an end of the stock house.

makes a secure assembly, but it should be strong enough to nail both ways. Even if you use bolts, it will be advisable to nail the overlapping plywood to the uprights.

Make the plywood panel for the door so it overlaps one upright. Make up a matching thickness on the other upright (FIG. 7-56A). Allow an overlap on the bottom rail (FIG. 7-56B), but leave some clearance so the door can open, even on rough ground. Frame the door to fit easily in the opening. Waterproof glue, as well as nails or screws would strengthen the door. Hinge the door, using two or three 3-inch hinges, which could be let into the edges or on the surface. You could fit a lock or some form of catch on the door, but for most situations a strip wood turnbutton will hold it (FIG. 7-53B).

The flap over the stock hole is made in a similar way to the door. Arrange it to fit between the thickened uprights (FIG. 7-53C), so it can be hinged at the top and will close against the bar at the bottom (FIG. 7-53D). Frame the flap to allow this overlap (FIG. 7-53E).

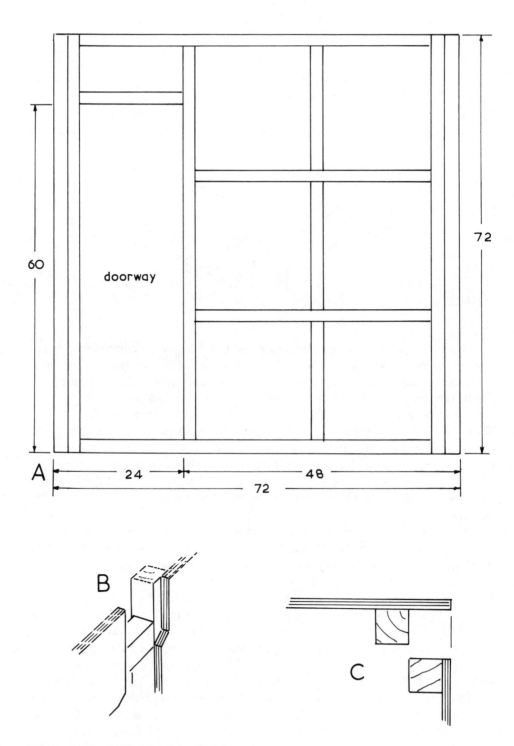

Fig. 7-55. *The high side of the stock house.*

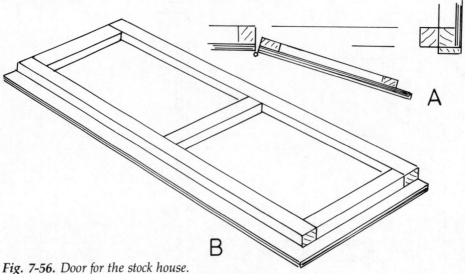

Fig. 7-56. Door for the stock house.

When you hinge the flap, make sure the knuckles of the hinges project far enough for the flap to swing up level with the surface of the end (FIG. 7-53F). Put a block and a wooden turnbutton there (FIG. 7-53G and H) to hold the flap open. Put turnbuttons at each side to hold the flap closed (FIG. 7-53J).

For some stock you might leave the bottom of the house open to the ground, but in most cases it is better to provide a floor. If you make the floor in two parts divided across the center, the sections are easy to take out for cleaning. For poultry (not ducks) a slatted floor is better than a solid one, so droppings go through. This can be 1-inch-×-2-inch strips on edge about 1 inch apart, held with strips underneath (FIG. 7-57A). Cut the floor parts so the slats rest on framework bottom rails. Notch at corners.

For stock needing a closed floor, use plywood cut to rest on the frame bottom rails, with notched corners and stiffen with 2-inch-square pieces across underneath (FIG. 7-57B). There is no need for very close fits when making floor parts.

If you want to be able to lift the house, there have to be handles. You can have a pair of extending handles at the stock hole end (FIG. 7-53K), but because of the door being in the way of a side handle, you should fit a rail at the other end (FIG. 7-53L). Make the handles with shaped and rounded extensions (FIG. 7-57C). Fit them with glue and screws driven from inside. Arrange a 2-inch-square rail at the other end (FIG. 7-57D)with end brackets. Make the assembly short enough to clear the framing inside, so glue can be used with screws driven from inside.

Leave work on the roof until you have done all other construction so it is easier to get at the inside of the walls and the floor. The roof is plywood, and it should overhang about 4 inches all around. This means it is larger than a standard sheet, and you will have to arrange a joint down the slope over a rafter

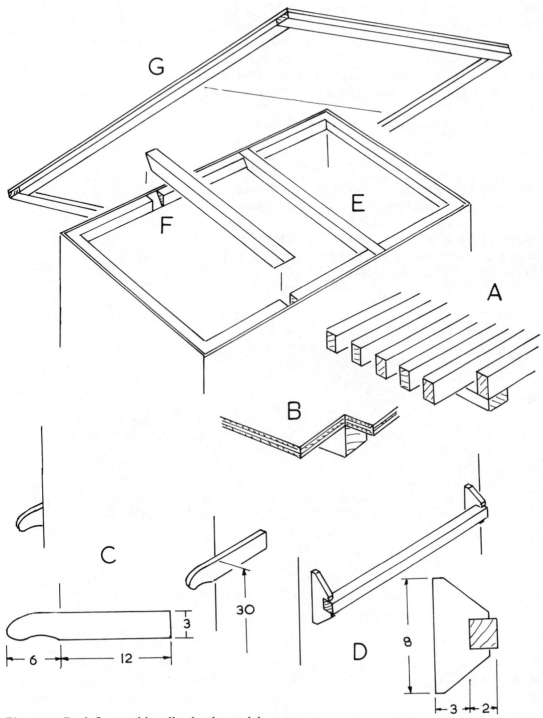

Fig. 7-57. *Roof, floor and handles for the stock house.*

inside (FIG. 7-57E). Notch the top wall rails so you can fit in the rafters (FIG. 7-57F). Position one rafter to suit the joint in the roof sheets.

Cut the plywood parts of the roof and edge them underneath to provide a thickness for nailing the covering (FIG. 7-57G). Nail the roof to the wall rails and the rafters, then cover with tarred felt or other covering material, tacking underneath around the edges. Nail battens down the slope of the roof at about 12-inch intervals.

Finish all the woodwork with preservative or paint.

Chicken Coop and Run

If you want to raise chickens using a brood hen, you need a house for the hen and a run for the chickens. It could be used directly on the ground and moved from time to time. This chicken coop and run (FIG. 7-58) has a house for the hen, with bars to keep her out of the run. Access to the house is by a hinged roof, and the run is exposed when you lift its top. Handles extending at the ends allow two people to carry the assembly easily.

Fig. 7-58. A portable chicken coop and run is intended for raising chickens with a brood hen, but it could be used for other small stock.

The same coop and run might be used for bantams, quail, rabbits, or other small stock. You might wish to alter sizes to suit them, but construction could be the same. Parts are strip wood covered with exterior plywood. Wire netting with about 1-inch mesh would be suitable for the run.

The house is first made complete (FIG. 7-59A), then the run is added with strips outside the house and the top pieces extended to make handles. The cover of the run is a separate framework.

Cut the two side pieces of plywood (FIG. 7-60A). Frame them inside with strips, notched to take the crosspieces (FIG. 7-60B). Two crosspieces are horizontal and notched to take the bars (FIG. 7-60C). The bottom bar fits in with its end full-width (FIG. 7-60D), but the other bars are notched (FIG. 7-60E). The spacing of 1-inch-square bars will suit chickens, but you might wish to alter the size of gaps for other birds or animals.

Join the sides of the house with the strips and cover the back with plywood. Put a solid wood or plywood strip across the front (FIG. 7-59B). Bevel top edges of crosspieces to suit the slope of the roof.

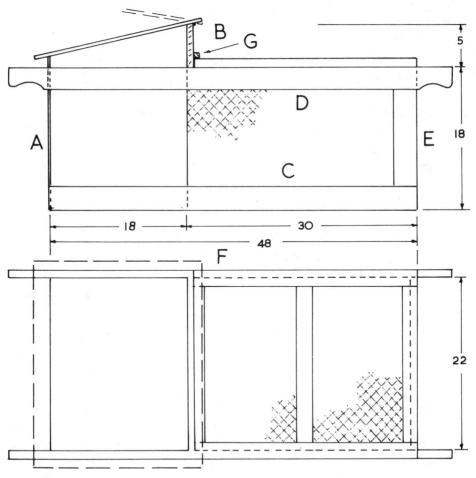

Fig. 7-59. Suggested sizes for the chicken coop and run.

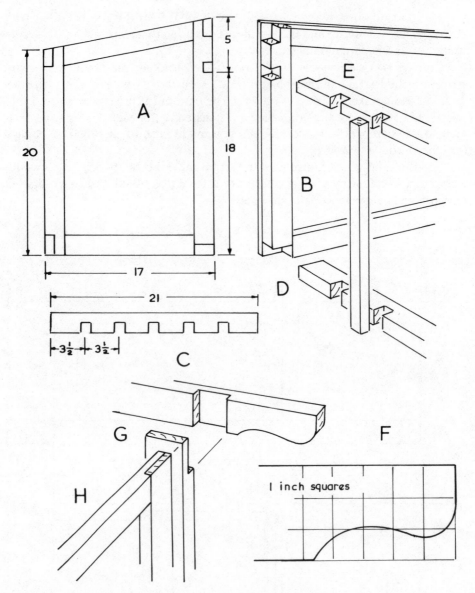

Fig. 7-60. *Construction of the chicken coop and run.*

Make the side rails (FIG. 7-59C and D). Extend the top one 5 inches at each end and shape the handles (FIG. 7-60F). Cut and halve uprights (FIGS. 7-59E and 7-60G). Assemble these parts to the house using waterproof glue and screws from inside the house.

With the house and side assemblies as a guide to sizes, make a frame to fit across the end of the run (FIG. 7-60H).

Materials List for Chicken Coop and Run

2 house sides	17 × 24 ×	1/4 or 1/2 plywood	
4 frames	1 × 2 × 24		
4 frames	1 × 2 × 17		
5 crosspieces	1 × 2 × 22		
5 bars	1 × 1 × 20		
1 house back	20 × 24 ×	1/4 or 1/2 plywood	
1 roof	24 × 30 ×	1/2 plywood	
1 house front	1 × 5 × 26		
1 cover stop	1 × 1 × 26		
2 base strips	1 × 3 × 50		
2 handle strips	1 × 3 × 60		
2 uprights	1 × 3 × 20		
2 end strips	1 × 2 × 24		
2 end strips	1 × 2 × 20		
2 cover sides	1 × 2 × 32		
3 cover strips	1 × 2 × 24		

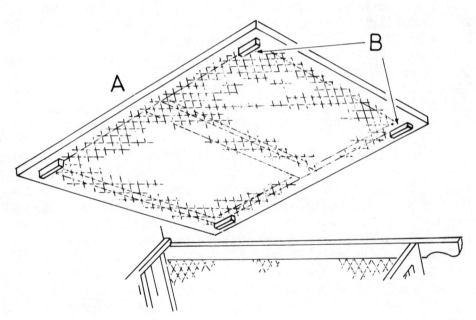

Fig. 7-61. Top of the chicken run.

The wire mesh is attached to the inside of the frame with staples. You might find it easier to do this before putting the end frame between the sides. Carry the wire a short distance over the edge of the house and staple it there.

Make the roof of the house from a sheet of plywood to overhang 2 inches all around (FIG. 7-59F). Hinge it under its front edge so it will swing up. Arrange a fastener under the rear edge so a predator cannot lift it.

The cover of the run is a frame with halving joints at the corners. A strip across the middle will prevent the wire sagging, particularly if an animal tries to get at the chickens (FIG. 7-61A). After you have stapled on the wire mesh, put locating blocks near the corners to stop the cover being moved about (FIG. 7-61B). A strip on the house front (FIG. 7-59G) will hold down that end. The weight of the cover will probably be enough to hold it down, but if you want to secure it, have a hook and eye or other fastening at the opposite end.

There is no built-in floor for the house, but if you want to provide one it could be a piece of plywood to drop in. This allows you to remove it for cleaning.

Field Poultry House

If you have sufficient area available and want to keep a reasonable number of hens on free range and protect them from predators at night, the building has to be big enough, but capable of being moved. For the number of birds involved, a light shelter that can be carried would not be sufficient, so the poultry house will have to be moved with a tractor. In this case you do not have to aim at exceptional lightness. It would be better for the house to be substantial enough to have a long life and possibly other uses if you change your interests.

This field poultry house (FIG. 7-62) is large enough for as many as 40 laying hens. There are perches and nest boxes inside. A door gives you access and there is ventilation in one end, but no windows. Skids under the sides keep the floor clear of the ground and allow the building to be moved with a rope bridle to a tractor or horse. The pop hole has a ramp to the ground and this is used to close the birds in at night.

It would be possible to build the poultry house from several materials. The walls and roof could be plywood. You could use weatherboarding or shiplap boarding on the walls and cover the roof with plywood or corrugated metal or plastic sheeting. For the strongest building, all of the covering, including the roof, could be boards about 1-inch-×-6-inch section, preferably tongued and grooved. That is the method suggested in these drawings and instructions.

If you decide to modify the sizes (FIG. 7-63A), the method of construction could be the same. Be careful not to err towards something tall and narrow, which might tip over when moved. If you expect to change the use of the building later, you might want a window, which can be arranged easily in the manner described for earlier designs. There could be a boarded screen to fit in the window space, which could be replaced by a glazed window later. The end ventilator is kept high to be out of reach of predators. If you need more ventilation, you could drill a row of holes in the sides under the eaves.

Start by making the pair of ends (FIG. 7-64). The door and pop hole could be arranged either way around. All of the framing is 2-inch-square strips. Corners and crossings should be halved (FIG. 7-65A). Where one piece meets another, a notch (FIG. 7- 65B) can supplement nailing.

A ridge piece has to be supported between two rafters (FIG. 7-64A). At the

Fig. 7-62. *This field poultry house is intended to provide overnight accommodation for freerange hens.*

door end arrange the long upright sufficiently to one side of center (FIG. 7-64B and C) to provide a guide at the side of the ridge. Put a rail across to support the ridge (FIG. 7-64D). At the other end put a supporting rail across (FIG. 7-64E).

Cover with vertical boards, level at all edges. Put a strip over the frame at the side of the door to make up to the same thickness as the boarding. A pop hole 9 inches wide and 12 inches high should suit most hens, but you might want to make it bigger for turkeys or geese. The ventilating space can be 12 inches deep.

The two sides are the same (FIG. 7-65C) except for the need to arrange the perch supports as a pair. Allow for the framing coming outside that of the ends, with the boarding overlapping (FIG. 7-65D). Arrange the end boards to project sufficiently (FIG. 7-65E). Cut level at top and bottom rails.

You can arrange any number of lift-out perches across the building (FIG. 7-65F). At this stage you can arrange more supports than you will probably need. In this case, five positions are suggested (FIG. 7-65G and H), even if you only start with three perches, which can be 1¹/₂-inch-square pieces with rounded top surfaces. Allow for them pressing into the end sockets fairly tightly.

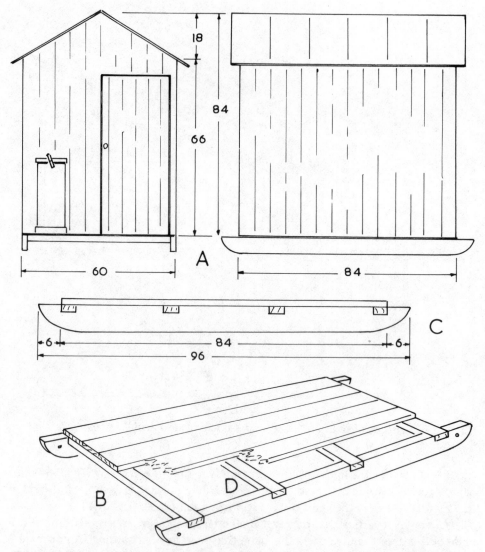

Fig. 7-63. Main sizes of the field poultry house, with details of the floor and skids.

The wall parts will give you the size of the floor and skid assembly (FIG. 7-63B). The floor width and length should match the outside sizes of the assembled walls. Cut the skids with curved ends (FIG. 7-63C) and arrange floor joists across (FIG. 7- 63D), notched into them. Drill the skids for towing ropes. Check squareness and lack of twist as you assemble these parts on a level surface. Accuracy here is important as it affects the rest of the building. Nail on floor boards, being careful that the overall size is correct.

Assemble the walls to each other and to the floor. You could nail the corners, but it would be helpful to use a few bolts through to pull the uprights tightly

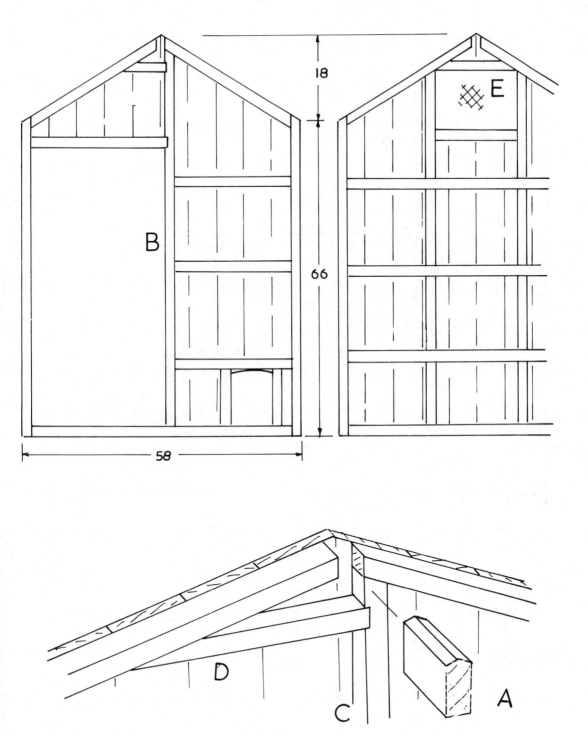

Fig. 7-64. Construction of ends of the field poultry house.

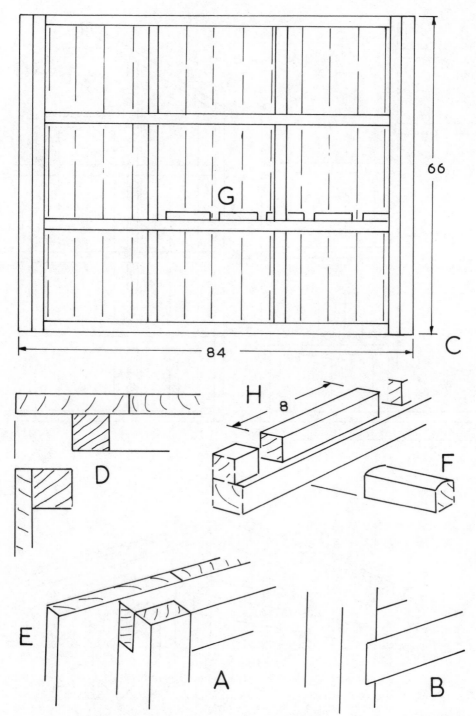

Fig. 7-65. Side and perch details for the field poultry house.

Materials List for Field Poultry House

Ends

4 uprights	2	×	2	×	70
3 uprights	2	×	2	×	90
5 rails	2	×	2	×	60
6 rails	2	×	2	×	30
4 rafters	2	×	2	×	48

Sides

8 rails	2	×	2	×	84
8 uprights	2	×	2	×	70
2 perch supports from	$1\,1/2$	×	$1\,1/2$	×	48
3 perches	$1\,1/2$	×	$1\,1/2$	×	60

Roof

1 ridge	2	×	6	×	86
10 battens	$1/2$	×	$1\,1/2$	×	40

Door

3 ledgers	1	×	6	×	30
2 braces	1	×	6	×	30

Pop hole

2 strips	1	×	2	×	12
1 ramp	1	×	12	×	24

Skids

2 skids	2	×	6	×	100
4 joists	2	×	4	×	62

Walls, roof and floor

boards (preferably tongued-and-grooved)	1	×	6		
Nest box					
5 divisions	$3/4$	×	16	×	20
1 bottom	$3/4$	×	16	×	54
1 back	$3/4$	×	19	×	54
1 top	$3/4$	×	17	×	54
1 front	$3/4$	×	5	×	54

together. Supplement these with nails between the posts and in the overlapping boards. Use long nails through the bottom rails into the skids and end joists.

Cut the ridge piece to fit into the end walls. It might be satisfactory to leave the top surface flat, but it will help the fit of the roof boards to bevel each side (FIG. 7-64A), if only partially. Beveling the tops of the side walls is less important.

Nail on the roof boards (FIG. 7-66A). Allow the end ones to extend about 2 inches over the end walls and cut the boards to overhang the side walls by 5 inches.

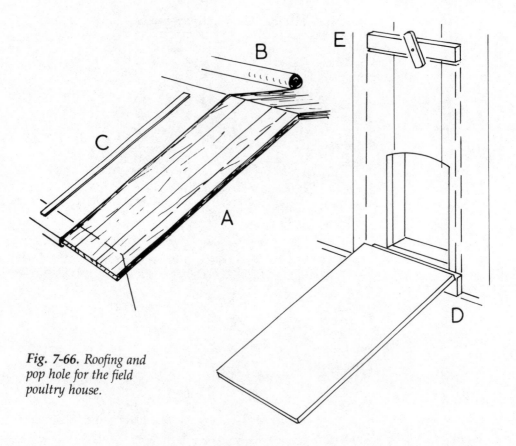

Fig. 7-66. Roofing and pop hole for the field poultry house.

Cover the roof with tarred felt (FIG. 7-66B), turned under and nailed at the eaves, then carried over the ridge to do the same at the other eaves. Allow a good overlap at joints and put battens (FIG. 7-66C) at about 15-inch intervals down both slopes. Cover the ventilating space with 1-inch wire or plastic mesh, held with staples.

Put a strip across below the pop hole (FIG. 7-66D) and experiment with the length of ramp you want. A board 24 inches long should do. Make this to overlap the pop hole 1 inch each side. Hinge it to the bottom strip. Swing it up to get the position of another strip to carry a wood turnbutton (FIG. 7-66E).

Make the door of upright boards ledgered and braced in the usual way. It should be sufficient for this type of building to fit the door into the opening as cut, but you could put edge strips around to cover the frame and board edges. Let the bottom of the door extend over the bottom frame rail. Hinge at one side and put a handle on the other side. You could use a turnbutton to hold the door closed, have a clasp and staple, or fit a lock. Arrange a stop strip inside.

The four nesting boxes are a separate unit (FIG. 7-67). It is a size that will allow you to put it across the end, at either side or rest it on the perches. The sloping

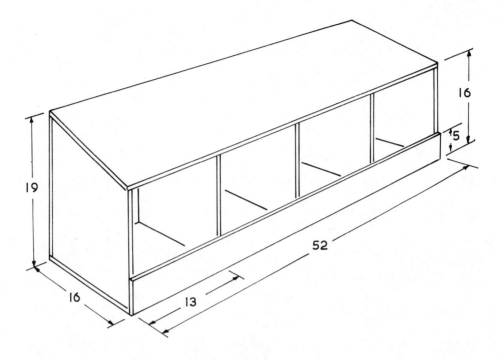

Fig. 7-67. *Nesting box for the field poultry house.*

top discourages birds from perching on it and fouling the box. Make it of solid wood or 3/4-inch plywood.

If the skids are not made of a rot-resistant hardwood, they should be soaked in preservative. The rest of the building could also be treated with preservative or painted. Hens and other birds can soon make the inside of the building very dirty. Cleaning will be easier if the inside is painted a light color, but let all smell of paint disappear before introducing the birds.

8

Children's Buildings

Children at play like to have something to get into. They might improvise shelters or use their imagination with the most improbable things. If you can provide them with an actual building to play in, they will probably go into raptures and be occupied for a long time. They can use such a house of their own for many hours of make-believe. They can furnish and decorate it and use it for many occasions over a long period. They do grow up, however, and no longer have a use for the building. An empty, unused building can be a problem, unless other children come along to take over. For the usual small family, any sort of play building probably should not be permanent.

You must consider if the building is to be long-lasting, or if it should be made portable so it does not have to stay outside when you no longer need it. If it is to be portable, where will you store it? If it is portable and folds, you might be able to place it against a garage wall or other place that will take length and width, and a reduced thickness.

A play building or "Wendy" house usually will be much smaller than a building used by adults. This feature could be one of its attractions—children can get into it, but their parents cannot. This design means that you can use lighter construction and the work is easier to handle, even if your shop is small and your tools and equipment are not very plentiful. You might want to use the building for only a few years, so it does not have to be very durable. You could use framed hardboard for a very economical building, but it might damage easily and it would deteriorate rapidly under moist conditions. Exterior-grade plywood is very suitable, as panels usually are smaller than a standard sheet. For many parts, plywood might be stiff enough without added framing.

If the building is to be permanently outside and must withstand any weather, you will have to make it more like a larger building, as described in earlier chapters. You might consider making it a combination building, even if it is small. Design the front to appeal to children, but place a large door at the back, which will allow you to put in a lawn mower and other garden equipment when the children no longer use the little house for play.

Children will get a lot of satisfaction out of a rather basic building. Most will not look for much fine detail. You may add trimmings that appeal to adults, but a child might not even notice them. The important items to remember are: a size that the child can enter, but not much bigger than that; a door that the child can close; some spaces to represent windows; and a place the child can call his own. You might get some satisfaction from painting the roof to look like shingles, but a child might be just as happy with a plain, painted roof.

The appearance should be something with which the child can identify. If his home, and all those around, have flat roofs, he might not appreciate a pitched roof. However, a pitched roof is more likely to fit his or her idea of a proper house. From your point of view, it might be better to convince the child that a building with a flat or sloping roof is a real house, if that suits your constructional ideas or method of folding.

Do not overlook safety requirements. Avoid sharp edges and corners. Make sure all woodwork is well-rounded. Be careful of wood that might split or splinter. Some softwood plywood might splinter too easily at the edges. You might have to file the sharpness off edges of hinges and other metal parts.

Windows may just be cutouts with rounded edges. Avoid glass; use soft, transparent plastic, if the child wants more than just a hole. Plain wood turnbuttons are better than more elaborate fasteners. If you arrange a door to fasten inside, make sure you can get at it in an emergency, possibly by reaching through a window or taking the roof off. If you make the building portable, be sure an adult is the only one who operates it. The child should not be able to unfasten anything that would bring the house down on him. Too simple a means of folding might not be a good thing. If you need a wrench on a few nuts and bolts, that puts the action beyond the young experimenting occupant. If you want to provide coat hooks and similar things, it is better to use rounded wooden pegs than nails, which could scratch the child. Be careful that the young users cannot turn the whole house over. If there is no built-in base or floor, you might have to anchor the walls down.

Consider scale. If you make a building to suit a child who is just starting to walk, it can be quite compact, but children grow rapidly. How long do you want the house to last? In only another two years, a child will need much more head room. He might not mind stooping through a doorway, but he should be able to stand up inside. If you want children up to 10 years of age to use the building, its size must become almost adult. If it is to be a recreational building for young people older than 10, you have to use adult sizes.

Basic Folding Playhouse

You can make the simplest small playhouse entirely from 1/2-inch plywood panels, hinging them together so it is portable. The house shown in FIG. 8-1 has a roof that lifts off and ends that are hinged centrally (FIG. 8-2A) so it is possible to fold the parts into a bundle under 5 inches thick. The greatest packed length is 48 inches, and the greatest packed width is 38 inches. Sizes are arranged so you can cut them economically from 48-inch-×-96-inch plywood sheets (FIG. 8-2B). As shown, there are openings for a window and a door. You could hinge on a plywood door and fit plastic sheet to the window, although for the age child this is intended for, simple openings should be satisfying.

Be careful to square all parts, or they will not fit and fold properly. Make four end pieces (FIG. 8-3A). With these sizes, the roof will slope at about 30 degrees.

Fig. 8-1. *You can make a basic folding playhouse from plywood sheets.*

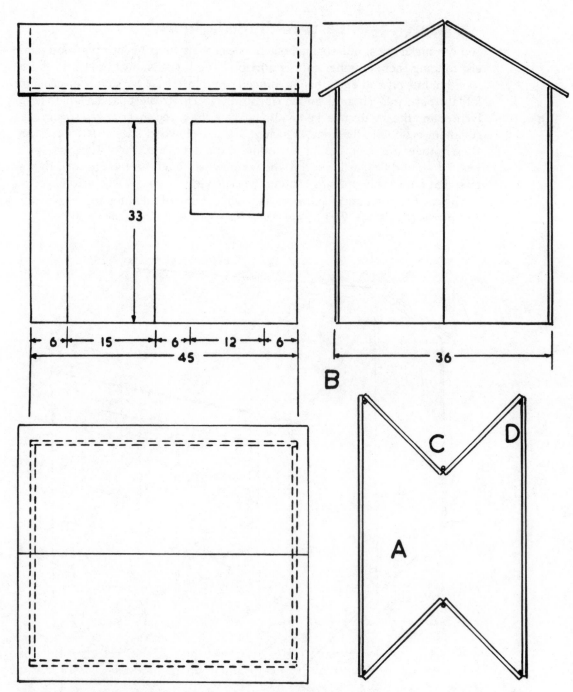

Fig. 8-2. Sizes of the playhouse and the method of folding the walls.

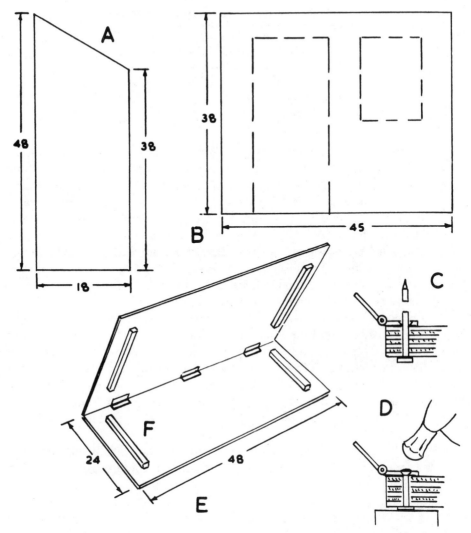

Fig. 8-3. Sizes of the folding playhouse parts and the method of riveting the hinges.

Make the back and front to match each other and as high as the eaves on the ends (FIG. 8-3B). Cut the door and window openings in the front. Remove sharpness from all edges and round the door and window edges thoroughly.

It should be sufficient to put three 2-inch hinges on each joint. So the parts will fold against each other, the hinges at the centers of the ends come outside (FIG. 8-2C), and those between the ends and the back and front are inside (FIG. 8-2D).

Screws probably will not hold adequately in 1/2-inch plywood. Although it

Materials List for Basic Folding Playhouse

4 ends	18- x -48- x -½ plywood
1 front	38- x -45- x -½ plywood
1 back	38- x -45- x -½ plywood
2 roofs	24- x -48- x -½ plywood
4 roof strips	1 x 1 x 21

might be possible to use small nuts and bolts, the neatest way of fixing the hinges is by riveting. The riveting avoids projections that could scratch young hands. You can make suitable rivets with soft-metal nails: Copper is particularly suitable. Drill slightly undersize for each nail, and drive it through from the other side. Cut off the nail end to leave sufficient length to hammer into the countersunk hole in the hinge (FIG. 8-3C). Support the nail head on an iron block, and work around the projecting end so as to spread it gradually, preferably using a light ball-peen hammer. Try to fill the countersink (FIG. 8-3D). Any excess may be filed off. Adjust the amount the hinge knuckle projects so the ends will open flat and the corners finish close when square to each other.

The two roof sections (FIG. 8-3E) will overlap the walls by a small amount. Hinge them together and locate them on the assembled walls so the overhangs are even. Mark the positions of the ends under the roof. Glue and nail strips to fit inside the ends (FIG. 8-3F). Their lower ends should come against the front and back, but the upper ends may be cut back about 2 inches. The roof then will hold the walls in shape. This procedure might be all you need to do, but if the child is able to push the roof, you could fit hooks and eyes outside, under the roof at the ends.

Finish the house in bright colors, with the outside walls a different color from the roof and the inside walls a lighter color. You could edge the openings with a darker color.

If you fit a door, it may be a piece of plywood hinged outside. Put a strip across a top corner inside to act as a stop. A wooden turnbutton outside will allow the child to "lock" the door when leaving the house.

General Store

Children like to play at shopkeeping. The little building shown in FIG. 8-4 is intended to give them a store into which they can put the things they want to pretend to sell. A counter in the window lets them serve customers, and they can close a door to stop anyone unauthorized from getting inside. There could be a back door if they have so much stock that some has to go outside.

Construction is with ½-inch plywood and some 1-inch- x -2-inch strip framing. Bolt parts together so the structure is semipermanent, but so you can fold flat sheets for storage. It is not intended to be very weathertight, but the parts would not suffer if rained on occasionally.

Fig. 8-4. *A child can use this general store to pretend to sell goods.*

Materials List for General Store

1 front	48- x -72- x -½ plywood
1 back	45- x -66- x -½ plywood
2 sides	36- x -39- x -½ plywood
2 roofs	36- x -39- x -½ plywood
1 door	18- x -36- x -½ plywood
1 counter	12- x -30- x -½ plywood
2 counter strips	1 x 2 x 30
8 framing strips	1 x 2 x 39

The sizes shown should suit most children of an age likely to use the building, but you might wish to modify them to suit your children or available space. You can cut the parts without much waste from standard 48-inch- x -96-inch sheets (FIG. 8-5A).

Make the back first. The roof has a shallow slope to give maximum head room at the sides. Put 1-inch- x -2-inch strips around the edges, level with the roof slopes, but in from the sides by the thickness of the side plywood (FIGS. 8-5B and 8-6A). Fit the sides in and bolt through them. Glue and screws are advisable to attach the framing to the end plywood.

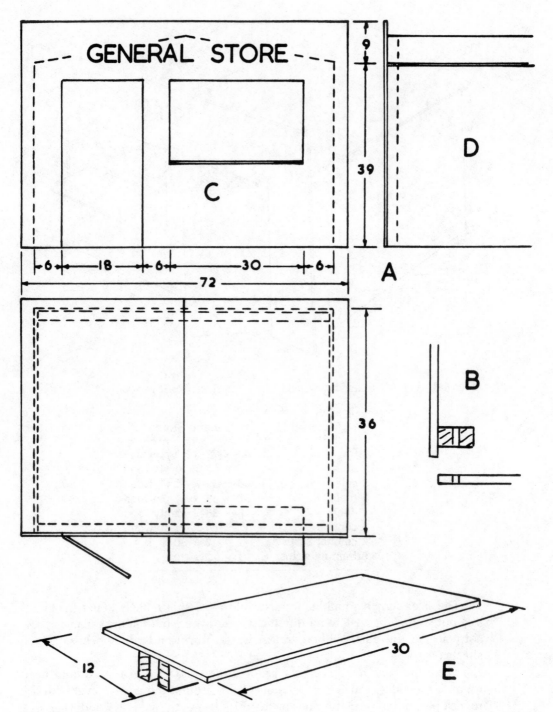

GENERAL STORE

Fig. 8-5. *Sizes of parts of the child's general store.*

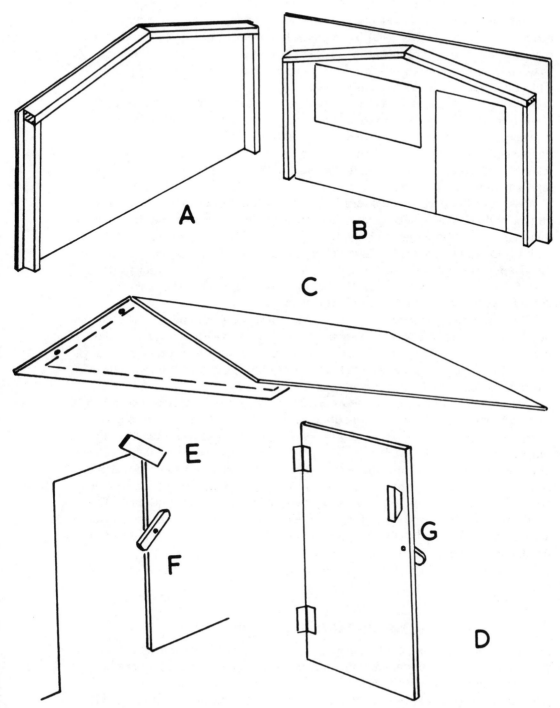

Fig. 8-6. Construction of the parts of the child's store.

Cut the front to size and use the back as a pattern to lay out a matching arrangement of strips (FIG. 8-6B). Also mark the positions of the door and window (FIG. 8-5C). It will be easier to cut these parts before you attach the strips. Take sharpness off the edges and round the upper parts of the window opening. Cut a door opening in the back, if you wish.

The two sides are plain rectangles (FIG. 8-5D). At each corner, drill for three 1/4-inch coach bolts. You can make a window opening in one or both sides, but it probably will be better if you leave them solid. In this size building, there should be no need to fasten the roof to the sides, but if you make the store longer from front to back, place a strip matching the slope of the roof along each top edge to take bolts through the roof.

Assemble the parts made so far so you can test the fit of the roof panels as you make them. Place them against the front, over the strips there. At the back, they can project about 1 inch and at the sides they should project almost to the width of the front (FIG. 8-6C). Hinge the panels together along the ridge, preferably riveting the hinges in the way described for the folding playhouse (FIG. 8-3C,D). At back and front, drill for two bolts on each slope. These bolts should be enough to keep the roof on and hold the assembly in shape.

You can make the serving counter set into the window opening permanent, but that would interfere with packing the house flat if you disassemble the building. Instead, you could make it with two strips underneath to press over the lower part of the window (FIG. 8-5E). This assembly should be firm enough in use, but you can lift off the counter.

Make a door from a piece of plywood (FIG. 8-6D). Allow easy clearance at the sides, and you can make the bottom up to 1 inch from the ground. A strip inside the top corner will act as a stop and be out of the way (FIG. 8-6E). Rivet on the hinges, although if you want to screw, place a thin strip of wood behind the doorway to take their points. There could be wooden turnbuttons inside and out so the shopkeeper can shut out intruders or fasten the door when he leaves his store. The outside turnbutton must be on the side of the doorway (FIG. 8-6F). The inside one must be on the edge of the door (FIG. 8-6G). The inside turnbutton will serve as a handle inside, but you should add a block of wood or some sort of handle on the outside of the door.

When you paint in bright colors, you could put the name of the store or the child's own name on the front.

Hardboard Playhouse

Hardboard is a convenient and cheap material, but if you decide to use it for a playhouse, you must understand its limitations. The cheapest grades have little strength. They still might be satisfactory, particularly if you do not expect the demand by the child to be very long. Oil-tempered hardboard is considerably stronger and has a resistance to moisture, so you might think it worth the extra cost. No hardboard is as strong as plywood. Because hardboard is only 1/8 inch thick, there has to be plenty of framing, including around any window or other cutout. Hardboard does not take paint as simply as wood does: You have to use a special sealer first.

The playhouse shown in FIG. 8-7 is an example of the way you must use hardboard with adequate framing. You can assemble the house in two ways. The framing may be on the inside so there is a smooth exterior, or it could be outside to give a "Tudor" appearance. Because one side of hardboard is smooth and the other side has a textured pattern, you must decide which way you want the hardboard to face. You can change the appearance at any time by turning over front and back panels and exchanging the end sections. The roof will suit either arrangement. You will have to make sure you can change over corner joints, if you want the option of two-way assembly.

Fig. 8-7. *You can make this playhouse of framed hardboard.*

You can economically cut all of the panels of the house shown in FIG. 8-8A from the usual 48-inch-×-96-inch sheets of hardboard. Nearly all the framing strips are 1-inch-×-2-inch sections, laid flat on the hardboard. You do not need to cut joints between frame parts, but if you want to strengthen meeting strips, you could drive in corrugated fasteners (FIG. 8-8B). Use glue between the strips and the hardboard, driving plenty of fine nails from the hardboard into the wood.

Make the front panel first (FIG. 8-9A). It is shown with a central door and two window openings, but you could alter the arrangement if you wish. Strips are around the edges and every opening. Make the back in a similar way. It is suggested that you do not make any cutouts, and it is 9 inches lower (FIG. 8-9B) than the front.

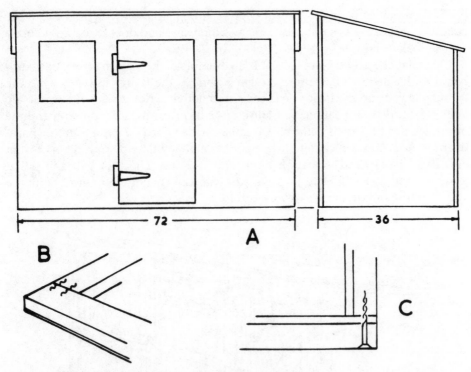

Fig. 8-8. Sizes and construction of the hardboard playhouse.

Materials List for Hardboard Playhouse

Front		Roof	
4 uprights	1 × 2 × 50	2 pieces	1 × 2 × 78
4 uprights	1 × 2 × 18	5 pieces	1 × 2 × 40
3 rails	1 × 2 × 74	1 piece	1 × 1 × 78
4 rails	1 × 2 × 26		
		Door	
Back			
		2 uprights	1 × 2 × 42
4 uprights	1 × 2 × 41	5 rails	1 × 2 × 20
3 rails	1 × 2 × 74		
		Floor (optional)	
Ends			
		4 pieces	1 × 2 × 72
1 upright	1 × 2 × 50	6 pieces	1 × 2 × 36
1 upright	1 × 2 × 41		
4 rails	1 × 2 × 35	**Covering**	⅛ hardboard

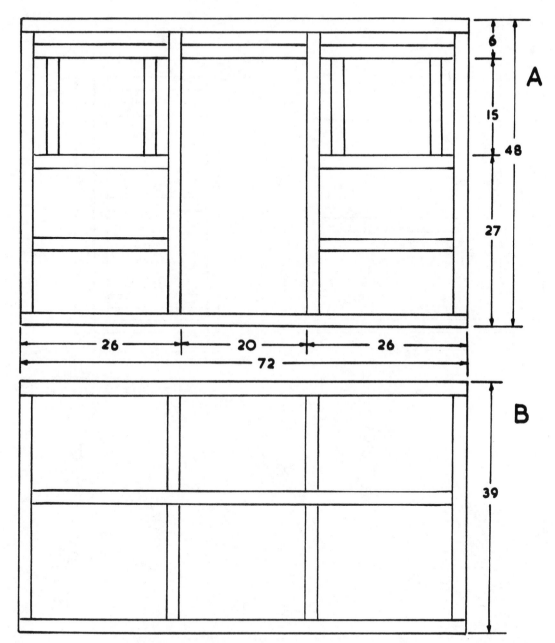

Fig. 8-9. Front and back of the hardboard playhouse.

Make a pair of ends (FIG. 8-10A) to give the width, front to back, that you want. As in the other frames, do not leave too much hardboard unsupported, or an unintentional knock might crack it.

Assemble the parts made so far. Eventually, they will be screwed together

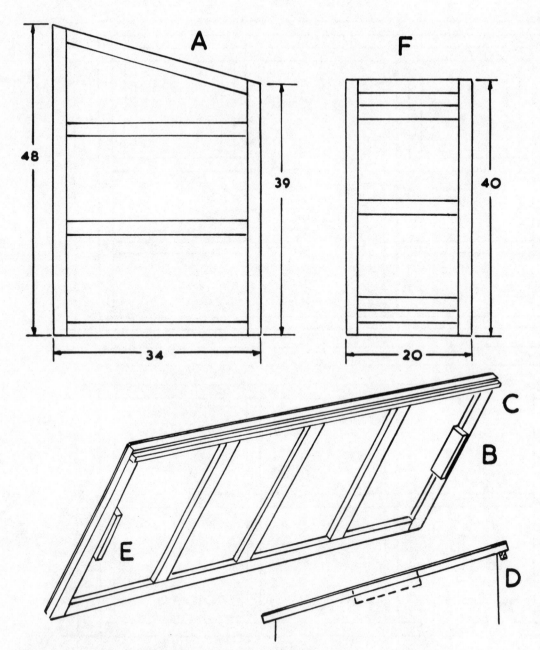

Fig. 8-10. *End, door, and roof of the hardboard playhouse.*

with 2¹/₂-inch wood screws at about 9-inch intervals (FIG. 8-8C). For the first assembly, two screws at each corner will be sufficient. You could make a floor to fit inside, if you wish, using hardboard or plywood on framing. The floor would hold the assembly in shape while you make and fit the roof.

Frame the roof like the other parts with the hardboard outside (FIG. 8-10B). Get sizes from the assembled other parts, and make it so it overhangs $1^1/2$ inches all around. Solid wood then will be bearing on the walls without gaps. Put a 1-inch-square strip along the front (FIG. 8-10C,D) to prevent the roof slipping down the slope if you do not screw it on. You can place pieces inside the ends (FIG. 8-10E) to locate the roof lengthwise. In the finished house, you might want to have the roof removable to provide some adult access.

Make the door by framing hardboard (FIG. 8-10F) to fit easily in the doorway. The two crossbars, a short distance in from top and bottom, are to take the hinges, which could be T type about 6 inches long. Arrange a stop in the corner of the doorway. The stop could be a spring or magnetic fastener, but a wooden turnbutton gives a child something to move.

You could glaze the windows with plastic, or you could fit them with curtains inside. If the playhouse is permanent or rarely taken apart, you could fit shelves, coat pegs, and other things, such as pictures and cupboards around the walls inside. Children can then treat it as a small home and learn to keep the place tidy.

If you want to complete the playhouse with the framing exposed on the outside, you can get a traditional effect by having the areas between the framing cream or another light color, while the "timbering" is black or dark brown. Any fairly neutral color will do for the other side, which will then look correct if you ever reverse the walls. The roof might be red-brown or even green, as a simulation of a full-size roof covering and a contrast to the paint on the walls.

Dual-purpose Playhouse

If you want to make a building that children can use for playing and that would be useful for storage for gardening tools as big as lawn mowers, it must be a reasonable size and stronger than anything intended purely as somewhere for younger children to play. It is likely to be permanent, so you must make it weatherproof. The requirements mean its construction will be very similar to other small buildings.

The dual-purpose building shown in FIG. 8-11 has a frontage that can be used as a play area, with a porch. It is large enough for children up to young teenagers, who might use it as a base for games and other activities. At the back is a large lift-out door, which gives access to a floor area about 60 inches × 72 inches to use for storage when children no longer need the building.

As drawn in FIG. 8-12A, the door is almost up to adult height at the front, with a glazed window alongside it. A porch that projects 24 inches shelters the door and window. You can lock the door so the building then becomes a storage place with wide access at the back. Construction is mostly of 2-inch-square strips covered by shiplap boards.

No floor is shown, but you should place the building on a concrete base. You can put a board floor inside, made with 2-inch-square framing covered with

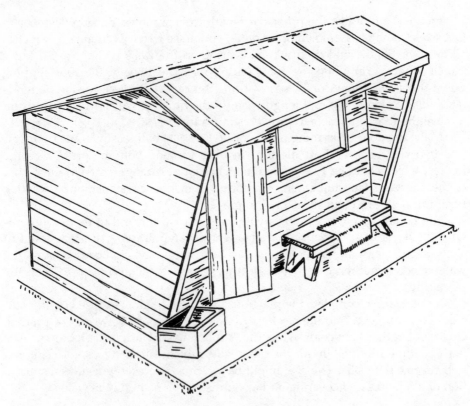

Fig. 8-11. *This roomy playhouse with a sheltered front has a dual use. A large back door allows you to put gardening equipment inside when the children do not need the house.*

1-inch boards that project onto the bottom parts of the frames. The frame that crosses under the door is intended to be left in place, but you could cut it away after you have anchored the other parts of the building if you want a clear floor for wheeling things in.

Start by making a pair of sides (FIG. 8-13A). You can use any of the normal framing joints, except two places need special treatment. At the apex, three pieces meet together. Miter the two sloping pieces together, then halve their meeting ends with the upright (FIG. 8-13B). Place a purlin halfway down the long slope (FIG. 8-13C). This placement requires cutting through the framing member. Put a piece under the cut (which does not go through the covering boards), and square its underside to meet the central upright (FIG. 8-13D).

The front (FIG. 8-14A) fits between the uprights under the apex, so check the height there as you put the frame together. All of the framing is 2-inch-square strips, except for the top, which forms the ridge. The top is 2 inches × 3 inches, and you must bevel to match the slopes of the roof (FIG. 8-14B). If you want the cladding to go close up, bevel that as well.

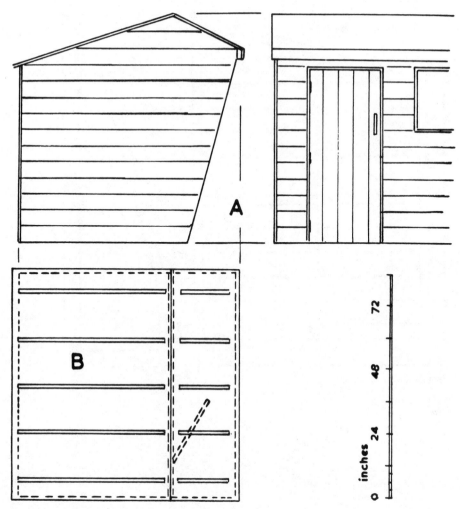

Fig. 8-12. Suggested sizes for the dual-purpose playhouse.

Carry the uprights to the full height, to give the best support to the horizontal shiplap boarding. Arrange rails between and across them for the doorway and the window. Check squareness by comparing diagonal measurements, as this frame controls the accuracy and symmetry of the building.

When you erect the building, the joints between the front and the sides will look best if the cladding of the front continues over the uprights on the sides (FIG. 8-14C). Allow enough boarding on each side of the frame to almost cover the adjoining upright.

You can line the building, but assuming it will serve your purpose without lining, edge the doorway and window opening with strips, allowing them to project a little inside and outside (FIG. 8-14D). When you make the back (FIG. 8-15A), its height must match the rear edges of the sides and its width should be

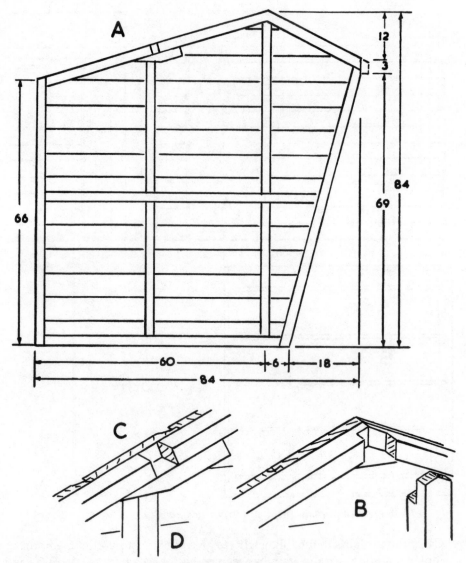

Fig. 8-13. *Details of an end for the dual-purpose playhouse.*

the same as the front. Framing is 2-inch-square strips, except the top, which is 2 inches × 3 inches. The doorway is 60 inches wide and 55 inches high. Because this doorway takes quite a lot out of the back, it is important that the remaining back is made strong to prevent distortion of that part of the building. Bevel the top edge to suit the slope of the roof (FIG. 8-15B).

When you assemble the building, the covering boards on the back should overlap the uprights on the sides, to leave a space for a filler piece (FIG. 8-15C). At the top of the doorway, take covering boards to the edge of the door. At the sides,

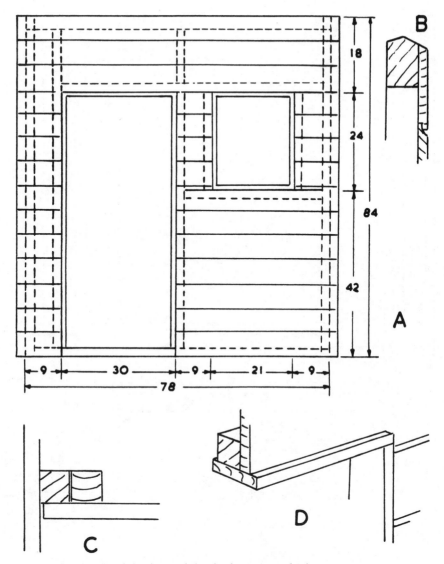

Fig. 8-14. *Details of the front of the dual-purpose playhouse.*

the covering boards on the door must overlap the uprights on the doorway, so cut back the ends of the shiplap boarding on the back to half the thickness of those uprights (FIG. 8-15D).

Make the door frame to fit easily in its opening (FIG. 8-15E). Use 2-inch-square pieces, except for the bottom, which is liable to get rougher use. It should be 3 inches deep. Fit diagonals to keep the door in shape. Fit covering boards level at top and bottom, but at the sides extend them to overlap the door uprights. Cut the door boarding so its lines match the boarding around the doorway.

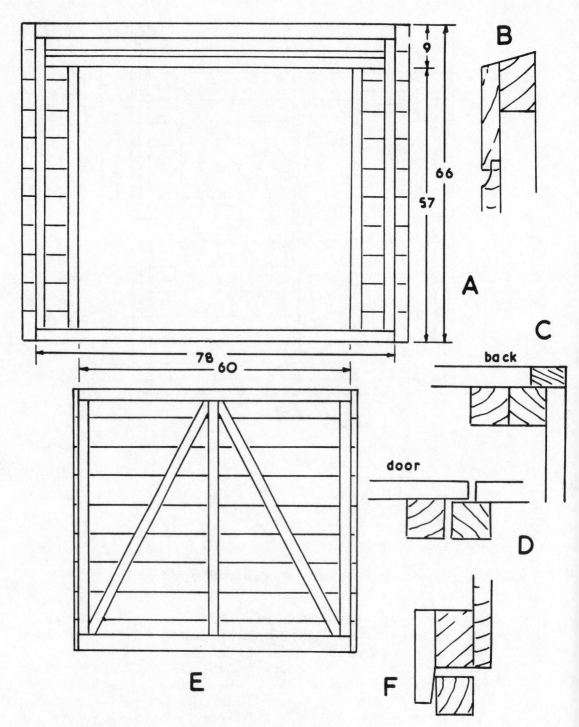

Fig. 8-15. The back of the dual-purpose playhouse, with a lift-out door.

Materials List for Dual-purpose Playhouse

2 uprights	2	×	2	×	86
6 uprights	2	×	2	×	74
2 rails	2	×	2	×	74
4 rails	2	×	2	×	70
2 rails	2	×	2	×	30

Front

4 uprights	2	×	2	×	86
2 rails	2	×	2	×	80
1 rail	1	×	3	×	80
1 rail	2	×	2	×	42
2 window posts	2	×	2	×	30
4 window edges	1	×	4	×	24
8 glazing bars	1	×	1	×	24
2 doorway sides	1	×	4	×	70
1 doorway top	1	×	4	×	32

Back

4 uprights	2	×	2	×	68
2 rails	2	×	2	×	80
1 rail	2	×	3	×	80

Back door

3 uprights	2	×	2	×	58
1 rail	2	×	2	×	62
1 rail	2	×	3	×	62
2 diagonals	2	×	2	×	70

Front door

3 ledgers	1	×	6	×	30
2 diagonals	1	×	6	×	40
6 boards	1	×	6	×	70

Roof

1 front strip	2	×	3	×	90
1 purlin	2	×	2	×	86
1 fascia	1	×	5	×	90
1 rear edge	1	×	1	×	90
Covering, boards about	1	×	6		
5 battens	½	×	1	×	65
5 battens	½	×	1	×	26
Cladding, shiplap boards	1	×	6		

This extended boarding on the door will prevent the door being pushed inwards. You now have to prevent it from pulling outwards. At the bottom, you can put a board across the width of the door, or make three pegs from 1-inch-×-3-inch wood to hook over the bottom member of the back frame (FIG. 8-15F). Taper slightly for easy fitting. Glue and screw to the inside of the bottom of the door. The pegs retain the bottom of the door. What you do at the top depends on the degree of security you desire. The simplest arrangement is a large wooden turnbutton on the back to turn down over the center of the door. You could fit a hasp and staple for a padlock alongside the turnbutton.

You can cover the roof in several ways. You could use corrugated metal or plastic sheets. Plywood would be satisfactory if you covered it with roofing felt or similar material. You can board and cover the roof, and that is the method suggested (FIG. 8-16A).

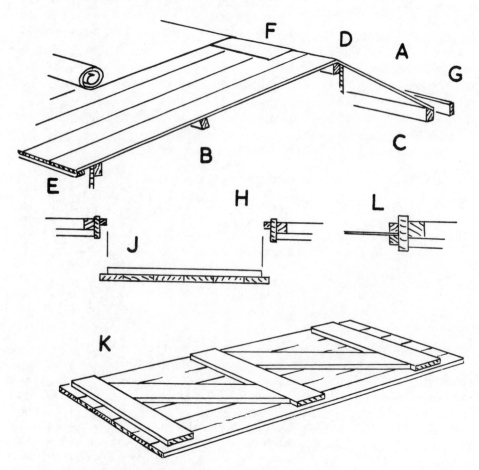

Fig. 8-16. *Roof and front door for the dual-purpose playhouse.*

Assemble the front, back, and sides using 3/8-inch coach bolts at about 18-inch intervals. Square the assembly and fasten it down to the base before adding the roof. Fit purlins between the slots in the sides (FIG. 8-16B). Fit the front piece to the ends (FIG. 8-16C). The roof boards extend 2 inches at each side, and the front piece should project the same amount. Cut the boards to meet closely at the ridge (FIG. 8-16D) and project 2 inches at the back. They could be plain boards, tongue-and-groove boards, or shiplap boards laid with the shaped parts underneath. Start at one side and allow for the overhang, then fit further boards tightly.

Put a strip under the ends of the boards at the back (FIG. 8-16E). Carry roof-covering material right over the ridge from front to back. Put a smaller piece over the ridge area only (FIG. 8-16F), which will give added protection there. Turn the covering material under and nail into the strip at the back. Turn it down at the front and nail there, then cover with a fascia board (FIG. 8-16G). Battens on the slopes (FIG. 8-12B) will prevent the covering material from lifting. It might be sufficient to turn the covering under at the sides, or you can nail battens on the edges there as additional security.

The front door may be ledgered and braced, with vertical-plain or tongue-and-groove boards. Put stops around the sides and top of the doorway (FIG. 8-16H), and cut back the ledgers on the door to clear them (FIG. 8-16J). Make the door with the bottom ledger high enough to clear the strip across the bottom of the doorway (FIG. 8-16K) and the top ledger a few inches down. Slope the braces up from the hinged side. You can make the door to swing either way. Use plain or T hinges. Either fit a lock or make a turnbutton. Fit a handle on the outside. You might need a catch and handle on the inside. When using the building for storage, you might want a bolt on the inside of the front door, so the only access then is via the rear door.

You could make a framed window to swing open, as described for some other buildings, but a simple fixed window has the glass held between fillets (FIG. 8-16L).

Play Barn

A traditional barn has an attractive appearance, and there is an appeal of the olden days to young people, which makes them want to use such a building in the ways they have read about. The scaled-down barn in FIGS. 8-17 and 8-18A has the traditional shape with a mansard or gambrel roof. The door is the stable type, so children can close the bottom part and look out above it. A lean-to commonly used as a cart shelter in a full-size barn now stores toys up to the size of bicycles. You can use a lean-to at the side as a porch for sitting out or playing with toys. The barn is large enough for many children to play in it at one time, and it makes a good store for outdoor equipment and the toys that are too large to be taken indoors.

Most of the construction is with shiplap boards on 2-inch-square framing.

Fig. 8-17. *A child-size play barn can provide storage, inside play area, shelter for toys, and a porch to sit under.*

Make the roof with boards on purlins, then cover with roofing felt or other similar material. The standard design has the door at one end and a window in the other end. You could have doors in both ends. There could be windows in one or both sides, and you might put a door from the barn into the lean-to.

Start with the two ends (FIG. 8-19A), which are the same, except in the closed end the central rail is taken right across (FIGS. 8-18B and 8-19B). The boarding goes across below the central rail and the space above becomes the window. The bottom rail across the doorway may stay there in the finished barn, or you can cut it away after you have anchored the building. If you wish to move the barn later, it is better to leave the bottom rail in place.

Take the shiplap boards to the edges of the doorway. When you erect the barn, the boards from the sides will overlap the end uprights (FIG. 8-19C). For a neat end finish, cut back the boards on the end to the center of each upright (FIG. 8-19D) so you can put a filler piece in each corner (FIG. 8-19E) after you bolt the parts together. Carry the boards to the edges on the roof slopes. Nail the purlins to the edges of the end frames and locate them with cleats, which you can put on now or later (FIG. 8-19F).

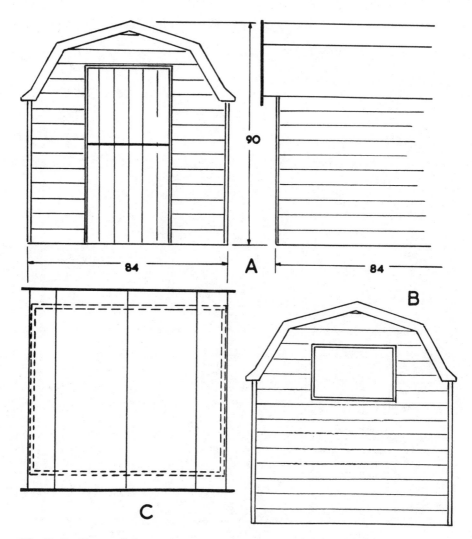

Fig. 8-18. Sizes and four views of the main building of the play barn.

If you are to line the building with plywood, deal with the ends now. Edge the door and window openings (FIG. 8-19G), going over any lining and extending a short distance inside and out.

The barn sides are simple rectangular frames (FIG. 8-20A). Leave the top edges square. Have the cladding level with the framing at top and bottom, but at the ends, extend the boards enough to overlap the end uprights.

Assemble the ends and sides. Use 1/4-inch or 1/16-inch coach bolts at about 18-inch centers in the corners, and cover them with the filler strips. Square the assembly by comparing diagonal measurements, then anchor the building to its base.

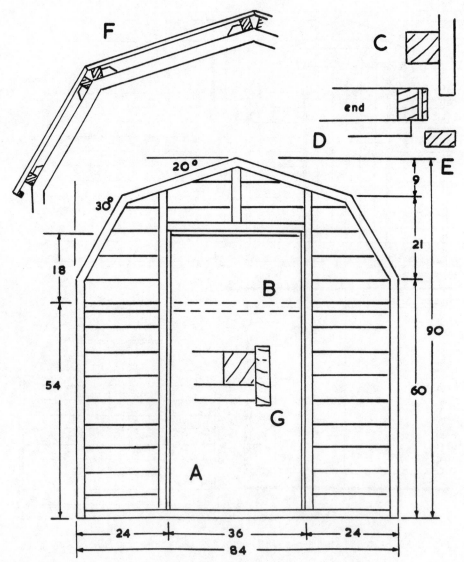

Fig. 8-19. An end and roof details of the play barn.

Fit the purlins against their cleats to extend about 5 inches at each end, so the bargeboards will be 6 inches from the barn ends (FIGS. 8-18C and 8-20B).

Place boards over the purlins with fitted ends where they meet on the ridge and at the angles. You will be covering these joints, but the covering will fit better if you avoid gaps. Boards may be plain or tongue-and-groove. As an alternative, you could use 1/2-inch or 3/4-inch plywood. Put strips of covering material along the joints (FIG. 8-20C). Roll the main covering material from eaves to eaves (FIG. 8-20D), where you should turn it under edge strips and nail it. Turn down at the

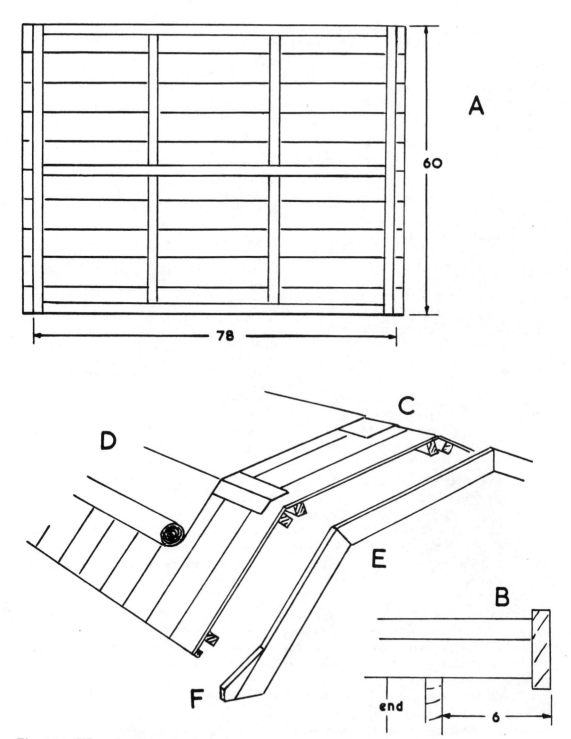

Fig. 8-20. *Side and roof details of the play barn.*

Door

4 ledgers	1	×	6	×	30
2 braces	1	×	6	×	34
2 sides	1	×	3	×	40
2 sides	1	×	3	×	30
6 boards	1	×	6	×	40
6 boards	1	×	6	×	30

Sides

8 uprights	2	×	2		62
6 rails	2	×	2	×	80
4 corner fillers	1	×	2½	×	62

Roof

8 purlins	2	×	2	×	10
8 bargeboards	1	×	5	×	24
16 battens	½	×	1	×	24

Covering

cladding	1-x-6-shiplap boards
roofing	1-x-6 plain or tongue-and-groove boards

Ends

4 uprights	2	×	2	×	90
4 uprights	2	×	2	×	64
2 uprights	2	×	2	×	24
4 rails	2	×	2	×	86
1 rail	2	×	2	×	40
8 rafters	2	×	2	×	30
2 door edges	1	×	4	×	74
1 door edge	1	×	4	×	40
4 window edges	1	×	4	×	40

Large lean-to

1 rail	2	×	3	×	86
1 rail	2	×	2	×	86
2 rafters	2	×	2	×	64
2 legs	2	×	2	×	52

Small lean-to

1 rail	2	×	3	×	86
1 rail	2	×	2	×	86
2 rafters	2	×	2	×	32
2 uprights	2	×	2	×	30
2 braces	2	×	2	×	32

ends so bargeboards will trap the material. Fit battens at about 18-inch intervals down the slopes on each surface to hold the covering.

Make the bargeboards to stand a little above the surface of the roof and extend below the purlins. Fit the boards to each other (FIG. 8-20E), and take the ends to a few inches below the roof level. Trim the ends parallel with the floor. Triangular additions (FIG. 8-20F) will give the traditional appearance. Gaps under the roof may be left as ventilation. To close them, you can fit pieces in or continue the cladding to touch the roof.

Make the door in the same way as the two-part door described for the barn in chapter 7 (FIG. 7-24D) and hinge it in the same way. You can leave the window at the other end open. You could hinge a shutter over it, or you could glaze it, either with glass between fillets, as in the last building, or with a separately framed window that you can hinge open.

The barn is a complete unit. If you are going to add lean-tos, they fit against the cladding, and you can screw or bolt the parts through to framework inside.

If the barn were full-size, the lean-to would form a shed for farm implements and be designed to suit that need. In this case, it is suggested to make the main lean-to as long as the barn and as high under the eaves as it can go. Then extend it 60 inches to its own eaves height of about 48 inches or 12 inches less than its higher edge. Two end supporting rafters will be sufficient (FIG. 8-21A). Use 2-inch-square strips, except for a 2-inch-×-3-inch piece against the barn wall. Screw this piece through the cladding or bolt it into the framing.

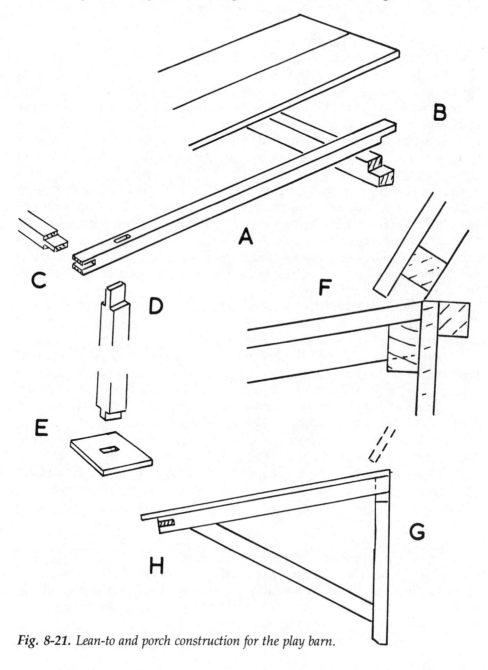

Fig. 8-21. *Lean-to and porch construction for the play barn.*

Make the lean-to length the same as the barn wall or take it to fit inside the bargeboards, if you want maximum roof length. Bevel the top of the 3-inch piece to suit the slope of the lean-to. Notch the rafters into it (FIG. 8-21B). At the other end, join in a matching lengthwise piece (FIG. 8-21C) and make legs to fit a short distance back from it (FIG. 8-21D). What you do with the bottoms of the legs depends on the ground or base. You can drive a leg into the ground or set it in concrete. It is shown with a broad base (FIG. 8-21E), which would spread the load on the earth or you could screw down to wood or concrete. The joints in the assembly could be open mortise-and-tenon or halving.

Allow for the lean-to roof to fit under the eaves of the main roof (FIG. 8-21F). You can board the lean-to in the same way as the main roof or you could use plywood. For 1/2-inch plywood, there should be a supporting purlin between the ends, halfway down the slope. Cover the roof to match the main roof. At the outer end, turn the material under and nail it. At the upper end, you may take it through and nail it to the top of the barn side. Arrange battens down the lean-to slope to match those on the barn roof.

You can make a narrower lean-to in the same way, but if it is no more than 30 inches wide, you could support it with end brackets, so there are no posts to the ground. This lean-to should be wide enough if the young people want to use it as a porch for sitting under. Arrange the brackets to come on the end uprights of the barn, but extend the roof over them. Place a 2-inch-×-3-inch piece along the barn wall, in the same way as for the large lean-to, but it may come between the brackets, without being joined to them.

Make the two brackets (FIG. 8-21G) with halved or mortise-and-tenon joints. Allow for a lengthwise piece similar to that on the large lean-to (FIG. 8-21H). Use boards or plywood for the roof and finish it in the same way as the other lean-to.

It is possible to add one or both lean-tos after you complete the barn, but if you intend to fit them at the same time as you build the barn, include them in the main work schedule and do their roofing as you do the main roofing. In that way, you can deal with the inner ends of some lean-to roof parts more easily.

How you finish the whole building depends on several factors. You may leave some woods, such as cedar, to weather without painting them. You could use a paint or a colored preservative. Traditionally, many of these barns were red, with a different color for the bargeboards. The roof probably will be black. The brighter colors might appeal to young users, but you might wish to choose them to fit in with the surroundings.

Fort

Because young people enjoy playing at pioneer days—with frontier activities and make-believe fights as wagon trains move west—a playhouse that looks like a fort and stockade obviously would be welcomed. The problem is that such a building would not look right if you made it of squared wood, and there would be no visible place for plywood and manufactured board.

You should make a fort with an authentic look with plenty of natural wood, at least for the external parts. This design means that you need a supply of logs and wood showing the natural bark or outside shapes. If you have access to a good supply of trees to fell or to those that are already in the form of poles or logs, the making of a fort and stockade playhouse should be easy. Even if none of this material seems possible, you could try a lumberyard or a sawmill for offcuts. When lumber is converted from the log to squared boards, a large number of outside slabs have to be cut away, and these pieces might be burned there or sold as firewood or garden decorations. Usually there are more of these offcuts than the sawmill can dispose of, and you might be able to get all you need. Although these pieces are comparatively thin, you can use them to face sawn and squared lumber, so the external appearance gives the effect of a structure built of logs.

Even if you have plenty of poles, you will have to cut many of them down the middle, either by splitting (which would have been the original way), or with a circular saw. For close fitting, you can cut some of these pieces parallel (FIG. 8-22A). For a fence, gaps caused by uneven edges might not matter, but for a building, a closer edge fit will be better. This fit is even more important if you are backing up with solid wood or plywood and you do not want it to show through.

It is advisable to peel off bark. With many woods, it comes away easily and the surface exposed still looks natural and rustic. Besides being rough for children to rub against, bark usually hides insects you do not want, and it could encourage rot. If you want to treat the wood with preservative, you cannot do that effectively if there is bark.

The original stockade had the tops of the logs in a palisade wall sharpened to lethal points (FIG. 8-22B). For a children's fort, they should have less acute angles, and you should round or flatten the tops (FIG. 8-22C). A fence will look authentic to the child, but should offer minimum danger if he clambers over.

A stockade wall could have sawn wooden rails. These would not be very obvious, and you could notch them into upright poles driven into the ground (FIG. 8-22D). At a corner, bring the rails in at different levels (FIG. 8-22E).

You could completely lift off some original gates, but for use by children, it would be better to hinge the gates inside. Closure might be by a substantial latch (FIG. 8-22F). Operation from outside might be by a rope through a hole (FIG. 8-22G). Inclusion of this rope is advisable if you want to be sure adults have access in an emergency (adults will probably not be able to reach over to work the latch).

Security against invaders was by a strong bar fitted into sockets (FIG. 8-22H). Knowing your children, you will have to decide if you should provide this.

Within the stockade, children will expect at least one enclosed building, preferably raised (FIG. 8-23). For strength and safety, this building probably is made best of sawn wood and plywood, with a facing to give a log cabin appearance. Some of the posts might also support the fence, but make sure they are secure—a cabin support that sinks or tilts would be difficult to rectify. If the ground does not offer much support unaided, sink a post in concrete, but keep that below the final level, so only soil shows (FIG. 8-24A).

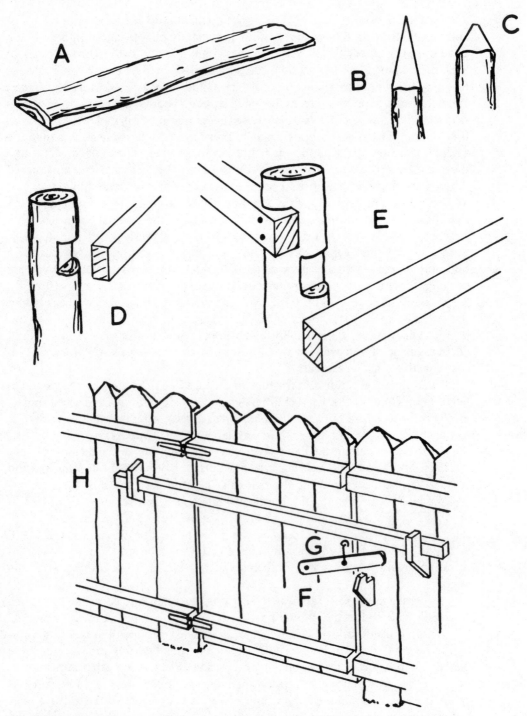

Fig. 8-22. The method of making a stockade fence for a child's fort. Avoid sharpness (B). Make blunt ends (C).

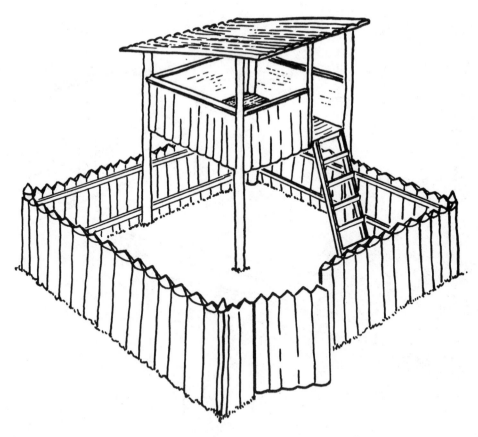

Fig. 8-23. A possible layout for a child's fort and stockade.

Notch in beams (FIG. 8-24B). If the stockade is 48 inches high, the beams could be 60 inches above the ground. For a building about 72 inches square, you could use 2-inch-×-3-inch wood. On this wood, arrange joists of the same section about 18 inches apart, and put ¹/₂-inch plywood on them (FIG. 8-24C).

Make the roof in a rather similar way, with beams across two pairs of poles and rafters and plywood over them (FIG. 8-24D). The slope need only be slight— 12 inches in 72 inches would be satisfactory.

Arrange walls at a height that will stop children from falling out—30 inches probably will do. Use plywood again on rails (FIG. 8-24E). At the entrance, put a post to the full height to support the wall and provide something on which to grab. Keep the entrance fairly narrow for safety.

Boxing in with plywood will provide safety, but you have to give the outside the correct appearance by covering with slabs of wood for the natural exterior (FIG. 8-24F). Cover tops for a safe edge to lean against. With squared wood, you can give it a more primitive appearance by scooping hollows out of the edges (FIG. 8-24G).

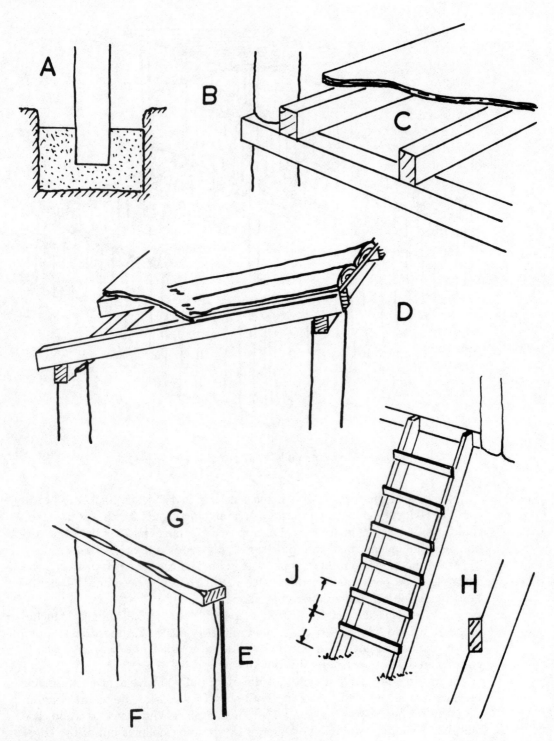

Fig. 8-24. Constructional details for the fort.

The access ladder could be upright, but it is easier to climb if it slopes. Attach securely at the top and let the bottom into the ground. Notch in rungs at about 8-inch intervals (FIG. 8-24H), with the same stepping distance at both ends (FIG. 8-24J), so an unexpected step height will not cause the child to trip. You can use waney-edge wood for the ladder sides, but if you cannot find suitable pieces, you may scoop the edges to simulate a more natural appearance.

There could be a gate opening inwards at the entrance. A spring closure would aid safety, even if the original defenders of the fort would not have known such things.

You can add several things. A raised platform inside the stockade fence would serve as a step for looking over and as a seat. Do not make it so high that a child could overbalance outwards. Holes in the fence would allow smaller children to look out. You can cut such gun slots in the cabin sides. If you build in benches in the cabin, be careful that a child standing on one could not topple over the side. It might be safer to arrange benches at ground level under the cabin.

If the fort is to stand for long, treat all the wood with preservative. Decay in the posts is most likely at ground level. Use plenty of preservative down to the concrete, before covering with soil. Some preservatives take a long time to dry, so you should keep children away during drying. Any renewal of preservative is best done at a time when the fort is not needed, at least for a few weeks.

Pack-flat Playhouse

If you want to provide a playhouse for a small child and do not have the space indoors or outdoors to store a complete little building, this project might be the answer for you (FIG. 8-25). The assembled house has an inside floor area about 28 inches by 44 inches, and the total height is 48 inches. You could alter the sizes, but those suggested allow for economical cutting from standard plywood sheets. When taken apart you have seven pieces of plywood without projections, so if you use 1/2-inch plywood, the packed thickness is 31/2 inches, or you can separate into lesser packages.

Materials List for
Pack-flat Playhouse
(all 1/2-inch plywood)

2 ends	32	× 48
2 sides	32	× 48
2 roofs	28	× 48
1 shelf	9	× 32

All parts are plywood. You could use 1/2-inch fir or other softwood plywood. Hardwood plywood need only be 3/8 inch thick. Exterior plywood is preferable, but if the playhouse is unlikely to get wet, any other plywood could be used. Cut

Fig. 8-25. *The parts of this playhouse hook together and can be disassembled to pack flat.*

edges carefully, both to ensure good fits and to avoid roughness that might hurt a child. Softwood plywood, in particular, should be cleaned free of splintery or rough edges, by thorough sanding.

For the sizes suggested (FIG. 8-26A), all of the parts can be cut alongside each other across standard 4-foot-×-8-foot sheets, as the walls and roof are all 48 inches long and the shelf a little shorter.

The four walls hook together (FIG. 8-27A). There is a shelf inside (FIG. 8-26B). For the smallest child this could be a table, but a bigger child will treat it as a seat. Its purpose structurally is to ensure squareness of the assembly, aided by the roof sections, which fit onto lugs in the ends (FIG. 8-27B).

Before marking out the walls, examine details of the hooks and sockets (FIG. 8-28). The sockets in the end walls are 4 inches long and wide enough to fit easily

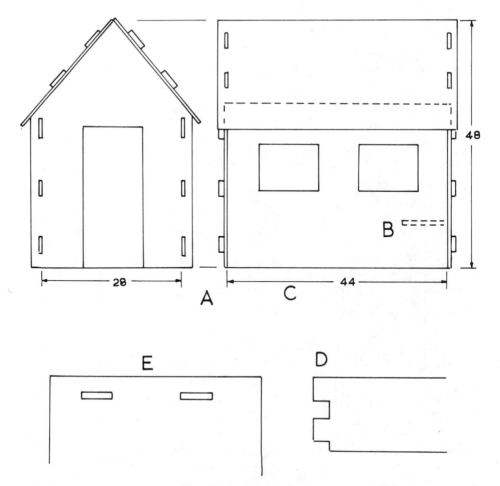

Fig. 8-26. Suggested sizes for the pack-flat playhouse. Roof and shelf details.

over the thickness of the plywood (FIG. 8-28A)—⁵/₈ inch would be suitable for ¹/₂-inch plywood. The hooks (FIG. 8-28B) are passed through the sockets, then moved down to fasten over the lower edges of the sockets, while bottom edges of the walls are brought level with each other. It is important in marking out that spacings all match (FIG. 8-27C). If possible, make corner joints interchangeable. If they do not match each other closely enough, mark the corners which should be fitted to each other.

Mark out and cut the two ends (FIG. 8-27D) with identical outlines, but only one with a doorway. The lugs on the roof slopes are 4 inches long and 3 inches from the corners. They should project 1¹/₂ inches, with rounded corners.

Make the two side walls (FIGS. 8-26C and 8-27E), with windows in one or both pieces. The key markings for the hooks are the positions of the bottom edges of the sockets on the end walls, so lower edges of walls will assemble level. Work

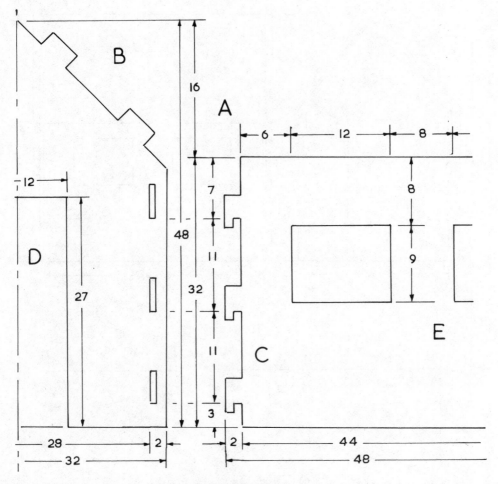

Fig. 8-27. Sizes of side and end of the pack-flat playhouse.

from these points to mark and cut the hook outlines. Check that the top of the side walls come level with the slopes of the end pieces.

While you test assemble the four walls, measure inside for the length of the shelf. Make it 9 inches wide, with lugs (FIG. 8-26D) to pass through sockets in the walls. Arrange the shelf to fit closely against the rear wall to hold the assembly square.

Make the roof sections 48 inches long and wide enough to overhang a little at the eaves. If you have worked to the sizes suggested, this will be 28 inches. Using a trial assembly of the walls and shelf, mark the positions of sockets (FIG. 8-26E). Round exposed edges and corners.

This completes the making of parts. Take off any roughness at edges before painting. You could just paint the walls one color and the roof another, but you might prefer to decorate by drawing on framing around door and windows and

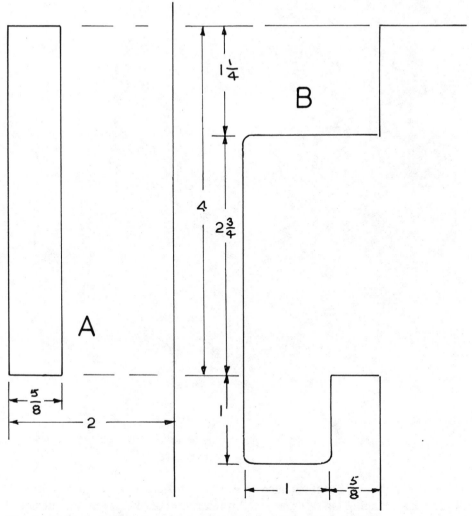

Fig. 8-28. Sizes of the hooks and slots used for assembly of the playhouse.

possibly marking lines to indicate siding. Inside there could be lighter paint, or you could stick on wallpaper. If thickness is to be kept minimal, you cannot add anything that projects, but you might glue on cloth to hang inside the windows.

Games Storage/Summerhouse

Children grow up, often more rapidly than you expect. If you provide a building as a play house, you might be faced with the problem of what to do with it when the children become too old to want to use it for its original purpose. This building (FIG. 8-29) is a multi-purpose structure that should be an attractive feature in your yard, whatever the stage of development of your children. It will serve as a

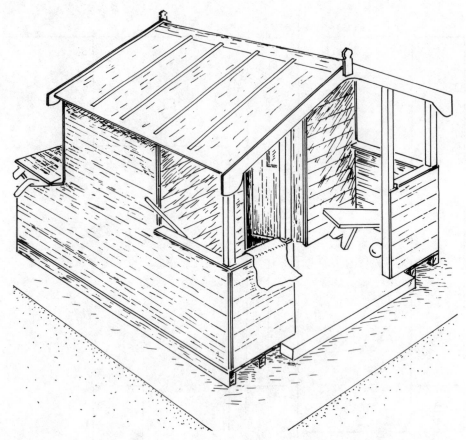

Fig. 8-29. This building combines storage for games equipment with changing room and summer house.

spacious play house, but it can also be a storage for games equipment and yard furniture, a changing room, or an area for relaxation on the porch. The design is for a permanent small building that should be of use to you and your family for a very long time.

The sizes suggested are for a floor area of 8 feet by 9 feet, with a total height of 8 feet (FIG. 8-30). Construction is mainly with 2-inch-square strips, which could be covered with plywood, clapboard, or shiplap boards. You could line the walls with plywood. The roof can be plywood or boarded. Covering can be tarred felt, but the building would look attractive with shingles.

The layout allows for a porch 36 inches deep with walls 36 inches high at the sides and a short distance in from each side at the front. The enclosed building is 48 inches deep, with a front door and a rear window. At the back there is an extension locker with a sloping lifting lid to give access to the contents, which can also be reached from inside the building. If you want to alter sizes or layout, do it at this stage.

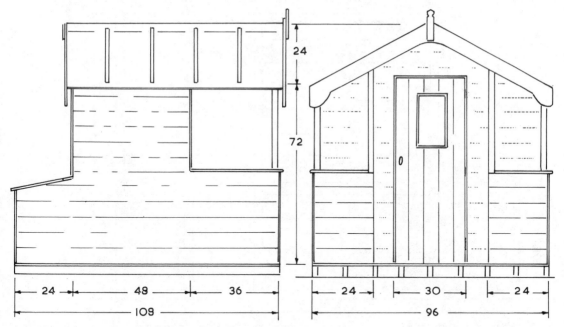

Fig. 8-30. *Main sizes for the games storage/summer house.*

You could mount the building directly on a concrete base and use that as the floor, but it will be better to have a raised wooden floor above the concrete and a step up at the front. The instructions allow for using a wooden floor.

Make the building in framed units. There are a pair of sides to construct first, then four walls to fit across between them. All of these assemblies can be prefabricated. The pair of sides control sizes of several parts.

The pair of sides (FIG. 8-31) extend over the locker and have the open space outlined beside the porch. It is advisable to use halving joints in the corners of the frames and where parts cross, but there can be shallow notches at other nailed joints. See that the assemblies are square by comparing diagonal measurements. Cover with plywood or boarding, as indicated, trimming level with the framing at edges.

Decide how you intend to deal with the eaves. For the closest fit of the roof, bevel the top rails of the sides (FIG. 8-33A), but leave the rails square if such a tight fit is not important (FIG. 8-33B). Arrange the heights of the sides of crosswise walls to suit the treatment you choose for the top side rails.

All of the crosswise numbered walls (FIG. 8-32) fit between the side walls and are the same width. The covering extends over the side uprights (FIG. 8-33C), then the outer corners are filled with strips of square section (FIG. 8-33D).

Make frame #1 first (FIG. 8-32A). Even if other 2-inch-square strips are not planed, the two uprights that stand clear should be, and their edges should be rounded (FIG. 8-32B), as they will be used as handholds. A 2-inch-×-4-inch-sec-

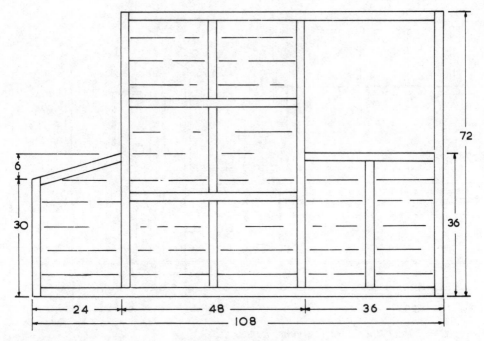

Fig. 8-31. A side of the games storage/summer house.

tion ridge piece passes through the frames. Put a rail across to support it and leave a gap between the rafters (FIGS. 8-32C and 8-33E). At the other frames, the joint will be supported by the boarding. Although there will be bargeboards on this frame, you must also make a 1/2-inch plywood strengthening piece to fit inside the rafters and the supporting rail, notched to pass the ridge piece. Board the area shown, extending enough at the edges to cover the side posts.

Use frame #1 as a pattern for the outlines of frames #2 and #3. The doorway is 78 inches high, but you could adjust this to suit your needs. Trim the covering level with the rafters and allow enough at the sides to cover the side uprights (FIG. 8- 32D).

Make frame #3 (FIG. 8-32E) in a similar way. The space to the bottom is for access to the bin from inside the building. The top edge of the rail over the space should be level with the top surface of the sloping rails on the sides. You could alter the size of the window opening, but the size suggested should give enough light and is too high for young children to reach. Cover so the boards extend to cover the side uprights, but leave out the board that will come above the locker until the locker top is made, as you will have to trim it to a close fit. You could leave out all boarding below this point at this stage, if you wish, and add it during assembly of the walls.

At the back of the bin, frame #4 (FIG. 8-32F) fits between the sides in the same way with boarding overlapping the corners and square strips to fill, as at the

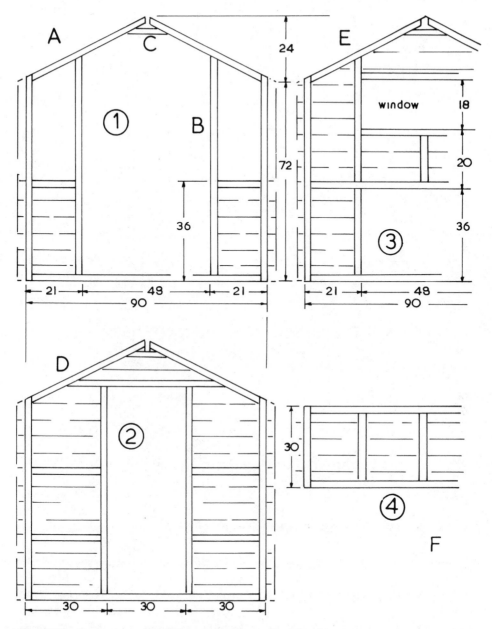

Fig. 8-32. Crosswise parts of the games storage/summer house.

front. You could bevel the top rail to match the slope, but that is not so important as the rails at the eaves.

With these parts made, you can measure them to get the exact sizes of the wood floor, which is best made to match the outside edges of the walls or be

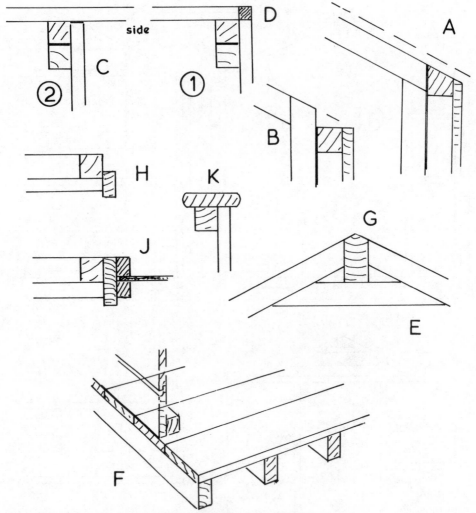

Fig. 8-33. Joints used in the game storage/summer house.

slightly less, rather than project and possibly collect rainwater that could find its way inside.

Make the floor with 1-inch planed boards on 2-inch- × -4-inch supports (FIG. 8-33F). Spacing of the supports will depend on the stiffness of boards, but 12-inch centers should withstand all loads you are likely to apply. Be careful to get the assembly square, as this will control the shape of the building. You could use 3/4-inch exterior plywood instead of floor boards, but seal the edges to prevent entry of water.

Position the floor on the concrete base. There should be sufficient weight in the building to prevent movement, but you might want to ensure exact location with a few attachments to the concrete. Erect one side and frame #1 on the floor.

Side walls					**Locker lid**				
8 uprights	2	× 2	×	74	17 boards	3/4	× 6	×	30
2 rails	2	× 2	×	110	2 boards	3/4	× 4	×	90
2 rails	2	× 2	×	86					
8 strips	2	× 2	×	50	**Door**				
4 strips	2	× 2	×	32	5 boards	1	× 6	×	73
					3 ledgers	1	× 6	×	31
Other walls					1 brace	1	× 6	×	36
12 uprights	2	× 2	×	86	2 strips	1	× 3	×	30
6 rails	2	× 2	×	92					
10 strips	2	× 2	×	32	**Trim**				
3 strips	2	× 2	×	52	2 door edges	1	× 2	×	74
6 rafters	2	× 2	×	52	1 door edge	1	× 2	×	32
					2 window edges	1	× 3 1/2	×	50
Floor					2 window edges	1	× 3 1/2	×	20
9 joists	2	× 4	×	110	4 window fillets	3/4	× 1 1/2	×	20
18 boards	1	× 6	×	98	window fillets	3/4	× 1 1/2	×	50
					4 door window fillets	1/2	× 1 1/2	×	24
Roof					4 door window fillets	1/2	× 1 1/2	×	15
1 ridge	2	× 4	×	90	2 porch wall covers	1	× 4	×	26
10 rafters	2	× 2	×	52	2 porch wall covers	1	× 4	×	38
8 battens	3/8	× 2	×	48	8 corner fillets	1	× 1	×	40
4 bargeboards	1	× 6	×	60					
Covering		3/4 plywood			Cladding: shiplap board, weatherboard or plywood				

Join the corner. You could use only nails both ways, but it will help in getting a close joint if you have one or two 3/8-inch bolts through the posts, to pull tight before finishing by nailing.

Add the other frames, joining in the same way and using the floor as a guide to squareness. When all parts are joined and correctly positioned, nail the bottom rails to the floor, except the parts across openings. Cut these away and discard them after the rails each side are fastened down. This should give you a rigid and upright structure.

Cut and fit the ridge piece. Bevel its top edge to match the slopes of the roof (FIG. 8-33G). It should fit inside the boarding at the back, drop into the intermediate frame and extend 2 inches in front of the rafters on the front frame.

The roof will look best with a small overhang at the ends. To allow this, put 2-inch-square strips down the outside of the slopes of the roof (FIG. 8-34A). These pieces come outside the boarding at the back but will double the thickness of the rafters at the front. You could get the same result at the front by making the rafters there 4 inches wide, but it is less trouble during construction to use 2-inch-wide pieces.

Although the roof plywood is stiff, it is advisable to support it with intermediate rafters that will prevent possible sagging later in the life of the building.

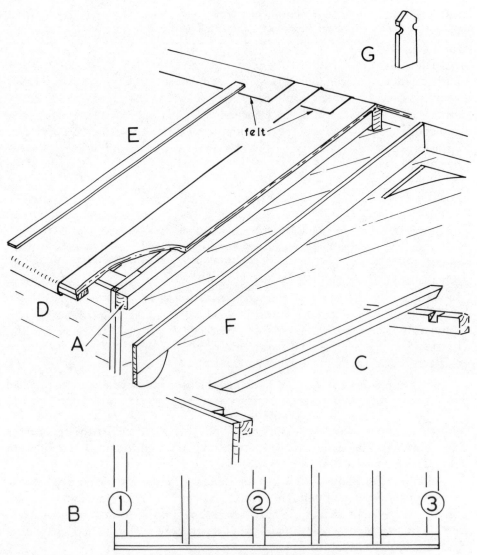

Fig. 8-34. *Roof layout for games storage/summer house.*

These could be at 16- to 18-inch centers (FIG. 8-34B). Notch the side rails and ridge to take the rafter ends (FIG. 8-34C). Notches could be cut before assembly, but be careful that rafter lines do not finish out of square. Sight along the rafters during assembly, and try putting a straight board across them to see they are level and in line with each other.

Fit the plywood roof. You will have to arrange joints down the slope of the roof over rafters. Put a strip of tarred felt along the ridge, then cover with more tarred felt tacked under at one eaves and taken over to tack under the other side (FIG. 8- 34D). Add battens down the slopes of the roof at 18-inch intervals (FIG.

8-34E). If you decide to use shingles on the roof, cover the plywood first with tarred paper or sheet plastic, then nail on the shingles, following the manufacturer's instructions.

The locker lid could be in one piece right across, or you could make it in two parts divided at the middle with an extra sloping rail there to support it. If you want to store long sports equipment, there will have to be a single locker lid, but otherwise a divided lid that can be opened in parts will be lighter to deal with. You could use plywood and frame it underneath, but a boarded lid will be more appropriate in most situations. Tongue-and-groove boards 3/4 inch thick would be suitable.

Put a rail across 4 inches down (FIG. 8-35A), halved into the side rails. Put a board across projecting inside far enough to cover with the cladding boards (FIG. 8-35B). Fasten this board down, and trim the cladding to fit against it. Complete the lower cladding on frame #3, if it has not already been fitted.

Make the lid(s) to overhang a little at the sides and about 2 inches at the bottom (FIG. 8-35C), to shed water and provide a grip for lifting. Join the boards with others across (FIG. 8-35D), cut short to fit easily inside. If you use plywood, frame similarly with narrower pieces, and arrange some down the slope of the lid. You could let butt hinges into the meeting edges, but it will be better to use T hinges, three on each divided lid and five on a wide lid. If you need to secure the lid, a hasp and staple inside will provide resistance to an unauthorized person trying to lift the lid from the outside, while you can release it from the inside.

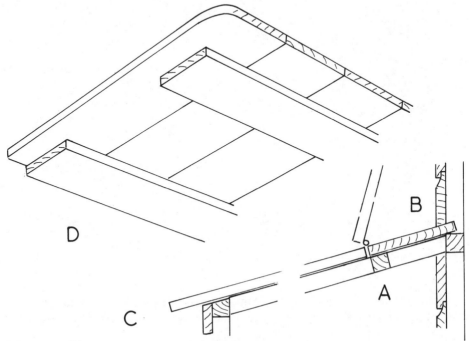

Fig. 8-35. *The locker lid at the rear of the game storage/summer house.*

Frame around the doorway sides and top with strips projecting 1/4 inch forward (FIG. 8-33H) and leaving a gap for the thickness of the door, which will open inwards. Frame around the window opening in a similar way (FIG. 8-33J). Fit the glass with fillets inside and outside. Use screws in the inside fillets so you can remove them easily if the glass has to be replaced.

Cover the boards around the porch walls with pieces that overhang both sides (FIG. 8-33K). Round the edges for comfort when leaning on them.

Bargeboards could be arranged decoratively in any way you wish. There could be curved outlines and pierced patterns. You will have to allow for covering the ends of the ridge piece, if plain boards are not wide enough. Nail the bargeboards to the thickened boards at the ends of the roof (FIG. 8-34F). A finial at the apex might be all you need to hide the ridge end (FIG. 8-34G). The rear bargeboards need not be as decorative as those at the front, depending on the situation.

The door could be made in any way. It could be plain ledgered and braced, but it is shown (FIG. 8-36A) with a window. It could be made to swing inwards or outwards, but it will keep the porch area free if it swings inwards (FIG. 8-36B).

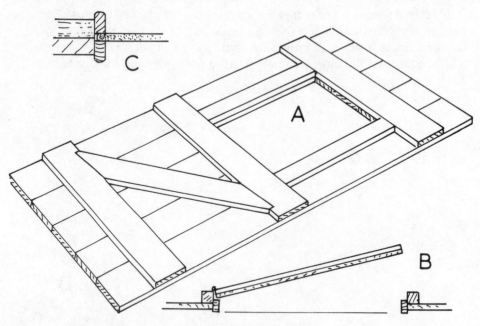

Fig. 8-36. Glazed door for the games storage/summer house.

Make it with a brace sloping up from the hinged side. For swinging inwards the ledgers can be the full width of the door. Outline the window opening with vertical strips.

Fit the glass with fillets, which will look neatest if they project a little with rounded edges (FIG. 8-36C). Use a 4-inch hinge at each ledger position. Fit a catch and a handle or knob at the other side. You will probably also want to provide a lock.

There could be a plywood lining in the main part of the building, either the full height or about halfway. Bright paint inside will suit use by children. The outside should be painted to match surroundings.

Raised Playhouse

A tree house appeals to children, but besides needing a tree, you have to ensure that any structure you build into it is safe. Using the natural branches often make the design difficult and you have to remember that the structure is probably temporary and you want to be able to leave the tree undamaged when whatever you build is removed. In most circumstances you are faced with an impossible design situation, unless you are very lucky. It will usually be better to satisfy this urge to climb by making a separate structure.

Materials List for Raised Playhouse

5 posts	2 × 4 × 130
2 posts	2 × 4 × 140
5 posts	2 × 4 × 110
4 joists	2 × 4 × 96
3 joists	2 × 3 × 96
6 house frames	2 × 2 × 50
3 house frames	2 × 2 × 62
16 house rails	2 × 2 × 48
1 house rail	2 × 2 × 96
3 deck rails	2 × 4 × 48
6 deck rails	2 × 2 × 48
1 deck rail	2 × 4 × 38
2 deck rails	2 × 2 × 38
12 deck uprights	2 × 2 × 32
6 climbing frame sides	2 × 4 × 60
6 climbing frame rails	2 × 2 × 48
2 ladder sides	2 × 4 × 70
7 ladder rungs	2 × 2 × 16
Roof 3/4 inch plywood	
Walls 1/2 inch or 3/4 inch plywood	
Deck 3/4 inch plywood or 1 inch boards	

This raised playhouse (FIG. 8-37) is a size that should be suitable for children aged 3 years to about 8 years. It is rigid and safe, with opportunities to climb and scramble or play making a home, fort, or anything else that appeals to the children's imagination. The platform is at adult eye level, and most children will be

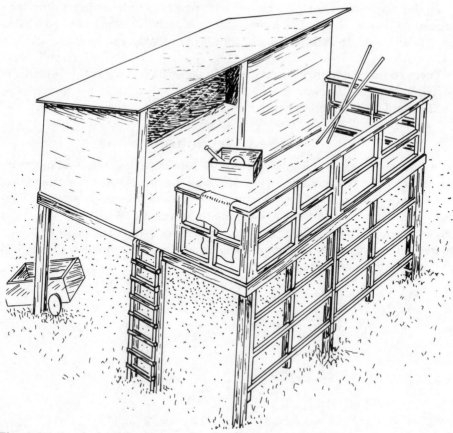

Fig. 8-37. *A raised playhouse combines the attractions of a tree house with a climbing frame.*

able to stand under the roof. You can arrange a toddler's swing under one side. The space below offers scope for a child's imagination during play and for storage of many things when the structure is out of use.

The suggested size of 90 inches square at ground level (FIG. 8-38A) allows you to cover the roof with an uncut standard sheet of plywood. The overall height is about 10 feet (FIG. 8-38B). You could build on a concrete base, but if children fall during play it would be better to erect on the softer soil or turf. Loads on the play house are unlikely to be great, and you might find it sufficient to let the posts directly into compacted ground. If something more seems advisable, let the posts into concrete, as suggested for some of the animal shelters. In the design it is assumed the posts will go 18 inches into the ground.

For safety reasons it would be advisable to choose the smooth surfaces of planed wood and to round all edges and corners. Some rounding can be done to pieces before assembling them, but where squareness is necessary for joints you must round parts that will be handled afterwards.

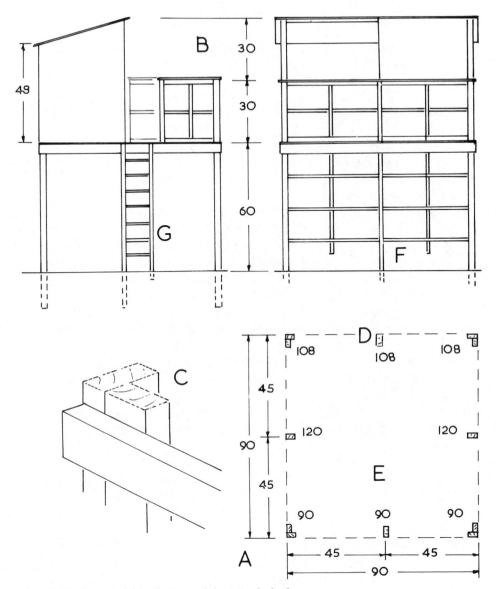

Fig. 8-38. Sizes and foundations of the raised playhouse.

All posts are 2-inch- × -4-inch-section wood. Join the corner posts with plenty of nails to make an L section (FIG. 8-38C). You could also use waterproof glue. Intermediate posts are single pieces.

Mark out the ground (FIG. 8-38D). Check squareness by comparing diagonal measurements, and see that intermediate posts are in line with the corners. Make the posts so they will stand at least the heights indicated above the ground (FIG. 8-38E) so they can be trimmed when other parts are joined to them. If the ground is uneven, allow for the platform being level at a height of about 60 inches.

Erect the posts vertically. Mark the height of the joists supporting the platform (FIG. 8-39A). Join the joists to the posts with an overlap at each corner (FIG. 8-39B). It will be strongest to use two 3/8-inch bolts at each corner crossing, but you can nail at intermediate posts. Use a spirit level to check the joists. Sight across and use temporary boards to check that there are no twists at deck level.

Put three floor joists across to divide the deck into 24-inch parts, in the direction of the width (FIG. 8-39C). They can be 2-inch-×-3-inch section, nailed through the edge joists and supported on cleats. Provide extra supports for the floorboards with blocks inside the corner posts (FIG. 8-39E).

Fit a post inside the joist to stand at least 30 inches above the floor at the side of the ladder opening (FIG. 8-39G). Screw or bolt it in place.

You could make a floor of 3/4-inch exterior-grade plywood. To prevent the entry of water into the plies, it would be advisable to glue narrow wood strips around the edges (FIG. 8-39F). You could use solid wood planed boards. Whatever you use, notch around the posts (FIG. 8-39G).

The house is made of framed plywood panels, with the frames fitting between the posts and the plywood extending over them. No windows are shown, but you could frame openings. For safety, any openings should be too small for a child to wriggle through.

Start with the side house frames (FIG. 8-40A). Make each frame wide enough to fit tightly between the posts. The heights shown are outside the posts, which should be cut to match the slope of the roof. Halve and nail all frame joints. Allow for the plywood extending over the corner post (FIG. 8-40B) and covering the intermediate post (FIG. 8-40C). Nail the covered frames to the posts and to the deck.

The back wall is made of two identical covered frames (FIG. 8-40D). Make them to fit closely between the posts. Extend the plywood at the corner to cover that on the sides. At the central post, allow enough plywood for the edges to meet (FIG. 8- 40E). For the best fit of the roof, you could bevel the upper surfaces of the top rails.

At the front of the house, which is at the middle of the deck, the frame goes halfway across and the plywood only goes to half the height, but the frame (FIG. 8-40F) has to support the roof. The central upright goes up to the top rail, which goes right across between the posts.

Notch the top of the post where the rail joins (FIG. 8-40G) so the rail can be nailed on. Bevel the top of this rail to match the slope of the roof.

The plywood roof will probably be stiff enough without extra support. If it needs stiffening, put strips across inside. Nail it on with an overlap all around. Take sharpness off the edges and corners.

The rails around the deck are 30 inches high and all fit between the posts. Make them from 2-inch-square wood except for the top rail, which is 4 inches

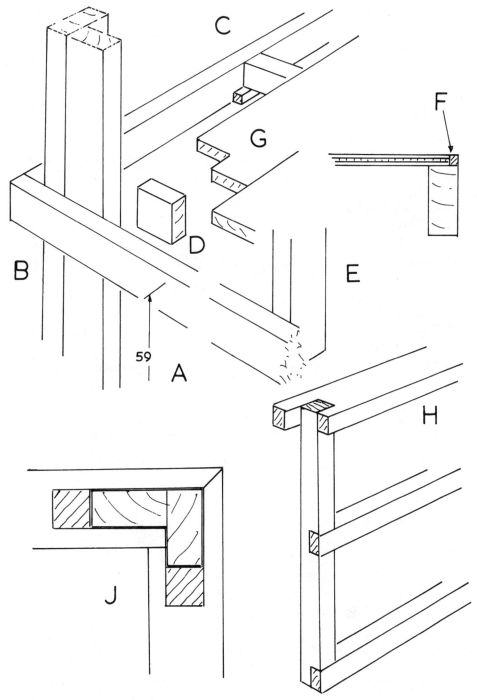

Fig. 8-39. *Joints used in the raised playhouse.*

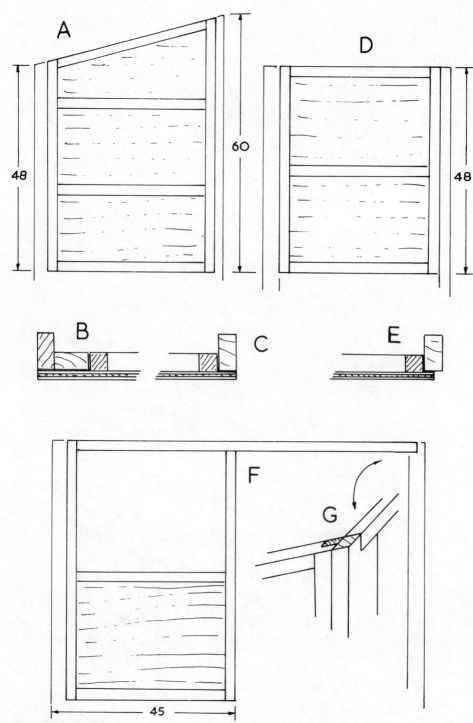

Fig. 8-40. Sizes of the shelter part of the raised playhouse.

wide, projecting equally both sides and forming a rail to lean on (FIGS. 8-39H and 8-41A). Round its edges. Make the frames with halving joints, but at the tops carry the uprights through. Cut the top rail level where it meets the house side. Notch it around the post at the ladder opening. For the neatest finish at the corners, carry the edges of the rail around the posts (FIG. 8-39J). Nail the frames to the posts and the deck. Drill the extending pieces of the top rail before screwing or nailing them, to reduce the risk of splitting.

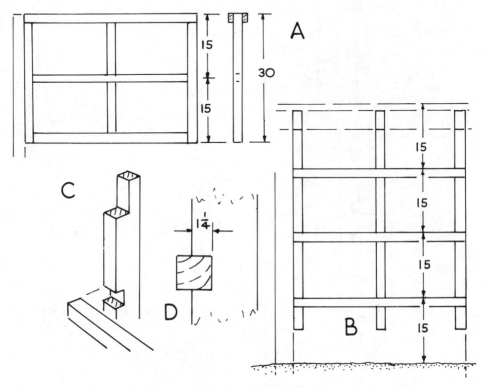

Fig. 8-41. Rails and climbing frame for the raised playhouse.

The two parts of the climbing frame (FIG. 8-38F) fit between posts and have rails that continue the same vertical spacing as the rails above the deck, all being 15 inches apart. Avoiding variations makes for less risk of a youngster scrambling. The rails are 2 inches square, but the uprights are 4 inches deep. The bottoms of the uprights need not reach the ground (FIG. 8-41B). Cut the tops of the uprights to fit behind the joists (FIG. 8-41C). Notch for the rails so they will stand forward 3/4 inch (FIG. 8-41D). Screw the cutaway tops of the uprights behind the joists, and nail the outer uprights to the posts.

The ladder (FIG. 8-42A) is made in a similar way to the climbing frame with rungs let into notches in the sides. It is shown (FIG. 8-38G) with one side over the intermediate post and the other 15 inches from it. Notch the tops of the ladder

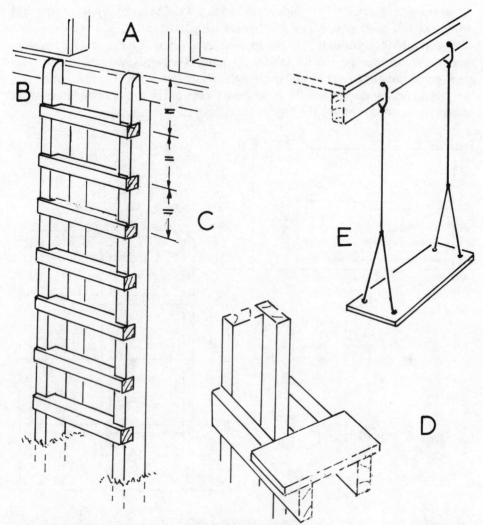

Fig. 8-42. *Ladder, swing, and seat for the raised playhouse.*

sides over the joist and deck (FIG. 8-42B). The post will steady one side, but both bottoms should be let into the ground a short way.

It is important for safety that the intervals of the steps up should be the same from the ground to the deck surface (FIG. 8-42C). The number of steps will depend on the sizes of children. The youngest will be happiest with not much more than 7 inches, while older children can manage up to 10 inches. Let the rungs in the same amount as the climbing frame (FIG. 8-41D). Well-round all edges of the rungs.

The climbing frame covers one side of the lower part, and the ladder is at another side. This leaves two sides open underneath. That might be the way you want them, particularly if the space is to form storage for a variety of things. It also leaves a clear play area for use in bad weather. If you want to provide a seat along one side, there could be two beams attached to the posts and a board on top (FIG. 8-42D). You could arrange a swing for a toddler, with the seat close to the ground (FIG. 8-42E).

Painting will probably be the best finish, but the parts for the posts and ladder in the ground should be soaked in preservative. The deck should have a non-slip treatment. The roof could be felted or kept well-painted. The climbing frame and the ladder rungs might be varnished in contrast to the other parts.

Tree House

The idea of a house in a tree appeals to young people. It is romantic, and there is a sense of adventure. Each tree house has to be an individual design because it depends on the tree, but in general you have to choose a tree that is strong enough, has a suitable arrangement of branches, and that will make a house of a suitable size at a convenient height. For peace of mind of parents, the height might only be 7 feet to the platform, but you have to arrange the layout to make best use of parts of the tree.

The tree should have a rigid trunk and sufficient branches that are strong enough to allow attachments. Driving nails into the tree or cutting off some branches should not affect the life of the tree. You can cut shallow notches into branches. You must avoid cutting away so much that there is little bark left: Much of the tree's lifeblood is in the sap that goes up and down under the bark.

Any tree house is basically a platform on which there could be a roofed shelter and an open area fenced around. There has to be space for access via a ladder, but except for that opening you must prevent the users' falling off.

For security, arrange the structures so outward-thrusting loads cannot break joints. If you nail a rail to a branch, have it on the inside (FIG. 8-43A) so anyone leaning on it pushes the parts together. If you nail on the outside (FIG. 8-43B), only the nail takes the load, and it could be pushed out. Similarly, any boarding that might have been put outside on a building on the ground is better arranged inside its framing on a tree house (FIG. 8-43C). You could notch as well as nail into a sloping branch (FIG. 8-43D). This takes downward loads without risk of slipping. A crook between branches could support a beam. You might cut off a branch so it comes under and supports the house, or you might prefer to let it pass through the platform.

The platform has to be mounted level (FIG. 8-43E). Relating that need to the form of the tree might determine the final height. Experiment with two strips of wood across what will be attachment points. You have to get two beams across, both at the same level and as near as possible to the width of the intended platform. You can expect to have to modify your ideas to suit supporting branches. It is unlikely the beams can be parallel, and they might not be as far apart as the size you want the platform.

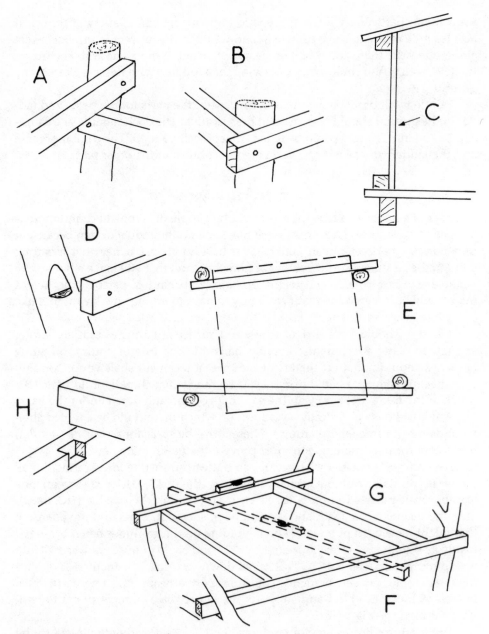

Fig. 8-43. *Suggested construction of the tree house.*

If the platform is to be about 7 feet square, the beams could be at least 2-inch-×-4-inch section. Get one beam level, probably fitted into notches and temporarily clamped or tied on. Locate the other one by sighting across to see that it is level and by checking the level across with strips (FIG. 8-43F). You might be able to

Fig. 8-44. *An example of a possible treehouse construction.*

arrange more than two beams at this level, depending on available parts of the tree to provide support. In any case, put other beams between the first two, with their tops level (FIG. 8-43G). Notched joints at the ends (FIG. 8-43H) can supplement nails. This pattern of beams provides the strength members. Make sure the beams are secure and will form a sound level base for anything you put on top.

The size and shape of the platform will depend on available space. Corners do not have to be square but are better that way. For the example, we assume you can arrange a platform 7 feet square (FIG. 8-44). This can project outside the supporting beams and possibly go around a branch. Use 2-inch- × -4-inch wood covered with 1-inch boards. Notch frame parts together. Attach them to the beams, and lay out uprights before putting down the floorboards. Nail or bolt the uprights into angles between frame parts (FIG. 8-45A). For the open parts, top the posts with rails (FIG. 8-45B). After you have put down the floorboards, fit strips

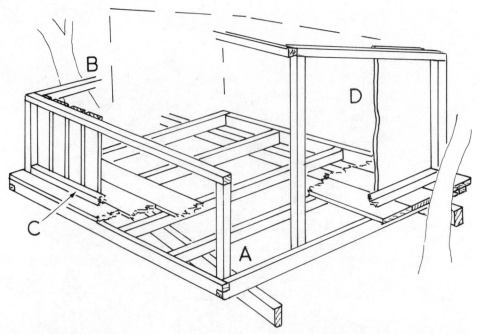

Fig. 8-45. Nail or bolt the uprights (A), and top the posts with rails (B). Fit strips along to take the palings (C) after you have put down the floorboards. Use boards or plywood inside for framing (D).

along to take the upright palings inside (FIG. 8-45C). The palings could be 1-inch-×-4-inch pieces with 1-inch gaps.

For the covered part, take posts to the heights needed. Frame in a similar way to the other buildings, except use boards or plywood inside (FIG. 8-45D). Children will probably be satisfied with less than full-standing head room. A plywood roof should be satisfactory. As you arrange posts, rails, and building framing, consider any further support the tree could provide. You might be able to extend a part to attach to another branch. Any additional support is worth having.

Access could be with an ordinary ladder leant in place and taken away when the house is not in use. There could be a rope ladder supported through holes in a beam.

Glossary

The making of wooden buildings is only part of the much wider craft of wood-working. The selection of words that follows includes some that are particularly appropriate to the subject of this book and might be helpful to readers unfamiliar with the language of this branch of the craft.

aggregate Stone, gravel or sand used with cement to make concrete.
anchor bolt Bolt set in concrete with its thread end projecting.
apex The top, particularly of a roof.
ark A building for small animals.
aviary A building to hold birds.

backfill Fill an excavation around a post or foundation.
bargeboards Covering boards at the gable end of a roof.
battens Strips of wood of light section, used on a roof to hold down the covering.
bay A space or section in a building.
brace A diagonal strut used to triangulate an assembly and prevent it distorting.
bridging Wood fitted between joists to spread a load.

chipboard Alternative name for particleboard, which is made by bonding wood chips with a synthetic resin.
cladding The covering of boards that forms the outside of a wall.

clapboarding Overlapping boards, usually tapered in section and used as cladding.

cleat A link between other parts. A strip of wood across other pieces. A support for a purlin on a rafter.

coach bolt Alternative name for carriage bolt. A bolt for use with a nut, having a shallow round head and a square neck to grip the wood.

coach screw Alternative name for a lag screw. A large screw for wood, with a square head for use with a wrench.

column An upright supporting member.

corrugated sheet Roofing material, which might be steel, other metal or plastic. Corrugations in the length provide stiffness.

dead pin A wedge or dowel.

drip groove A groove cut along the underside of a sill or other projecting wood to prevent water running back.

eaves The angle between the roof and a wall. The overhang of a roof over a wall. Never spelled without the s, even if there is only one.

exterior-grade plywood Plywood in which the glue used is waterproof.

eye screw Alternative name for screw eye. A screw for wood with a ring or eye as head.

fascia A long flat wooden surface, such as the front of a lean-to roof. The casing of a door.

feather edge Wood tapered in section so one edge is thin.

gable The end of a roof, usually one with a ridge.

galvanizing A method of coating steel with zinc as a protection against rust. Used on corrugated steel roof sheets.

gambrel roof Alternative name for mansard roof. A roof with two slopes on each side.

gazebo A structure intended to be decorative and, usually, from which you can obtain a view.

girder A horizontal supporting member, similar to a joist.

handed Made as a pair.

hardboard A thin board made from compressed shredded wood.

hardwood Wood from broad-leafed trees, which shed their leaves in the winter.

hip roof The end of a ridge roof that slopes inwards instead of having a vertical gable.

joist A supporting beam, as in a floor.

lag screw Alternative name for a coach screw.

lean-to   A building with a roof having a single slope. It could be against another building or be free-standing.

ledger, ledge   A piece across the vertical boards of a door, used with braces to keep the door in shape.

lintel   Support for a load over a doorway or other opening.

mansard roof   Alternative name for a gambrel roof.

nominal   When applied to lumber, this is the sawn size and wood finished by machine planing will have smaller sections.

palisade   A fence of upright boards.

particleboard   Alternative name for chipboard.

pergola   A wooden structure covered with growing plants.

pitch   Slope of a roof. Distance between tops of a screw thread.

plywood   Manufactured board made by gluing thin pieces of wood (veneers or plies) with the grain of alternate pieces arranged at right angles.

pole construction   A barn or other building made with poles as the main structural parts.

pop hole   The entrance for poultry into their house.

purlin   A lengthwise support for roof covering, usually supported on rafters.

rabbet (rebate)   Recess in the edge of wood, as in a picture frame.

rafter   A support for a roof.

rail   A horizontal structural member.

ridge   The apex of a roof made like an inverted V.

roofing felt   A flexible roof covering material to lay over boards or plywood, made of felt impregnated with tar, asphalt or other waterproof substance.

roof truss   A braced framework with rafters for supporting a roof.

screw eye   Alternative name for eye screw.

shiplap boards   Cladding boards, to be laid horizontally, with the upper edge of each one fitting into a rabbet in the one above.

sill (cill)   A projecting horizontal board, such as the bottom of a window, to shed water away from the wall below.

softwood   Wood from needle-leaf trees.

stable door   A door in two parts, so you can open the top part while the lower part remains closed.

staple   A nail in the form of a U, so it has double points.

stove bolt   A bolt threaded to the head, which has a screwdriver slot.

stressed skin   An assembly in which the skin plays a major part in providing strength.

stringer   Support for cross members, as at the sides of a stair.

stud   Vertical support in a wall.

surfaced wood   Wood with machine-planed surfaces.

sway bracing Diagonal pieces to triangulate an assembly and provide a resistance to distortion, particularly in strong winds.

tack A small tapered nail. Harness and other equipment used with a horse.

tempered hardboard Hardboard treated with oil, to strengthen it and give it a resistance to water.

tie A member under tension in a structure, as across a roof truss, where it prevents rafters spreading.

tongue-and-groove boards Boards prepared so a tongue on the edge of one piece fits the groove on the edge of the next piece.

triangulation Placing a member diagonally across a four-sided figure to divide it into triangles, so it keeps its shape.

truss A supporting structural framework. In a building, rafters might be supported by truss.

waney edge The shape of the outside of a tree retained on the edge of a board that has not been squared.

weatherboarding Cladding boards to be laid horizontally, tapered in the width so the thin edge of a lower board goes under the thicker lower edge of the one above it.

wind bracing Sway bracing arranged in the roof, diagonally between trusses or purlins, to resist distorting loads in the roof due to strong winds.

Index

Other Bestsellers of Related Interest

GIFTS FROM GRANDPA'S WORKSHOP
—Howard V. French

Whether you're a beginner or a skilled craftsman, these projects are sure to be both interesting and rewarding. For each item, you'll find step-by-step instructions, detailed illustrations, and a photograph of the finished project. Projects include chicken bookends, plant stands, goose baskets, shelves, deluxe picnic tables, country cupboards, and more! 352 pages, 379 illustrations, 8 full-color pages. Book No. 4113, $14.95 paperback, $29.95 hardcover

TRADITIONAL FURNITURE PROJECTS
—Percy W. Blandford

If you enjoy pioneer, colonial, and country-style decorating themes, this book's for you. It features pieces patterned after early American designs. Most of the projects can be completed in only 12 hours using readily available woods. All projects include clear, step-by-step instructions and exploded-view assembly drawings. The historical significance of each piece is also discussed. 216 pages, 200 illustrations. Book No. 3707, $12.95 paperback, $22.95 hardcover

PERCY BLANDFORD'S FAVORITE WOODWORKING PROJECTS—Percy W. Blandford

Here, Blandford gives do-it-yourselfers and woodworking hobbyists plans and instructions for everything from chairs to kitchen utensils, magazine racks, and gardening tools. There are 800 pages' worth of woodworking projects in all, for every room of your home, plus the yard and garden. As always, Blandford includes drawings of the finished projects, materials lists, and step-by-step instructions. 800 pages, 800 illustrations. Book No. 3896, $39.95 hardcover only

BUILD YOUR OWN FRAME HOUSE
—S. Blackwell Duncan

The step-by-step illustrations and procedures in this detailed manual will show you how to construct a wood-frame house to your specifications. From initial site preparation to finishing touches, you'll find it all here in one easy-to-use reference. This convenient source for technical guidance details the latest building techniques and gets you professional-quality results—all while staying within your budget. 528 pages, 400 illustrations. Book No. 3453, $19.95 paperback, $32.95 hardcover

WHOLE HOUSE REMODELING GUIDE
—S. Blackwell Duncan

This book features hundreds of remodeling, renovating, and redecorating options described and illustrated step-by-step! Focusing on interior modeling, the possibilities that exist for floors, windows, doors, walls, and ceilings are comprehensively explored. Complete detailed, illustrated instructions for projects are easy to follow. 448 pages, Illustrated. Book No. 3281, $19.95 paperback, $28.95 hardcover

HARDWOOD FLOORS—2nd Edition—Dan Ramsey

Hardwood floors have begun to reappear in new and remodeled homes because they are both beautiful and practical. If you yearn for the mellow look of wood, let Ramsey guide you through the selection of the proper tools and materials. He explains how to install or restore plank, tongue and groove, parquet, and block hardwood floors and then finish them to match your home's special decor. 192 pages, 222 illustrations, 4 full-color pages. Book No. 3529, $14.95 paperback, $22.95 hardcover

ROOFING THE RIGHT WAY—2nd Edition
—Steven Bolt

Why pay a contractor thousands of dollars to put a new roof on your home when you can do it yourself? Roofing isn't as difficult or as costly as you might think. Follow the guidelines presented here, you can install a watertight roof that will add to the beauty and value of your home for years. You'll find in-depth details on every aspect of roofing—from choosing the proper tools and materials to step-by-step application techniques for nearly any type of roof. 240 pages, 277 illustrations. Book No. 3387, $14.95 paperback only

BUILD YOUR OWN KIT HOUSE—Jonathan Erickson

Learn exactly what a kit house is, details about what a package includes, how it compares to a conventional, stick-built home, and construction techniques. The author gives a start-to-finish process for choosing, buying, and building a kit home using a two-by-four wood frame home as the model. Because the common tasks associated with all kit home construction are presented in this guide, you can apply this information to log homes, geodesic dome designs, and others, as well. 272 pages, 167 illustrations. Book No. 2873, $14.95 paperback, $22.95 hardcover

**ATTIC, BASEMENT, AND GARAGE
CONVERSION: A Do-It-Yourselfer's Guide**
—Paul Bianchina

Achieve the space, appearance, and functional practicality you want in your home using the space that already exists. This book combined with your own creative imagination will produce professional results. Information on tools and techniques is featured along with complete step-by-step instructions for converting underutilized basements, garages, and attics into spacious, attractive living spaces. 208 pages, Illustrated. Book No. 3271, $16.95 paperback, $24.95 hardcover

Prices Subject to Change Without Notice.

Look for These and Other TAB Books at Your Local Bookstore

To Order Call Toll Free 1-800-822-8158

(in PA, AK, and Canada call 717-794-2191)

or write to TAB Books, Blue Ridge Summit, PA 17294-0840.

Title	Product No.	Quantity	Price